Principles of Color Technology

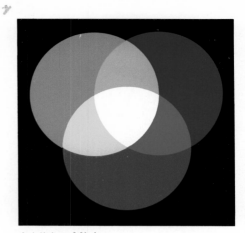

Additive Mixing

Simple-Subtractive Mixing

These illustrations show the results of additive and simple-subtractive color mixing, discussed in Chapter 5A. The overlapping of the three additive primaries, red, green, and blue (light), in pairs give the colors yellow, magenta, and cyan (blue-green). Where they all three overlap, in the correct amounts, white light results. The primaries for simple-subtractive mixing are yellow, magenta, and cyan, and their overlapping in pairs give the colors red, blue, and green. Where they all three overlap, in the correct amounts. black results.

Principles of Color Technology

Fred W. Billmeyer, Jr.

Professor of Analytical Chemistry
Rensselaer Polytechnic Institute
Troy, New York

Max Saltzman

Senior Scientist
Allied Chemical Corporation
Morristown, New Jersey
  and
Adjunct Professor of Chemistry
Rensselaer Polytechnic Institute
Troy, New York

INTERSCIENCE PUBLISHERS
a division of John Wiley & Sons
New York   London   Sydney

First Corrected Printing, September, 1967

Preface

Over the years we, the authors, have been closely involved with the use of color in various industries. We have been asked many questions by colleagues and associates, and by customers and suppliers. In many instances, the same questions are asked over and over again. The answers to most of these questions are found in the literature. Often these answers are in such excellent (and available) books as *An Introduction to Color* (Evans 1948), *Color in Business, Science, and Industry* (Judd 1952; 1963), *The Science of Color* (OSA 1953) or *The Measurement of Colour* (Wright 1964)—all advanced and authoritative works in the field.

To us, the persistence of these questions indicated the need for a truly elementary book serving as an introduction to the field of color and the use of color in industry. This book attempts to answer some of these questions in a relatively simple way, drawing its examples from daily practice in the field.

Our book is primarily for use (and we hope it will be *used*, not merely *read*) by people who are actively working with color; in the production of colorants or the coloring of materials in industry. It presupposes some technical background, but places no emphasis on mathematics. Secondarily, the book is directed towards those who use color, as in design, sales, and advertising, but whose needs are somewhat different from those working directly in the production of colored materials.

We make no claim that this book is either complete or comprehensive. It represents largely our personal opinions, although we have drawn heavily on, and referred heavily to, the published literature.

Originally, and only partly in jest, we considered titling this book *What Everybody Knows About Color. Or Do They?* Again and again, in our experience, we have found complicated arguments and important decisions based on the assumption that "everybody knows . . ." It is to attempt to supply these elusive facts that "everybody knows" but people so often forget that we have written this book.

Contents

Chapter 1. What is Color?   1

A. What This Book is About   **1**

B. The Physical Stimulus   **2**

     Sources of Light   **4**

     How Materials Modify Light   **8**

       Transmission   **8**

       Absorption   **9**

       Scattering   **10**

       Other Aspects of Appearance   **11**

       The Spectral Characteristics of Materials   **12**

     Detecting Light and Color   **12**

     Summary   **12**

C. The Description of Color   **14**

     The "Desert Island" Experiment   **15**

     Color Coordinates   **17**

D. The Appearance of Color   **18**

     Light Sources, Color Rendition, and Adaptation   **18**

     Metamerism   **20**

Chapter 2. Color-Order Systems   25

A. Systems Based on Physical Samples   **25**

     Random Arrangements   **25**

     Orderly Arrangements   **26**

     Arrangements Based on Principles   **26**

       The Munsell System   **26**

       The Ostwald System   **30**

B. The CIE System   **31**

     Mixing Colored Lights   **31**

     The 1931 CIE Sources, Observer, and Coordinates   **38**

C. Uniform Chromaticity Systems   **45**

     Transformations of the CIE System   **45**

     Other Perceptually Uniform Systems   **46**

D. Single-Number Color Scales   **50**

Lightness Scales   **51**

Yellowness Scales   **51**

Whiteness Scales   **52**

Other One-Dimensional Color Scales   **52**

E. Summary   **52**

Chapter 3. Color Measurement, Specification, and Tolerances   53

A. Basic Principles of Measuring Color   **53**

Examination   **53**

Assessment   **54**

THINK and LOOK   **54**

B. The Sample   **55**

Samples for Analysis   **55**

Form Suitable For Inspection   **55**

Again, LOOK   **57**

C. Visual Color Measurement   **57**

Sample and Single Standard   **57**

Sample and Multiple Standards   **58**

D. Instruments Using the Eye as Detector   **60**

Disk Colorimetry   **60**

Color Comparators for Liquids   **61**

More-Refined Instruments   **62**

E. Fully Instrumental Color Measurement   **63**

Classification of Methods   **64**
  Unaltered Light   **64**
  Three-Colored Lights   **65**
  Monochromatic Light   **65**

Colorimetry   **66**
  Source-Detector Response   **66**
  Sample Viewing   **67**
  Coordinate Scales   **69**
  Instrument Metamerism   **69**
  Standardization and Differential Use   **71**
  Typical Commercial Instruments   **72**
  Abridged Spectrophotometry   **73**

Spectrophotometry   **74**
  Source of Spectrum   **74**
  Sample Viewing   **75**
  Standardization and Accuracy   **77**
  Calculation of CIE Coordinates   **77**
  Typical Commercial Instruments   **79**

F. The Use of Instruments in Color Assessment   **83**

Assessment with Limit Standards   **83**

Assessment by Color Difference   **84**

       Perceptibility Versus Acceptability   **87**

       Color Tolerances   **88**

  G. Summary   **89**

Chapter 4. Colorants   91

  A. Some Matters of Terminology   **91**

  B. Dyes Versus Pigments   **93**

       Solubility   **93**

       Chemical Nature   **94**

       Transparency   **94**

       Presence of a Binder   **94**

       Summary   **95**

  C. Classification of Colorants   **95**

  D. Selecting the Colorants to Use   **97**

       Sources of Information   **97**

          Experienced Personnel   **97**

          Suppliers of Colorants   **97**

          Books and Periodicals   **97**

          The User's Experience   **97**

       General Principles in Choosing Colorants   **100**

  E. Summary   **100**

Chapter 5. The Coloring of Materials in Industry   103

  A. Color Mixing Laws   **103**

       Additive Mixing   **104**

       Simple-Subtractive Mixing   **107**

       Complex-Subtractive Mixing   **110**

  B. Color Matching   **112**

       Selecting the Colorants   **112**

          Invariant Matches   **113**

          Colorant Identification   **113**

          Conditional Matches   **113**

          Summary   **114**

       The Initial Match   **114**

          Visual Matching   **115**

          Instrumental Aids   **115**

          Computer Techniques   **119**

       Adjusting the Match   **123**

  C. Color Control in Production   **124**

       Monitoring   **125**

          The Value of Instruments   **125**

          The Effect of Process Variables   **125**

          More than Measurement Alone   **125**

       Adjusting   **125**

       Controlling   **128**

  D. Those Other Aspects of Appearance   **128**

Chapter 6. Color Technology–Present and Future   129

   A. Color as an Engineering Material   **129**

      The Various Meanings of Color   **129**

      Engineering Properties of Colorants   **131**

      Color Gamuts   **132**

      The Selection of Colorants   **136**

   B. Some Guesses About the Future   **136**

      Colorimetry and the CIE System   **137**

         New Illuminants   **137**

         New Reflectance Standards   **138**

         New Supplementary Standard Observer   **138**

         Uniform Chromaticity System   **140**

         New Color-Difference Formula   **141**

      Instrumentation   **141**

      Colorants   **143**

      Color Matching   **143**

      Education   **144**

Chapter 7. Annotated Bibliography   145

   A. Books   **146**

   B. Journals, Yearbooks, and Other Serials   **148**

   C. Color Perception and Appearance   **149**

   D. Color-Order Systems   **150**

   E. Color Measurement   **152**

   F. Color Difference   **154**

   G. Colorants   **155**

   H. Color Matching and Formulation   **156**

Bibliography   161

Author Index   173

Subject Index   177

CHAPTER **1**

What is Color?

A. What This Book is About

This is a book about *color, colorants,* and the *coloring* of materials. *Color* can mean many things. In this book, color may mean a certain kind of light, its effect on the human eye, or (most important of all) the result of this effect in the mind of the viewer. We shall describe each of these aspects of color, and relate them to one another.

Colorants, on the other hand, are purely physical things. They are the dyes and pigments used in the process of coloring materials. *Coloring* is itself a physical process, that of mixing dyes and pigments into suitable material media. A part of this book is devoted to describing these physical substances and processes.

But color is much, much more than something physical. Color is what we *see*—and we shall repeat this many times—the result of the physical modification of light by colorants as observed by the human eye (called a psychophysical process) and interpreted in the brain (which introduces psychology). This is an enormously complicated train of events. To describe color and coloring, we must understand something of each aspect of it. A large portion of the book deals with this problem.

With an understanding of color in this broad sense, we can approach some commercial problems involving color. These problems are concerned with answering such questions as: "Does this sample have the same color as the one I made yesterday—or last week, or last year?" (Or, more simply: "Do these two colors match?") "How much of what colorants do I use to produce a color just like this one?" "How can I choose colorants which will perform satisfactorily in a certain application?"

"For the Rays (of light) to speak properly are not coloured. In them there is nothing else than a certain Power and Disposition to stir up a Sensation of this or that Colour."

Newton 1730

1

Traditionally, most of these questions have had only subjective answers, based on the skill and memory of the trained color matcher. Fortunately, through the application of the principles of color technology and the use of color measurement, it is now often possible to provide objective answers. We shall consider the industrial application of color technology largely in this objective vein.

In summary, we provide a brief résumé of the present state of the art of color, coloring, and colorants—a very complex field. To simplify, we have omitted much. Among our omissions are conflicting points of view: We tend to present our best current opinion rather than a studied evaluation of all sides of any question. We hope our readers will be stimulated to seek more detailed and more varied information on many of the subjects we touch upon only briefly.

To this end we provide—and consider of major importance—an annotated bibliography (Chapter 7). In listing these references we have tried to indicate content, depth, level of presentation, and usefulness as a source of further information. We hope that our readers will recognize with us that this book can be no more than a beginning, and that they will make use of its bibliography as a guide into the extensive and often complex literature on color.

This book is *not* a "how to do it" manual for any process or any industry. It will not tell you the best way to make a pink shade in vinyl plastic at the lowest cost. Nor will it provide a detailed study of what colorants to avoid in making outdoor paints. It *will* tell you in principle how to avoid having that pink go off-shade in tungsten light; it *will* tell you how to locate pigments with good light fastness and other technical properties.

This book is *not* an instrument manual nor a catalog of instruments; it will not tell you how to operate any specific color-measuring instrument to measure samples of a given material. It *will* tell you what types of instruments are available, and for what purposes they can or cannot be used.

This book is *not* a mathematical treatise on color theory. But, there are some things we cannot say without numbers, and some things that can be said much easier with a simple graph or equation than with many words. We do not hesitate to use the best and simplest means to express our thoughts.

This book does *not* attempt to give the "best" ways to use color, the "best" ways to use colorants, or the "best" colorants to use for any application. These are important practical questions, but to answer them would require much more detail than can be put into this elementary book. For these subjects, as for others we do not discuss, there are references to the literature.

B.   The Physical Stimulus

To describe color, we must talk about both physical actions, such as producing a stimulus in the form of light, and subjective results, such as receiving and interpreting this stimulus in the eye and the brain. Since color exists only in the mind of the viewer, these latter effects are the more important to us. To aid

"What you see is your best guess as to what is out front."

A. Ames, Jr.

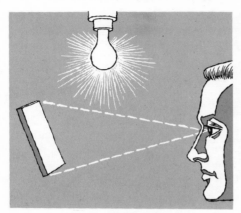

A source of light, an object, and the eye and brain . . .

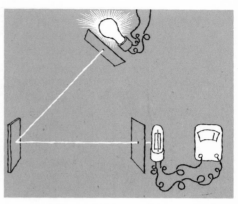

. . . or a source of light, an object, and a photo-electric detector and meter.

in understanding them, we first consider the physical aspects of color, which are simpler.

From the purely physical point of view, the production of color requires three things: a source of light, an object which it illuminates, and the eye and brain to perceive the color. Alternatively, the eye may be replaced by a photosensitive detector and auxiliary equipment which approximate its action in detecting light. While a light source may be seen directly as having color without illuminating anything but the eye (the *illuminant mode* of viewing; see Evans 1948, Judd 1961), we always refer to seeing a material sample illuminated by a light source (the *object mode* of viewing) unless we specify otherwise.

The illuminant mode of viewing.

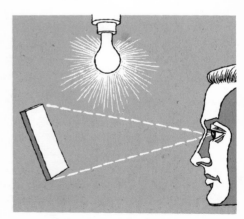

The object mode of viewing.

Sources of Light

Visible light is a form of energy, part of the family which includes radio waves and x-rays, as well as ultraviolet and infrared light. Light can be described by its *wavelength*, for which the *millimicron* (mμ) or *nanometer* (nm) is a convenient unit of length. One nm is 1/1,000,000 millimeter.

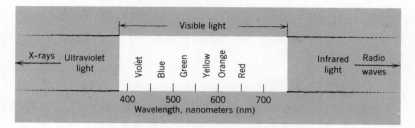

The visible spectrum and its relation to other kinds of radiation.

The relation of visible light to the other members of its family is shown in the figure on this page. The relative insensitivity of the eye limits the visible part of the spectrum to a very narrow band of wavelengths between about 380 and 750 nm. The hue we recognize as blue lies below about 480 nm; green, roughly between 480 and 560; yellow, between 560 and 590; orange, between 590 and 630; and red at wavelengths longer than 630 nm.

Many of the objects we think of as sources of light emit light which is white or nearly white—the sun, hot metals like the filaments of light bulbs, and fluorescent lamps, among others. Sir Isaac Newton showed many years ago (Newton 1730), by using a prism to disperse light into a spectrum, that white light is made up of all the visible wavelengths. The light from any source can be described in terms of the relative energy (or amount of light) emitted at each wavelength. Plotting this energy against the wavelength gives the *spectral energy distribution curve* for the light source. A typical example is the spectral energy distribution of average daylight, shown on the facing page.

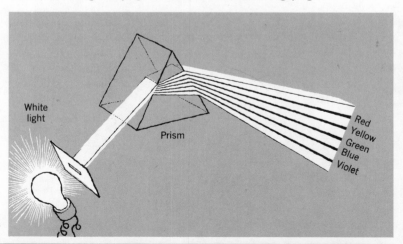

Dispersing white light into a spectrum.

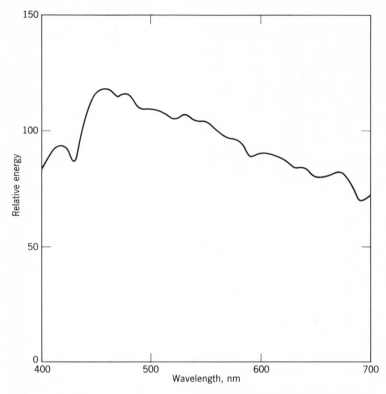

The spectral energy distribution, or relative energy at each wavelength, for typical daylight (Judd 1964).

One very important group of light sources is that called *blackbodies*, which belie their name in that they do not look black except when cold. On being heated, they glow like metals, first a dull red like a hot poker or stove, then progressively brighter and whiter like the filaments of incandescent light bulbs. Real blackbodies are hollow heated chambers, important because their spectral energy distribution, and therefore their color, depends only on their temperature and not on their composition. The temperature of blackbodies is called their *color temperature.* Tungsten filaments, such as those in common incandescent lamps, are close approximations to blackbodies, but their color temperatures are not exactly equal to their actual temperatures.

The spectral energy distribution curves for two blackbodies, representing the range of color temperatures of interest in color problems, are shown on page 6. The curve for 2854°K is typical of the spectral energy distribution from a 100-watt tungsten filament lamp, while that for 6500°K is in the color range of actual daylight.

(The symbol °K stands for degrees Kelvin, or "absolute" temperature. Degrees Kelvin are obtained by adding 273 to degrees centigrade or Celsius, °C.)

While blackbodies are important because of their simplicity, many practical light sources, including the sun and daylight, fluorescent lamps, and various arc lamps, are not blackbodies.

Most arc lamps, such as the mercury, neon, and sodium arcs, do not emit light of all wavelengths but of only a few specific wavelengths (lines) characteristic of the material of the arc. Their spectral energy distributions are not continuous, as are those described so far. Rather, all the light energy they emit is concentrated in a few very narrow wavelength regions. Fluorescent lamps have continuous spectral energy distributions on which are superimposed a few lines (page 7).

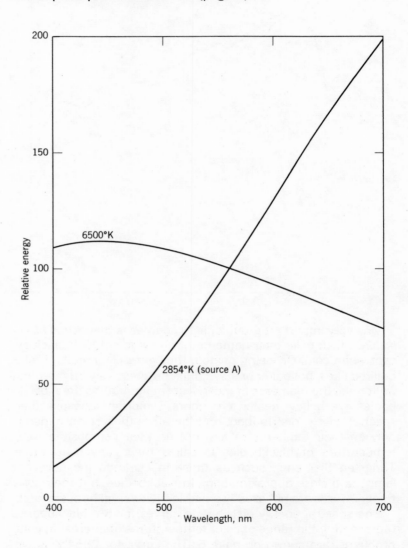

The spectral energy distributions of blackbodies with color temperatures of 2854°K (Source A) and 6500°K. (Pivovonski 1961) (The curves are adjusted to a relative energy of 100 at 560 nm.)

Several standard light sources have been defined for use in describing color (CIE 1931, Hardy 1936, OSA 1953). One of these, CIE Source A, is a tungsten filament lamp operating at a color temperature of 2854°K; its spectral energy distribution curve is shown on this page. CIE Sources B and C are derived from Source A by passing its light through liquid filters. Source B, with a color temperature of about 4800°K, is an approximation of noon sunlight; Source C, about 6500°K, is an approximation of average daylight. Another light source widely used in color

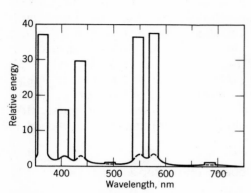

The spectral energy distribution of a typical line source, a mercury arc lamp (IES 1966).

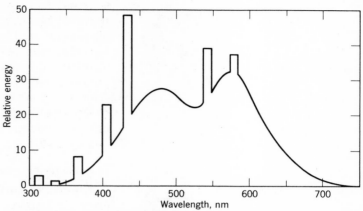

The spectral energy distribution of a daylight fluorescent lamp (IES 1966).

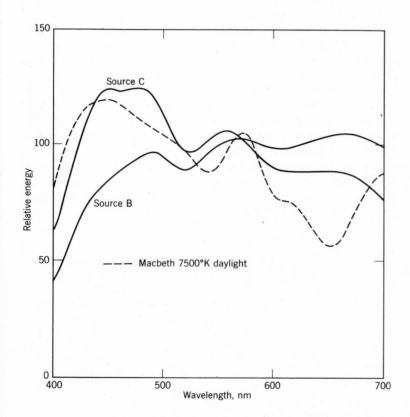

The spectral energy distributions for some standard light sources used in describing color (OSA 1953).

matching is Macbeth 7500°K Daylight, obtained by modifying light from a tungsten filament lamp with glass filters. The spectral energy distribution curves for these sources are shown on this page.

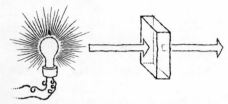

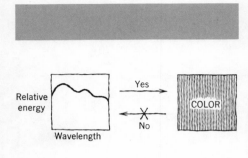

The transmission of light through a transparent object.

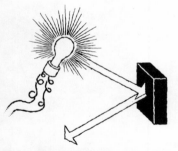

The reflection of light from the surface of an object.

Many of these non-blackbody light sources can be described by the color temperature of the blackbody which they most nearly resemble. This is called their *correlated color temperature.* However, as the drawings on pages 5–7 show, many of these sources have spectral energy distributions quite different from those of blackbodies. This important observation, recognized over a hundred years ago (Grassmann 1853), will be encountered again as we consider the light reflected from or transmitted through material objects: Many different spectral energy distribution curves can yield the same visual effect which we call *color.* It follows that the perceived color of an object or a light source does *not* tell us the nature of its spectral energy distribution. The reverse, however, *is* true: Knowledge of the spectral energy distribution *does* allow the description of perceived color.

How Materials Modify Light

When light strikes an object, one or more things pertinent to color can happen:

1. Transmission. The light can go through essentially unchanged. It is said to be *transmitted* through the material, which is described as *transparent.* If the material is colorless, all the light is transmitted except for a small amount which is reflected from the two surfaces of the object.

This reflection, and the more important scattering of light, described below, occurs whenever there is a change in a quantity called the *refractive index,* which measures how much light is slowed down in a material, relative to its speed of travel in air. At every boundary between two different materials, light changes its speed. As a result, a small fraction of the light is reflected and (unless the boundary is hit straight on) the direction of the light beam is changed. For many common materials, with refractive index near 1.5, the amount reflected is about 4% at each boundary with air. The change in direction, by an amount dependent on the wavelength, explains how light is dispersed into a spectrum by a prism.

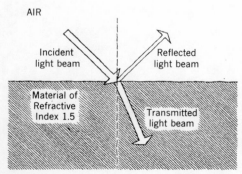

At every boundary where there is a change in refractive index, some of the light is reflected. The direction of the light beam is changed by an amount depending on the change in refractive index and the original direction of the beam.

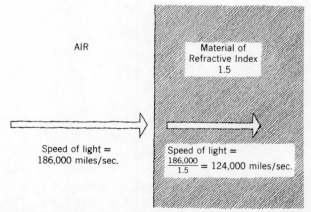

Refractive index is equal to the speed of light in air divided by the speed of light in the material. Therefore, air has a refractive index of exactly 1.

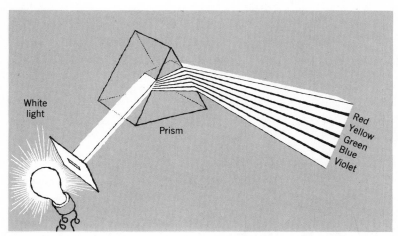

Since refractive index changes with the wavelength of the light, different colors of light change direction by different amounts on passing through a prism.

2. *Absorption.* In addition to being transmitted, light may be *absorbed,* or lost as visible light. (If a very large amount of light is absorbed, we can sense that at least part of it is converted into heat.) If the material absorbs part of the light, it appears colored but is still transparent; if all the light is absorbed, the material is black and is said to be *opaque.*

The fundamental law of light absorption (Lambert's law) states that equal amounts of absorption result when light passes through equal thicknesses of material. If one inch of material absorbs half the light incident on it, another inch behind it absorbs half of the amount passing the first layer, so that only $\frac{1}{2} \times \frac{1}{2}$ or $\frac{1}{4}$ of the original light emerges from two inches of material, and so on. If each wavelength is considered separately, Lambert's law is always true *in the absence of scattering.*

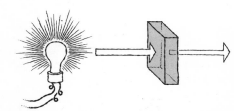

The absorption of light by a transparent, colored object.

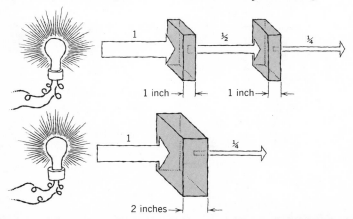

Lambert's law states that equal thicknesses of material cause equal amounts of absorption.

A second absorption law, Beer's law, states that equal amounts of absorption result when light passes through equal amounts of absorbing material. This law is important in explaining the effect of colorant concentration on the color of a transparent material. Like Lambert's law, Beer's law must be applied to each wavelength of light separately. Not all materials follow Beer's law.

Beer's law states that equal amounts of absorbing material cause equal amounts of absorption.

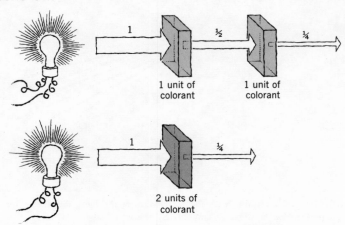

1 unit of colorant   1 unit of colorant

2 units of colorant

3. Scattering. Finally, light may be *scattered* when it passes through matter. It may be reflected, partly in one direction and partly in another, until ultimately some light travels in many different directions. The effects of light scattering are both common and important, accounting for the blue color of the sky and the white colors of clouds, smokes, and most white pigments.

If only part of the light passing through a material is scattered, and part is transmitted, the material is said to be *translucent;* if the scattering is so intense that no light passes through the material (some absorption must be present, too), it is said to be *opaque.* The color of the material depends on the amount and

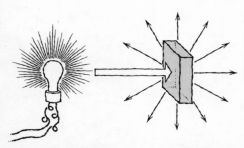

The scattering of light by a turbid or translucent material. In such a material, some light is transmitted and some is reflected by scattering.

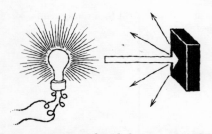

In an opaque material, no light is transmitted, but some is reflected by scattering.

If particles are placed in a medium of the same refractive index there is no scattering, but if there is a difference in the refractive indices, scattering results.

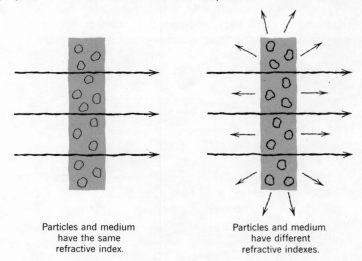

Particles and medium have the same refractive index.

Particles and medium have different refractive indexes.

kind of absorption present: If there is no absorption, a scattering material looks white; otherwise, colored.

It should be pointed out here, however, that scattering is caused by light falling on small particles with refractive index different from that of the surrounding material. (When the particles are very large, we call the similar thing that happens reflection; see p. 8). The amount of light that is scattered depends strongly on the difference in refractive index between the two materials. When the two have the same refractive index, no light is scattered and the boundary between them, as every microscopist knows, cannot be seen. The amount of light scattering

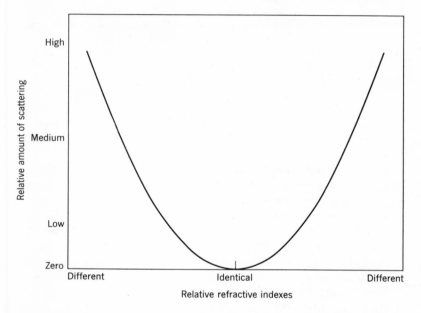

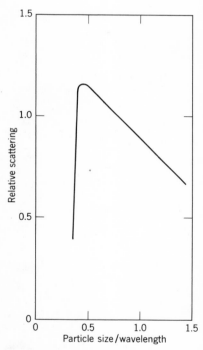

Scattering as a function of particle size for **titanium dioxide**, a common white pigment (**Mitton 1958**).

also depends strongly on the size of the scattering particles. *Very* small particles scatter very little light. Scattering increases with increasing particle size until the particles are about the same size as the wavelength of light, and then decreases for still larger particles.

For these reasons pigments are most efficient as light scatterers when their refractive index is quite different from that of the resin with which they are to be used and their particle diameter is about equal to the wavelength of light. When pigments are of very small particle size and have about the same refractive index as the resin with which they are used, they scatter so little light that they look transparent.

The laws of light scattering are much more complex than Lambert's or Beer's law, and we leave their statement to the discussion of complex-subtractive color mixing on page 110.

Other Aspects of Appearance. In this book on color, we place almost no emphasis on phenomena other than color which contribute to the appearance of objects, such as gloss and metallic reflex, haze and turbidity, or fluorescence. Although they are often important in determining the appearance of things, we mention them only briefly as required (but see Evans 1948, Judd 1961, Hunter 1963a,b).

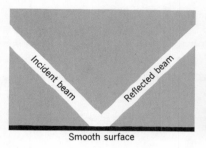
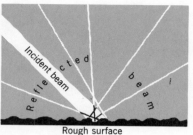

Smooth surface   Rough surface

Reflection of light from a glossy material and from a matte (nonglossy) material.

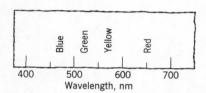

Hue names of the spectrum colors. Purple, a color which does not appear in the spectrum, is a mixture of blue or violet with red.

"... the eye—that superb trick of adaptation which Nature has brought off . . . in the course of evolution."

Rushton 1962

"... The eye is the external part of the central nervous system. The magnificence of man's central nervous system sets him apart from the beasts ..."

Kodak 1965

It should be mentioned here, however, that *gloss* results from the *specular* or mirror reflection of light from a smooth surface. As the surface becomes rougher, the gloss is reduced as indicated in the accompanying figures.

The Spectral Characteristics of Materials. From the standpoint of color, the effect of an object on light can be described by its *spectral transmittance* or *reflectance curve* (for transparent or opaque materials, respectively; both are needed for translucent objects). These curves show the fraction of the light at each wavelength transmitted by or reflected from the material, describing it just as the spectral energy distribution curve describes a source of light. The spectral reflectance curves of several opaque colored materials are shown on page 13. By comparing these figures with the hue names of the colors of the spectrum, and noting that colored materials always reflect light of their own color and (except yellow) absorb other hues, one can readily develop the ability to recognize colors in a general way from their spectral reflectance or transmittance curves.

Detecting Light and Color

By far the most important detector of *color* is the system comprising the eye, the nervous system, and the brain. We do not know exactly how it works, but all other detector systems attempt to duplicate its results in one way or another (Southall 1937, Wald 1964, Ciba 1965).

For color measurement, photodetectors (phototubes and photocells) are the only important detectors of light other than the eye. Their response is different for different wavelengths. The *spectral response* curves of these detectors and the eye are shown on page 14. As developed in Section D, the fact that the spectral response curves of photodetectors are unlike that of the eye is of considerable importance in color measurement.

Summary

In this section we said that the physical production of color requires three things: a source of light, an object which it illuminates, and a detector of some sort, usually the eye and brain.

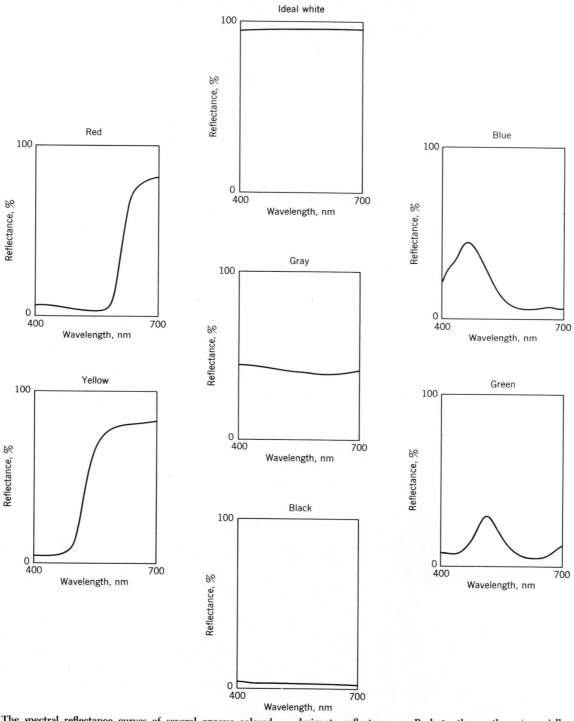

The spectral reflectance curves of several opaque colored materials, with their color names (Kelly 1955, 1958). We designate reflectance as **R**, but other authors (especially European) may use the symbol β.

The spectral response curves of the eye and of some photoelectric detectors of light.

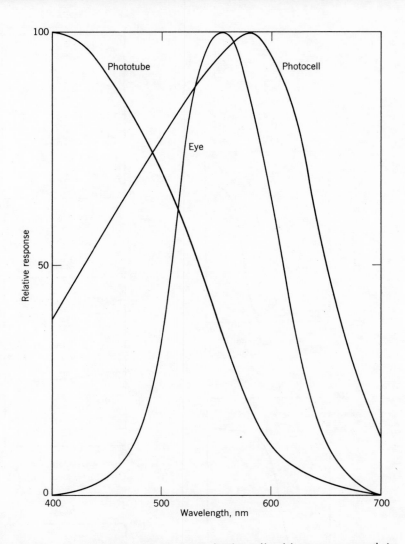

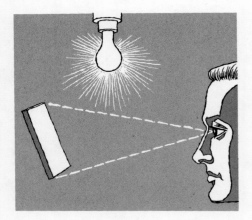

We saw how each of these three is described by an appropriate curve plotted against the wavelength: the light source, by its spectral energy distribution curve; the object, by its spectral reflectance or transmittance curve; and the detector, by its spectral response curve.

The combination of these provides the *stimulus*, or signal, which the brain converts into our perception of color. We must now consider some psychophysical and psychological, rather than physical, concepts which are essential to understanding and talking about the appearance of color.

C. The Description of Color

At this point we invite the reader to approach the subject of color with us from an entirely different point of view, setting aside for the moment almost everything that was said in Section

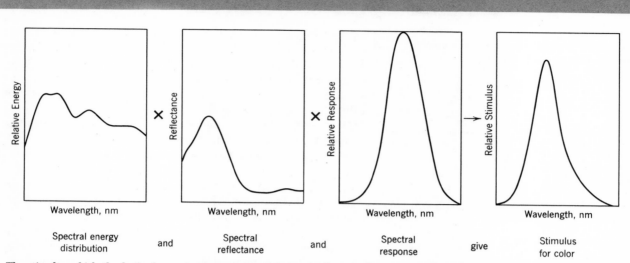

| Spectral energy distribution | and | Spectral reflectance | and | Spectral response | give | Stimulus for color |

The stimulus which the brain (or an instrument) interprets as a color is made up of the spectral energy distribution curve of a light source times the spectral reflectance or transmittance curve of an object times the spectral response curve of a detector. (Although the stimulus curve looks superficially like the spectral response curve of the eye, careful examination will show that they are really quite different.)

B. Almost, but not quite: We will not be allowed to forget the importance of the triad of source, object, and observer.

Our first objective is to describe color as we see it. In this section we shall simplify this problem by considering only the description by a single observer of how colors appear to him when illuminated by one source of light. Specifically, we shall ask how a person with normal color vision describes colors seen in daylight. In Section D we shall add to this picture some of the variations which can be obtained by changing the characteristics of the source or the observer or both.

The "Desert Island" Experiment

One of the many possible approaches to describing color is the so-called "desert island" experiment discussed by Judd (1952, 1963) and others. Suppose a person with no previous experience in dealing with colors were idling away his time on a desert island, surrounded by a large number of pebbles having a wide variety of colors. Suppose, further, he wished to arrange these pebbles in some orderly way, according to their color. How can we describe color in terms of what he might do?

One can think of many different ways in which our lonely castaway might solve this problem. We shall describe only one, which may not be the most obvious, or the most logical, or the best, but which will serve our purpose well enough.

Let us assume that our experimenter, thinking about color in terms of the common names red, blue, green, etc., as most of us do, chooses first to separate the colored pebbles from those without color—that is, those which are white, gray, or black. In

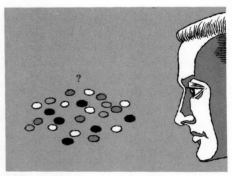

In the "desert island" experiment, an observer is faced with a large number of colored pebbles. To arange them in an orderly way by color . . .

more sophisticated terms, we can say he separates the *chromatic*, or colored, pebbles from the *achromatic*, or colorless, ones.

On examining the achromatic stones, our observer would find that they could be arranged in logical order in a series going from white through light gray to dark gray and finally black. This arrangement in terms of a single varying quality, *lightness*, provides a place for every achromatic pebble in the collection. Another common name for this quality is *value*.

The colored pebbles provide a more complicated situation, because they differ from one another in several ways, not just by differences in lightness. Our experimenter could separate them first by *hue*—that is, into different piles he calls red, yellow, green, blue, etc. Each of these piles might be further subdivided as finely as he wants, for example by separating the green group into yellow-green, green, and blue-green piles.

Each group of pebbles of a given hue could then be separated by *lightness* just as the achromatic stones were. The red pebbles, for example, could be separated into a series starting with the lightest pinks and becoming gradually darker, ending with very dark cherry reds. Each red pebble would be recognized as being equivalent in lightness to one of the gray pebbles in the colorless series and, if the subdivisions were fine enough, equivalent in hue to all the other reds in its group.

But our friend would recognize that some of his red pebbles (and those of other hues too) differ from others in some way besides hue and lightness. He might, for example, compare a

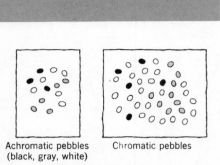

Achromatic pebbles   Chromatic pebbles
(black, gray, white)

... he first separates out the achromatic or colorless stones ...

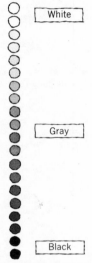

White

Gray

Black

... and arranges them in order of *lightness*, from white through gray to black. ...

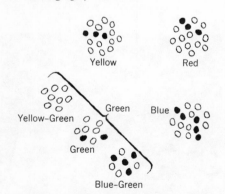

Yellow   Red

Yellow-Green   Green   Blue

Green

Blue-Green

... Next he separates the chromatic or colored stones, first by *hue* ...

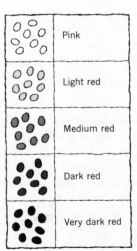

Pink

Light red

Medium red

Dark red

Very dark red

... and then by lightness within each hue. ...

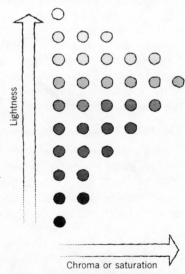

Lightness

Chroma or saturation

... Recognizing that the stones in each pile are still not all alike, he subdivides them, finally, on the basis of difference from gray or color content, which we call *chroma* or *saturation*.

brick-red stone with one having a vivid tomato-red color. He would have to admit they have the same hue: Neither is a yellower or bluer red than the other. Likewise, he would see that they have the same lightness, being equivalent in that quality to the same medium-gray stone taken from the achromatic series. Yet they are distinctly different. He might, after some thought, recognize that this third kind of difference relates to how much the colors of the stones differ from gray—in crude terms, how much color, or chromaticness, or *chroma*, they contain. Another common name for this third variable quantity in color is *saturation*.

Color Coordinates

Once our castaway had separated all his stones by hue, lightness, and saturation (or hue, value, and chroma) he would find that his systematic arrangement provided a place for all the pebbles on the island. None, in fact, that he could imagine to exist would be left out. He would conclude, correctly, that three and only three quantities (let us call them *color coordinates*) must be specified to describe color.

Note that we said three and only three quantities must be specified to describe *color*, but this does not completely describe the *appearance* of objects. As we mentioned on page 11, other qualities, such as its size, gloss, and surface texture, and the colors of nearby things (the *surround*), also affect the appearance of an object (Evans 1948).

The scheme we have described, with hue, value, and chroma as its color coordinates, is widely used to describe color in a systematic way, as in the Munsell color-order system described on page 26. Although these three coordinates are widely used, it would be possible to pick others on which to base the systematic description of color. For example, one might choose *brightness*, a combination of lightness and saturation, as one of the variables. This does not mean that more than three coordinates at a time are needed to describe color.

The word brightness is, unfortunately, used in several ways. We talk here about "dyer's brightness," a combination of saturation and lightness (Davidson 1950). When applied to the appearance of light sources, brightness is a quantity equivalent to the lightness of objects.

Now that we have a description of color as it appears to the observer, can we relate these psychological concepts of what color is to the physical picture which was developed in Section B, where the color of an object was stated to depend on its spectral reflectance curve? The answer is "yes" or at least "almost." As we will develop in Chapter 2, we can calculate, from the spectral reflectance or transmittance curve, sets of three numbers which describe color. If we make the calculations complex enough, the numbers begin to correlate with what we see as hue, lightness, and saturation. Quite probably we shall never be able to improve the calculations to the point where the numbers represent *exactly* what the marvelous human eye sees, or even to recognize when or how we have failed to do this. For practical purposes, this is not very important.

HUE
VALUE or LIGHTNESS
CHROMA or SATURATION

Color coordinates

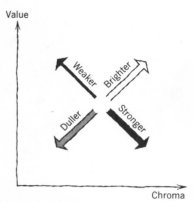

Color coordinates commonly used in the dyeing industry. Hue or "shade" is another variable not considered here.

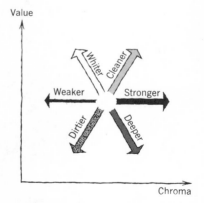

Color coordinates commonly used in the paint industry. Again, hue is another important variable.

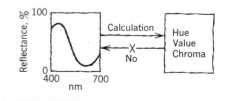

D. The Appearance of Color

Now that we have developed a framework for describing the way colors appear to an observer, we may consider how this appearance changes when the three important factors influencing color—the source of light, the object, and the observer—are changed.

Light Sources, Color Rendition, and Adaptation

Let us consider first a common situation in which the object and the observer remain constant but the light source changes. As a familiar example, you purchase a rich-brown suit in the tailor's shop, lighted with warm-colored tungsten bulbs, only to find it has a distinctly unpleasant greenish hue when you get it under daylight in the street. What has happened?

In the summary on page 12 we pointed out that the physical stimulus which the brain converts into our concept of color is made up by combining (by multiplying, wavelength by wavelength) the spectral energy distribution of the source, the spectral reflectance curve of the object, and the spectral response curve of the detector (here, the eye). The curves on pages 19 and 20 illustrate this combination and show that the stimuli to the brain do differ: we can expect the perceived colors to differ also. In terms of the psychological description of Section C rather than the physical description of Section B, we may say that the change in illumination has made the object appear greener, darker, and less saturated. We conclude also that the color coordinates of an object, like its perceived color, change when the illuminant changes.

This situation is quite analogous to that of an observer looking at two different objects under the same light source, as the curves on page 19 suggest. We expect that similar effects take place if the source and the object remain the same but the observer changes. This is harder to prove, but some people have been found whose eyes differ sufficiently in their spectral response curves to bear this out.

The eye and brain are wonderful devices, and they usually try to compensate for the changes presented to them. In one of his famous demonstration lectures, Ralph M. Evans shows a series of very similar color slides, modifying the illuminant slightly for each one until the last is shown with tungsten light whereas the first was seen in daylight. The eye adapts to the small changes differentiating each slide from the next and the audience is usually unaware of what is going on until, at the end, the first and last slides are shown side by side in startling contrast.

The point we wish to make is that the power of adaptation of the eye is such that if everything changed in the same way with change in illuminant (or object or observer), even large effects might go unnoticed. But there are many examples where this is not the case, and they are quite important for the practice of making and selling colored objects.

It is a common (and sometimes unpleasant) fact that the same object can have different colors when seen by the same observer under different light sources . . .

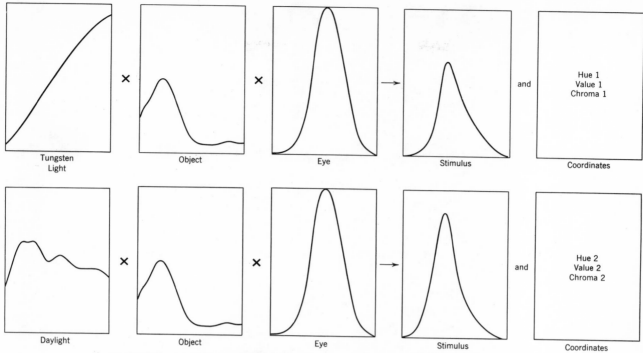

... but this is only natural if we recall that the sensation of *color* requires a light source *and* an object *and* an observer. If any one of these changes, with no compensating change in another, the color must change. . . .

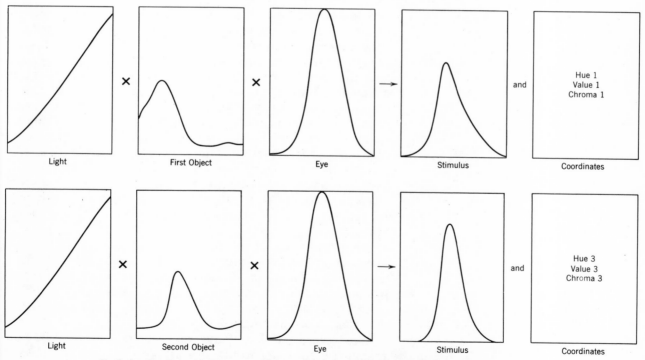

... Similarly, the colors of different objects are different even if the light source and observer are the same . . .

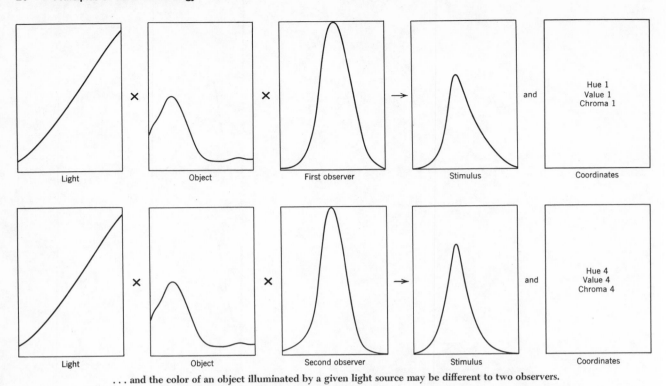

| Light | × | Object | × | First observer | → | Stimulus | and | Hue 1
Value 1
Chroma 1
Coordinates |

| Light | × | Object | × | Second observer | → | Stimulus | and | Hue 4
Value 4
Chroma 4
Coordinates |

. . . and the color of an object illuminated by a given light source may be different to two observers.

Metamerism

Since we are now looking for differences in the way objects behave when the illuminant or the observer changes (but not both at once), we must think in terms of pairs of objects. The specific situation of importance is this: Two objects are seen to have the same color—that is, to *match*—when viewed under one illuminant. They do not match, however, under another illuminant. From what we have seen, and as shown in the figures on page 21, this must mean that the two objects have different spectral reflectance curves. If they do match under one illuminant, they must have the same color coordinates. There is no conflict between these two statements, for the spectral reflectance curve contains much more information than the set of three color coordinates derived from it. Many different spectral reflectance curves correspond to the same set of color coordinates.

We define a pair of objects, having different spectral reflectance curves but the same color coordinates for one illuminant, as *metameric objects*, or a *metameric pair*. They are said to exhibit *metamerism*. Pairs of objects having the same spectral reflectance curve and, therefore, the same color coordinates for all illuminants, are *non-metameric*.

We deplore the use of the word isomeric to describe non-metameric pairs, for to the chemist who is in the business of color and coloring, metameric and isomeric mean the same, not opposite, things (Hackh 1944, Webster 1961).

The concept of metamerism can also be applied to cases where a pair of objects appear to some observers to have the

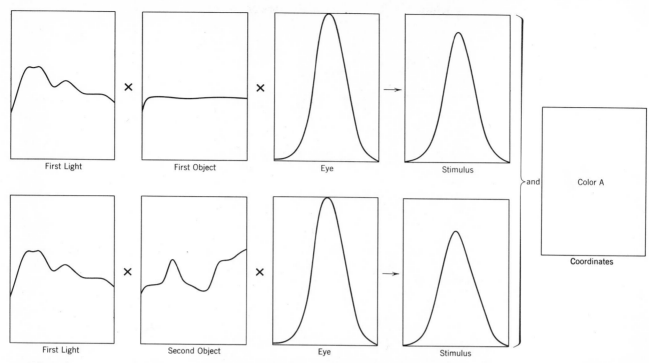

The two members of a *metameric pair* of objects have the same color for one light source even though they have different spectral reflectance curves . . .

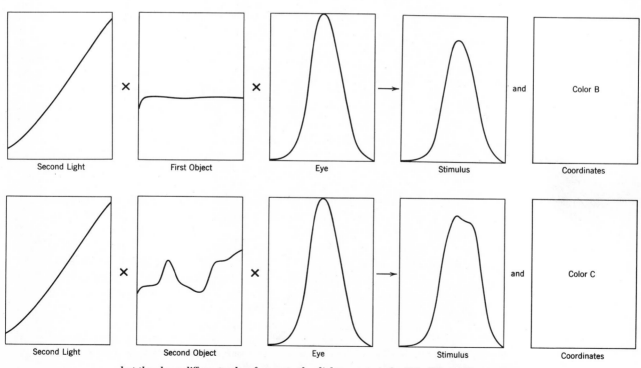

. . . but they have different colors for most other light sources (color B is different from color C) . . .

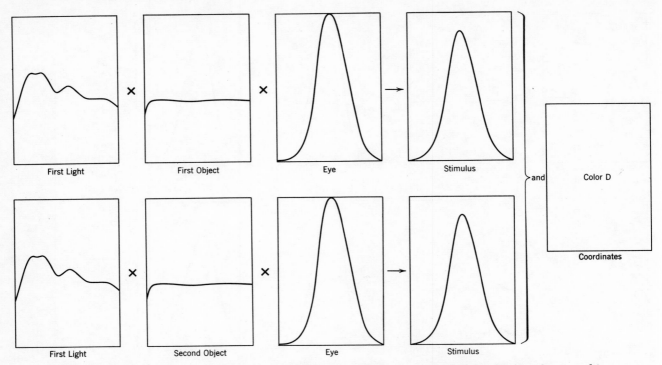

... whereas the members of a *nonmetameric* pair of objects always yield the same stimulus and therefore have the same color. . . .

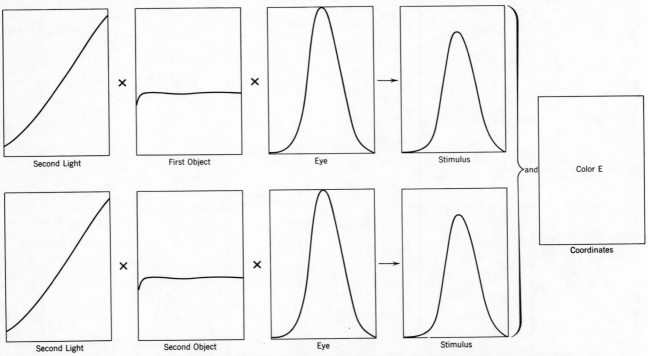

... When the illuminant is changed, the two members of a nonmetameric pair still yield the same stimulus and have the same color. But note that color **D** is *not* the same as color **E**.

same color, but to other observers the same objects do not match. We call this *observer metamerism*. It results from minor differences in the spectral response curves of the observers, none of whom can be said to be color blind. It is important to note, as described on page 69, that the two "observers" need not be human, but can be two instruments with significantly different spectral response characteristics.

An understanding of metamerism is important in color matching. As discussed further in Chapter 5B, if two objects are to match invariably, under all illuminants, they must have identical spectral reflectance curves. This can be achieved in practice only by using the same colorants for the two samples. If this cannot be done, as for example when different materials such as a textile and a paint are to be matched, such invariant matches are virtually impossible to achieve, and conditional or metameric matches must be accepted.

The properties of the eye are important in many other ways in color matching, as anyone familiar with this art knows. Some examples are the effects of adaptation, sample size, surroundings, and separation between samples (Evans 1948, p. 168; Interchem 1965).

It is perhaps not as often realized that instruments vary in their sensitivity to other aspects of appearance, and this affects their usefulness for color matching and color measurement. Regardless of the nature of the detector, the important fact we leave with you at the close of this chapter is that three factors are essential for the production, perception, and measurement of color: the source of light, the illuminated object, and a human or instrumental observer.

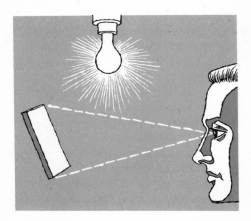

CHAPTER **2**

Color-Order Systems

The orderly description and specification of color is an essential part of solving problems of talking about color. Universally accepted languages are needed to express across a distance, over a span of time, or in the absence of the right physical samples, our ideas about the appearance of colored materials. Since we may wish to talk about color measurement, color perception, or the description of a particular product, we require many different languages to describe all aspects of color. In this chapter we describe and classify existing systems for arranging and describing color—that is, *color-order systems* or *color spaces*—with the objective of facilitating the choice of one most appropriate for a given purpose.

Of the many ways of classifying color-order systems, we choose to distinguish between collections of physical samples and systems which are not based on actual samples. The first group is subdivided according to the presence or absence of a guiding principle (such as equal visual perception) followed in building up the collection. Within each class and subdivision we describe one or more typical examples, but our list is not meant to be all inclusive. Many other systems are described by Wyszecki (1960) and Judd (1963, pp. 264–361).

A. Systems Based on Physical Samples

Random Arrangements

Collections of physical samples put together without major concern for a guiding principle are quite common. They range from completely random atlases to semiordered arrays. Most collections of samples designed to illustrate the colors available in a given product are random or nearly random groups of

> "Dining Room. To be yellow, and a very *gay yellow*. Just make it a bright sunshiny yellow and you cannot go wrong. Ask one of your workmen to get a pound of the A&P's best butter and match it *exactly*."
>
> **Hodgins 1946**

samples. Mode shade cards (for seasonal fashions), color cards (for telephones or damask napkins), and other manufacturers' catalogs are typical examples. The *Federal Color Card for Paint* (Federal Specification TT-C-595), the *House and Garden Colors*, and the *Color Forecasts of the Color Association of the United States, Inc.* are well-known collections of this type. An important defect of this type of array, which might be considered a criterion for calling a collection "random," is that it is *not* possible to deduce the colors of intermediate samples from those of the samples displayed.

Orderly Arrangements

In several industries, such as paint and printing ink, it is common to produce a wide variety of colored samples by the systematic mixing of a relatively few highly colored samples with one another and with white, black, and gray. Not only are the samples produced in this manner, but the product which is sold is made in the same way. Most major producers of house paint, as well as makers of industrial and automotive finishes, have systems of this type utilizing either custom mixing, frequently from elaborate dispensing and mixing devices, or factory pre-packaged units. Similar systems are offered in the printing ink industry and by suppliers of colorants for plastics. Two collections of considerable historical importance, produced in this manner, are the Maerz and Paul *A Dictionary of Color* (Maerz 1930) and the Ridgway *Color Standards and Color Nomenclature* (Ridgway 1912). A unique collection of this type is the transparent *Lovibond glasses* (Schofield 1939), with which a wide gamut of colors can be produced (Judd 1962a,b) by subtractive mixing in a visual color comparator, the *Lovibond Tintometer* (p. 62).

It is characteristic of most of these systems that interpolation between samples *is* possible. Moreover, some of the samples, such as the Lovibond glasses, have been measured and can be related, in an approximate way, to other color-order systems.

Arrangements Based on Principles

The Munsell System. Perhaps the best known of all color-order systems is the *Munsell System* (Munsell 1929, 1963; Nickerson 1940, Kelly 1943). Based on the guiding principle of equal visual perception of small color differences, the Munsell system is both a collection of samples painted to represent equal intervals of visual perception of color difference between adjacent samples, and a system for describing all possible colors in terms of its three coordinates, *Munsell Hue*, *Munsell Value*, and *Munsell Chroma*. These coordinates correspond to three variables commonly used to describe color; *hue* is that quality of color which we describe by the words red, yellow, green, blue, etc.; *value* is that quality by which a color can be classified as equivalent in lightness to some member of a series of gray samples ranging from white to black; *chroma* is the quality which describes the degree of difference between a color (which is itself not a white, gray, or black) and a gray of the same value or lightness.

Hue: that quality of color which we describe by the words red, yellow, green, blue, etc.

Value: that quality of color which we describe by the words light, dark, etc., relating the color to a gray of similar lightness.

Chroma: that quality which describes the extent to which a color differs from a gray of the same value.

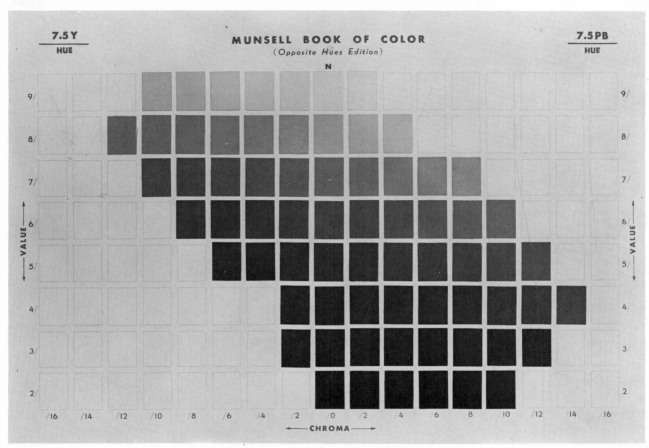

Arrangement of samples in the *Munsell Book of Color*.

The samples of the *Munsell Book of Color* (Munsell 1929) are usually arranged in planes or pages of constant hue. On each page, samples are arranged by Munsell Value in the vertical direction and by Munsell Chroma in the horizontal direction. A scale of grays, with white at the top and black at the bottom, may be thought of as the "trunk" of the Munsell color "tree," or as the zero-chroma column on each page. Each sample carries a *Munsell Notation* denoting its position; this notation consists of three symbols representing the Munsell Hue, Value, and Chroma in that order. Munsell Hue is expressed by a number and letter combination such as 5 Y or 2 GY where the letters are taken from the ten major hue names (*R*ed, *Y*ellow, *G*reen, *B*lue, *P*urple, and the five adjacent pairs of these, e.g., *G*reen-*Y*ellow) and the numbers run from 1 to 10. Munsell Value and Munsell Chroma are written after the hue designation and are separated by a diagonal line (/). A typical complete Munsell designation is 5 Y 5/6; the location of this designation is shown in the figure on the following page.

Two outstanding features of the Munsell System contribute to its usefulness and wide acceptance. The first is its conform-

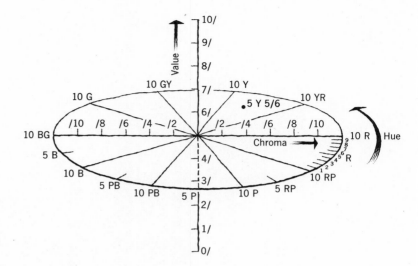

In the Munsell color-order system, colors are arranged by *hue* in a hue circle, by *value* or lightness from top to bottom, and by *chroma* or saturation according to distance out from the scale of grays making up the center column.

ance to equal visual perception. Within the limits of chroma (6–10) set by the samples of the original *Munsell Book of Color,* there is very little evidence for deviation from equal steps of perception in any of the Munsell coordinates. No other color system is as good in this respect; the Munsell System is the standard to which all other systems are compared.

The second major advantage of the Munsell System is that its notation is not linked to or limited by existing samples. Any conceivable color can be fitted into the system, whether it can be produced with existing colorants or not. In contrast, most collections of physical samples are based on highly colored specimens and could not accommodate a still more highly colored sample if one were found.

The Munsell designations of the original, matte finish, Munsell samples were subsequently adjusted somewhat to correct certain obvious errors in the original spacing. The new designations are known as *Munsell Renotations,* and the revised system as the *Munsell Renotation System* (Newhall 1943). Glossy samples were later painted (Davidson 1957) to whole-number Munsell Renotation designations. The Munsell Renotation System is related to the results of color measurement for all possible colors even though they cannot be produced by existing colorants.

The Munsell System was used as the basis of the ISCC-NBS system for designating color names (Kelly 1955), which was developed as an aid to standardizing the verbal description of color by names (see also Chapanis 1965). The published method tells how to assign an ISCC-NBS name to a color from its Munsell notation and includes a dictionary of common color names with their ISCC-NBS equivalents. Samples have been painted to represent the center of each region in Munsell color space corresponding to an ISCC-NBS name (Kelly 1958, NBS 1965).

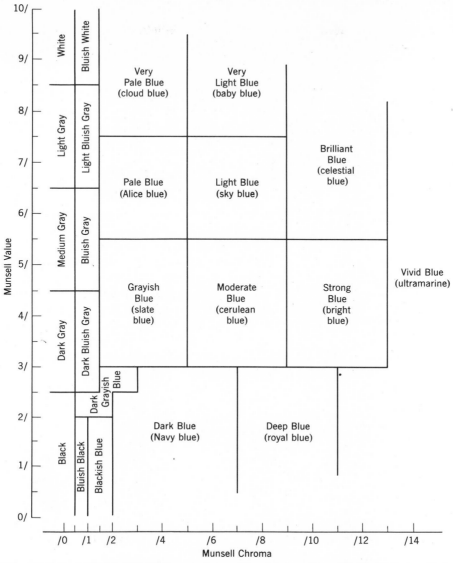

This page from the ISCC–NBS Dictionary of color names (Kelly 1955) shows the ISCC–NBS names assigned to colors with various Munsell Values and Chromas, and Munsell Hues between 9B and 5 PB. We have added some corresponding common names in parentheses.

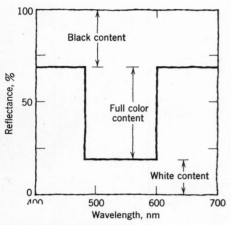

The spectral reflectance curve of a sample ideally fitting the Ostwald system would look like this and would be divided as indicated into black content, white content, and full-color content. Obviously, such a straight-sided curve cannot be obtained with real colorants.

The Ostwald System. In the Ostwald system (Ostwald 1931, Foss 1944, Jacobson 1948) colors are described by their *full color content*, *white content*, and *black content* in terms of idealized spectrophotometric curves, not attainable with existing colorants. The organization of the Ostwald system emphasizes scales of colors having approximately constant hue, constant black content, and constant white content. It is particularly convenient for artists, painters, ink makers, and others who work with mixtures of a colored pigment with black and white pigments.

A collection of samples arranged on the Ostwald principle is the *Color Harmony Manual* (Granville 1944, Container Corporation of America 1958). It contains over 900 samples, with glossy and matte sides, arranged in groups by Ostwald hue. Each group contains a pigment approximation to an Ostwald *semichrome* (color with no black or white content) and mixtures of it with black and white forming approximate scales of constant black content, constant white content, and constant "full-color" content. Like all real systems based on the Ostwald concept, it cannot be "extended" to include all possible colors.

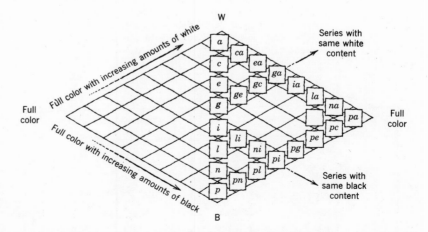

One set of color coordinates in the Ostwald system is *hue* (determined by the wavelengths of the vertical parts of the ideal spectral reflectance curve), *white content*, and *black content*.

Unlike the Munsell system, the Ostwald system suffers from a serious defect in that the same notation corresponds to different colors if different colorants are used to set up the system. Thus, as pointed out by Judd (1963, p. 243) an Ostwald notation is useful *only* to designate *a specific sample in a particular collection.*

B.   The CIE System

We come now to the description of color-order systems which are only incidentally, if at all, associated with collections of physical samples. By far the most important of these systems, which are usually used in connection with instruments for color measurement, is the CIE system (*C*ommission *I*nternational de l'*E*clairage or International Commission on Illumination) (CIE 1931, Judd 1933, 1950). This system is based on the concept of additive color mixing as derived from experiments in which colors are matched by mixing colored lights.

Though logical and straightforward, the arguments leading up to the rational basis of the CIE system are not the simplest to write down or to grasp. The reader who is more interested in the "how" than the "why" of the CIE system may wish to skip the following section at this time and pick up the story again on page 38.

Mixing Colored Lights

In a very old experiment (Newton 1730, Grassmann 1853), light from a test lamp shines on a white screen and is viewed by an observer. A nearby part of the screen is illuminated by light from one or more of three lamps, equipped to give light of three widely different colors, say, red [Ⓡ], green [Ⓖ], and blue [Ⓑ]. (In this section only we use the encircled letter R, Ⓡ, to designate a red light. Elsewhere in this book, R stands for reflectance.)

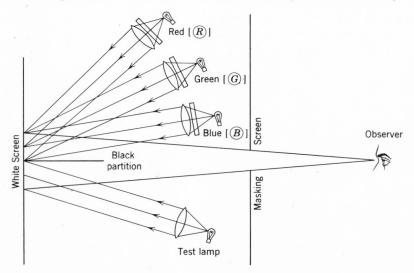

An arrangement for producing a large number of colors by mixing the light from three different colored lamps.

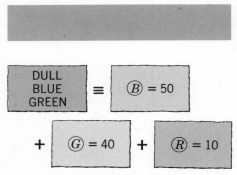

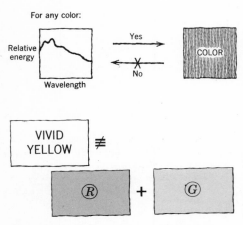

DULL BLUE GREEN ≡ Ⓑ = 50

+ Ⓖ = 40 + ⓇR = 10

The symbol ≡ means "is matched by," so this statement means that a dull blue green light is matched by 50 parts of blue light plus 40 parts of green light plus 10 parts of red light.

For any color:

Relative energy — Wavelength

Yes → COLOR

← No

VIVID YELLOW ≢

Ⓡ + Ⓖ

The symbol ≢ means "cannot be matched by."

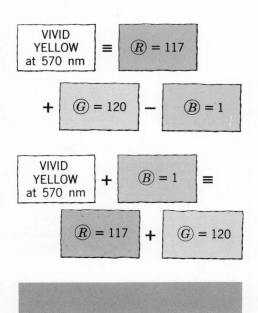

VIVID YELLOW at 570 nm ≡ Ⓡ = 117

+ Ⓖ = 120 − Ⓑ = 1

VIVID YELLOW at 570 nm + Ⓑ = 1 ≡

Ⓡ = 117 + Ⓖ = 120

For convenience, we may refer to these as *primary* lights. By adjusting the intensities of these lights, the observer can make their combined color on the screen match that of the test lamp. The purpose of the experiment is this: Colors can be specified in terms of the three numbers representing the amounts of the three primary lights added together to make the match; thus the term *additive color matching* is used. For example, a dull greenish-blue test light might be matched by 10 parts of [Ⓡ], 40 parts of [Ⓖ], and 50 parts of [Ⓑ].

The amounts of the three primaries, which are the three numbers describing the test color, are called the *tristimulus values* of that color. If we call the amount of red primary Ⓡ, the amount of the green, Ⓖ, and the amount of the blue, Ⓑ, the dull greenish-blue test light can be described by writing down Ⓡ = 10, Ⓖ = 40, and Ⓑ = 50.

It should be noted that the spectral energy distribution of the test light will usually be different from that of the combination of primaries matching it. They will form a metameric pair of light sources (p. 20) and their spectral energy distributions cannot be inferred from their colors.

If the colors of the three primary lights are quite different, a wide variety of test colors can be matched in this way (Grassmann 1853). It is found experimentally, however, that in no case can all possible test colors be matched with combinations of any one set of primaries, even if the spectrum colors are used as primaries. Thus, a bright yellow test light cannot be matched by any combination of red and green.

This problem can be overcome in several ways. In one, light from one of the primaries can be added to the test color, rather than mixed with that from the other two primaries. For describing the test color, this light can be thought of as being subtracted from the other primaries. Thus, the test color can be described by a combination of negative and positive amounts of primary light colors. Thus, the bright yellow test lamp is matched by [Ⓡ] plus [Ⓖ] minus [Ⓑ], or the yellow test light plus [Ⓑ] is matched by [Ⓡ] plus [Ⓖ].

By use of negative amounts of light as described above, we can match any test light by mixing only three colored lights. For example, all of the spectrum lights can be matched by combining positive and negative amounts of three primary lights. If we select for these primaries the spectrum colors in the red at 700 nm, in the green at 546 nm, and in the blue at 436 nm, the figure on page 33 shows the relative amounts, which we call $\bar{r}$, $\bar{g}$, and b, of these needed by a person with normal color vision to match any of the other spectrum colors, provided each of the spectrum light sources emits the same amount of energy.

Since we will ultimately be interested in objects instead of just lights, let us generate the test color by shining the light from a standard lamp through a transparent colored object onto one side of the screen. (With a slightly different arrangement an opaque reflecting object could just as well be used.) Let us put an entire series of spectrum lights on the other side of the screen, for example, a set spaced every 10 nm across the spec-

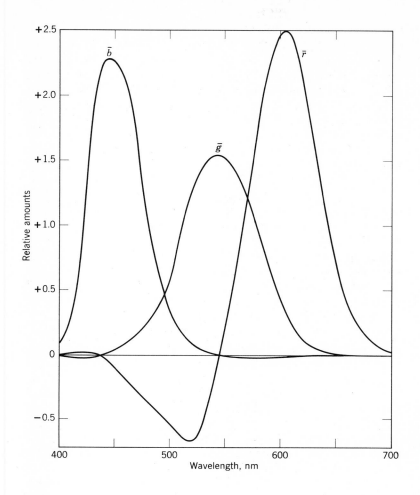

These curves show, for each wavelength, the amounts $\bar{r}$, $\bar{g}$, and $\bar{b}$ of the 700 nm red [Ⓡ], 546 nm green [Ⓖ], and 436 nm blue [Ⓑ] primaries needed by a normal observer to match each of the colors of the equal-energy spectrum (CIE 1931 Ⓡ-Ⓖ-Ⓑ system).

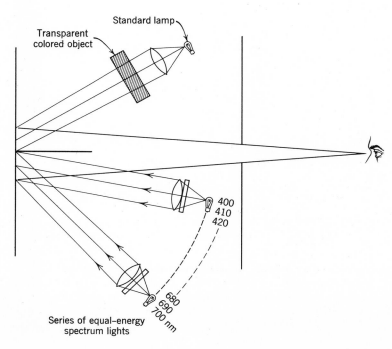

Arrangement for using spectrum lamps to duplicate the spectral energy distribution of a source and a transparent object.

trum from 400 to 700 nm, and all having initially the same energy. Now we can adjust the energy of a spectrum lamp until it equals that from the standard lamp and object at the wavelength of the spectrum lamp. By doing this for each of the spectrum lamps we will have duplicated, at 10 nm intervals, the energy distribution curve reaching the observer from the standard lamp and object.

Alternate arrangement for an opaque object.

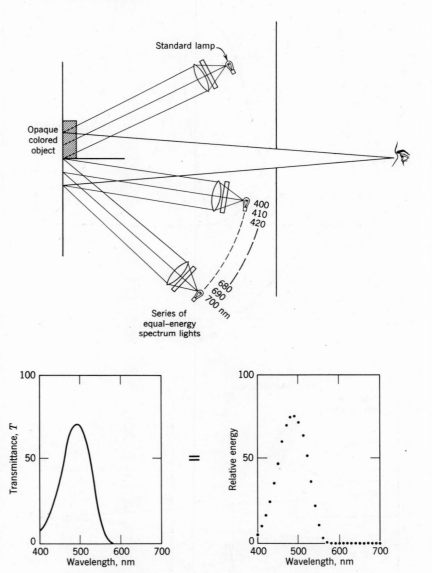

At each wavelength, the amount of light coming to the observer is obtained by multiplying E times T: $E \times T = ET$.

Now let us replace the standard lamp and object with our [Ⓡ], [Ⓖ], and [Ⓑ] primary lights and match the color from the series of spectrum lamps with these primaries. This gives us tristimulus values Ⓡ, Ⓖ, and Ⓑ, which are the correct tristimulus values for the test object and standard lamp.

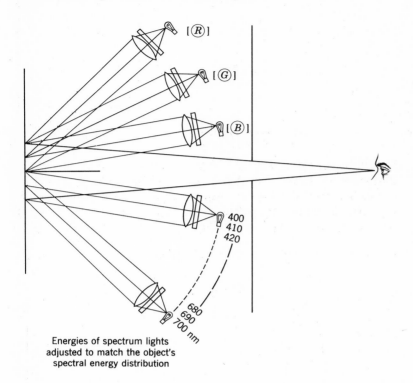

[Ⓡ]

[Ⓖ]

[Ⓑ]

400
410
420

680
690
700 nm

Energies of spectrum lights
adjusted to match the object's
spectral energy distribution

We have found a new way of calculating tristimulus values, as follows: If each spectrum lamp had unit energy, it would take an amount of light $\bar{r}$ from the red primary [Ⓡ], plus $\bar{b}$ from [Ⓑ], plus $\bar{g}$ from [Ⓖ], to match it, as we saw earlier. But each spectrum lamp has instead an energy $E \times T$ because we adjusted it to match the combination of the standard lamp and object. Therefore, it will take amounts $\bar{r} \times E \times T$, plus $\bar{g} \times E \times T$, plus $\bar{b} \times E \times T$, to make the match. If we add these amounts up for all of the spectrum lamps, we find the desired tristimulus values of the object as illuminated by the chosen standard lamp and seen by an observer with normal color vision. Thus, we can find tristimulus values if we know the spectral energy distribution of the standard lamp, the spectral transmittance (or, for an opaque object, reflectance) curve of the object, and the color-matching functions $\bar{r}$, $\bar{g}$, and $\bar{b}$ of the normal observer, bringing us around full-cycle to what was said in the summary of Chapter 1B on page 12.

But we still have the problem of negative numbers, and we wish to find some way of getting rid of these. On the other hand, we can now get the tristimulus values without actually performing the color-matching experiment with real lamps. Freed from this restriction, we can adopt another solution to the problem.

Tristimulus value Ⓡ = Sum over all wavelengths of $E \times T \times \bar{r}$, or in mathematical terms

$$Ⓡ = \sum_\lambda E\,T\,\bar{r}$$

similarly,

$$Ⓖ = \sum_\lambda E\,T\,\bar{g}$$

$$Ⓑ = \sum_\lambda E\,T\,\bar{b}$$

The symbol Σ means to take the sum and the symbol λ means over all wavelengths.

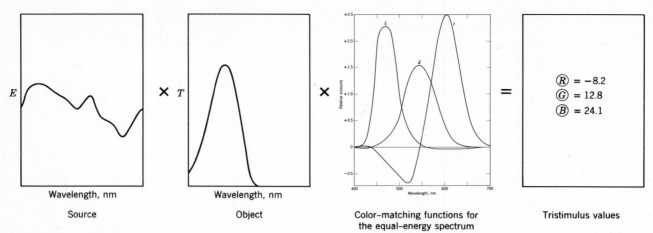

Source · Object · Color–matching functions for the equal–energy spectrum · Tristimulus values

$$\mathbb{R} = -8.2$$
$$\mathbb{G} = 12.8$$
$$\mathbb{B} = 24.1$$

The tristimulus values ®, ©, and ® of a color are obtained by multiplying together the relative energy E of a standard lamp, the transmittance T (or the reflectance) of the object, and the tristimulus values (or color-matching functions) of the equal-energy spectrum. The products are summed up for all the wavelengths in the visible spectrum to give the tristimulus values, as indicated in the diagrams and by the mathematical equations on page 35.

This is the use of unreal or imaginary primary lights, chosen so that their mixtures *do* match all possible real colors. This alternative has proved the most useful one devised so far for describing color in numerical terms. A particular set of unreal primaries, selected in 1931 by the CIE (CIE 1931, Judd 1933, 1950)

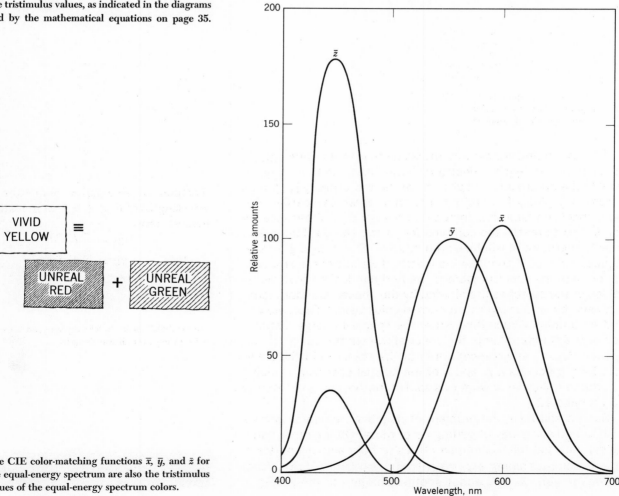

VIVID YELLOW ≡ UNREAL RED + UNREAL GREEN

The CIE color-matching functions $\bar{x}$, $\bar{y}$, and $\bar{z}$ for the equal-energy spectrum are also the tristimulus values of the equal-energy spectrum colors.

The CIE Color-Matching Functions $\bar{x}$, $\bar{y}$, and $\bar{z}$ Tabulated at 5 nm Intervals of Wavelength (OSA 1953)

Wavelength, nm	$\bar{x}$	$\bar{y}$	$\bar{z}$	Wavelength, nm	$\bar{x}$	$\bar{y}$	$\bar{z}$
380	0.0014	0.0000	0.0065	580	0.9163	0.8700	0.0017
385	0.0022	0.0001	0.0105	585	0.9786	0.8163	0.0014
390	0.0042	0.0001	0.0201	590	1.0263	0.7570	0.0011
395	0.0076	0.0002	0.0362	595	1.0567	0.6949	0.0010
400	0.0143	0.0004	0.0679	600	1.0622	0.6310	0.0008
405	0.0232	0.0006	0.1102	605	1.0456	0.5668	0.0006
410	0.0435	0.0012	0.2074	610	1.0026	0.5030	0.0003
415	0.0776	0.0022	0.3713	615	0.9384	0.4412	0.0002
420	0.1344	0.0040	0.6456	620	0.8544	0.3810	0.0002
425	0.2148	0.0073	1.0391	625	0.7514	0.3210	0.0001
430	0.2839	0.0116	1.3856	630	0.6424	0.2650	0.0000
435	0.3285	0.0168	1.6230	635	0.5419	0.2170	0.0000
440	0.3483	0.0230	1.7471	640	0.4479	0.1750	0.0000
445	0.3481	0.0298	1.7826	645	0.3608	0.1382	0.0000
450	0.3362	0.0380	1.7721	650	0.2835	0.1070	0.0000
455	0.3187	0.0480	1.7441	655	0.2187	0.0816	0.0000
460	0.2908	0.0600	1.6692	660	0.1649	0.0610	0.0000
465	0.2511	0.0739	1.5281	665	0.1212	0.0446	0.0000
470	0.1954	0.0910	1.2876	670	0.0874	0.0320	0.0000
475	0.1421	0.1126	1.0419	675	0.0636	0.0232	0.0000
480	0.0956	0.1390	0.8130	680	0.0468	0.0170	0.0000
485	0.0580	0.1693	0.6162	685	0.0329	0.0119	0.0000
490	0.0320	0.2080	0.4652	690	0.0227	0.0082	0.0000
495	0.0147	0.2586	0.3533	695	0.0158	0.0057	0.0000
500	0.0049	0.3230	0.2720	700	0.0114	0.0041	0.0000
505	0.0024	0.4073	0.2123	705	0.0081	0.0029	0.0000
510	0.0093	0.5030	0.1582	710	0.0058	0.0021	0.0000
515	0.0291	0.6082	0.1117	715	0.0041	0.0015	0.0000
520	0.0633	0.7100	0.0782	720	0.0029	0.0010	0.0000
525	0.1096	0.7932	0.0573	725	0.0020	0.0007	0.0000
530	0.1655	0.8620	0.0422	730	0.0014	0.0005	0.0000
535	0.2257	0.9149	0.0298	735	0.0010	0.0004	0.0000
540	0.2904	0.9540	0.0203	740	0.0007	0.0003	0.0000
545	0.3597	0.9803	0.0134	745	0.0005	0.0002	0.0000
550	0.4334	0.9950	0.0087	750	0.0003	0.0001	0.0000
555	0.5121	1.0002	0.0057	755	0.0002	0.0001	0.0000
560	0.5945	0.9950	0.0039	760	0.0002	0.0001	0.0000
565	0.6784	0.9786	0.0027	765	0.0001	0.0000	0.0000
570	0.7621	0.9520	0.0021	770	0.0001	0.0000	0.0000
575	0.8425	0.9154	0.0018	775	0.0000	0.0000	0.0000

has been widely used ever since for describing colors in the *CIE system*. These imaginary primary lights were selected so that (*1*) all possible real colors can be "matched" (an imaginary experiment, of course) by positive amounts of the primaries, so that negative numbers do not appear in the CIE system; (*2*) a relatively large range of colors in the yellow-red region can be "matched" with only two primaries; and (*3*) the intensity of the light needed to make the "match" (the luminosity or lightness of the color) is specified by one of the primaries alone.

It should be emphasized that, despite the use of imaginary primaries, the CIE system is very real indeed, for the amounts of these primaries needed to "match"—that is, to *specify*—any color can be calculated easily. This results from another of

VIVID YELLOW at 570 nm $\equiv$

$X = 76$ + $Y = 95$

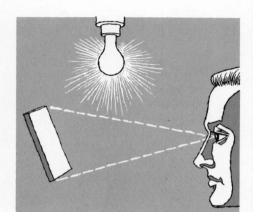

CIE Standard
Source

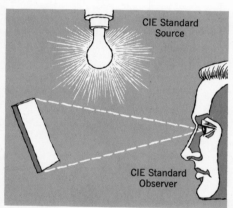

CIE Standard
Source

CIE Standard
Observer

The CIE system for describing colors is no different from any other except for its standardization of light sources and of an observer.

CIE Source A = Incandescent light (2854°K blackbody)

CIE Source B = Simulated noon sunlight

CIE Source C = Simulated overcast-sky daylight

$$X = \sum_{\lambda} E\,R\,\bar{x}$$
$$Y = \sum_{\lambda} E\,R\,\bar{y}$$
$$Z = \sum_{\lambda} E\,R\,\bar{z}$$

Grassmann's laws (Grassmann 1853) which states that the color-matching functions or tristimulus values of the spectrum colors can be calculated for any specified set of primaries if they are known for one set of primaries. Thus if we call the 1931 CIE primaries [X], [Y], and [Z], the color-matching functions $\bar{x}$, $\bar{y}$, and $\bar{z}$ can be calculated from $\bar{r}$, $\bar{g}$, and $\bar{b}$ (which were originally determined experimentally). The figures on the preceding pages give the CIE color-matching functions $\bar{x}$, $\bar{y}$, and $\bar{z}$.

The 1931 CIE Sources, Observer, and Coordinates

Just as color invariably involves three components—a source of light, an illuminated object, and an observer—the CIE system requires and provides both standard light sources and a standard observer to complete the description of the color of objects. The 1931 *CIE standard observer* is a numerical description of the response to color of the normal human eye, as expressed by the color-matching functions $\bar{x}$, $\bar{y}$, and $\bar{z}$. The *CIE Standard Sources* A, B, and C—simulating incandescent light, noon sunlight, and overcast-sky daylight, respectively—exist in physical form as lamp–filter combinations, providing standard light sources for viewing colors. The CIE system describes the colors of objects illuminated by these sources and viewed by observers with normal color vision.

Here we must point out a distinction, in CIE terminology, between a source and an illuminant. A *source* is a real physical light which can be turned on and off and used in real color-matching experiments. A, B, and C are sources, although B and C are very seldom used in this way. The spectral energy distribution of a *source* is determined by experiment (for Sources A, B, and C, see Davis 1953). An *illuminant,* on the other hand, is defined by a spectral energy distribution, and it may or may not be possible to make a *source* representing it. The proposed CIE Illuminant D_{6500} described on page 137 is an illuminant by definition, representing average natural daylight, but there are artificial sources available duplicating D_{6500} closely (McLaren 1965). A source can be used as an illuminant, as are A, B, and C for calculating tristimulus values from spectrophotometric data, and in such cases it is correct to speak of Illuminants A, B, and C.

The standard coordinates of the 1931 CIE system are the *CIE tristimulus values X, Y, and Z*. These coordinates can be either determined directly in color matching or measuring experiments with colored lights or calculated from spectral reflectance curves with the aid of tables giving the tristimulus values of the pure spectrum color at each wavelength, that is, $\bar{x}$, $\bar{y}$, and $\bar{z}$. These numbers are multiplied, wavelength by wavelength, by the reflectance of the sample and the relative energy of the light source, and the products are added up for all the wavelengths in the visible spectrum. The sums are the tristimulus values of the sample.

If any one of the tristimulus values can be said to be the most important, it is Y, for this coordinate is the *luminance* or intensity of the matching light, equal to the *luminous transmittance* or *luminous reflectance* of the object. It is usual to describe the

Source:	A physically realizable light, whose spectral energy distribution can be experimentally determined. When the determination is made and specified, the source becomes a *standard source.*			*Illuminant:*	A light defined by a spectral energy distribution, which may or may not be physically realizable as a *source*. If it is made available in physical form, it becomes a *standard source.*		

Spectral Energy Distributions of CIE Standard Sources A, B, and C

Wavelength, nm	E_A	E_B	E_C	Wavelength, nm	E_A	E_B	E_C
380	9.79	22.40	33.00	580	114.44	101.00	97.80
385	10.90	26.85	39.92	585	118.08	100.07	95.43
390	12.09	31.30	47.40	590	121.73	99.20	93.20
395	13.36	36.18	55.17	595	125.39	98.44	91.22
400	14.71	41.30	63.30	600	129.04	98.00	89.70
405	16.15	46.62	71.81	605	132.70	98.08	88.83
410	17.68	52.10	80.60	610	136.34	98.50	88.40
415	19.29	57.70	89.53	615	139.99	99.06	88.19
420	21.00	63.20	98.10	620	143.62	99.70	88.10
425	22.79	68.37	105.80	625	147.23	100.36	88.06
430	24.67	73.10	112.40	630	150.83	101.00	88.00
435	26.64	77.31	117.75	635	154.42	101.56	87.86
440	28.70	80.80	121.50	640	157.98	102.20	87.80
445	30.85	83.44	123.45	645	161.51	103.05	87.99
450	33.09	85.40	124.00	650	165.03	103.90	88.20
455	35.41	86.88	123.60	655	168.51	104.59	88.20
460	37.82	88.30	123.10	660	171.96	105.00	87.90
465	40.30	90.08	123.30	665	175.38	105.08	87.22
470	42.87	92.00	123.80	670	178.77	104.90	86.30
475	45.52	93.75	124.09	675	182.12	104.55	85.30
480	48.25	95.20	123.90	680	185.43	103.90	84.00
485	51.04	96.23	122.92	685	188.70	102.84	82.21
490	53.91	96.50	120.70	690	191.93	101.60	80.20
495	56.85	95.71	116.90	695	195.12	100.38	78.24
500	59.86	94.20	112.10	700	198.26	99.10	76.30
505	62.93	92.37	106.98	705	201.36	97.70	74.36
510	66.06	90.70	102.30	710	204.41	96.20	72.40
515	69.25	89.65	98.81	715	207.41	94.60	70.40
520	72.50	89.50	96.90	720	210.36	92.90	68.30
525	75.79	90.43	96.78	725	213.26	91.10	66.30
530	79.13	92.20	98.00	730	216.12	89.40	64.40
535	82.52	94.46	99.94	735	218.92	88.00	62.80
540	85.95	96.90	102.10	740	221.66	86.90	61.50
545	89.41	99.16	103.95	745	224.36	85.90	60.20
550	92.91	101.00	105.20	750	227.00	85.20	59.20
555	96.44	102.20	105.67	755	229.58	84.80	58.50
560	100.00	102.80	105.30	760	232.11	84.70	58.10
565	103.58	102.92	104.11	765	234.59	84.90	58.00
570	107.18	102.60	102.30	770	237.01	85.40	58.20
575	110.80	101.90	100.15	775	239.37	86.10	58.50
				780	241.67	87.00	59.10

The spectral energy distribution curves of the CIE standard sources are shown on pages 6 and 7 and tabulated above.

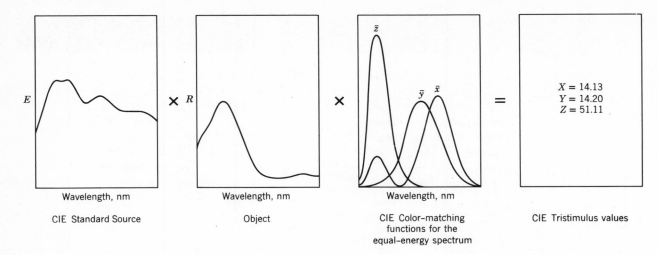

CIE Standard Source   Object   CIE Color-matching functions for the equal-energy spectrum   CIE Tristimulus values

The CIE tristimulus values X, Y, and Z of a color are obtained by multiplying together the relative energy E of a CIE standard light source, the reflectance R (or the transmittance) of the object, and the tristimulus values of the equal-energy spectrum colors $\bar{x}$, $\bar{y}$, and $\bar{z}$. The products are summed up for all the wavelengths in the visible spectrum to give the tristimulus values, as indicated in the diagrams and by the mathematical equations on page 38.

Wavelength, nm	R, %	$E_c\bar{x}$	$E_cR\bar{x}$	$E_c\bar{y}$	$E_cR\bar{y}$	$E_c\bar{z}$	$E_cR\bar{z}$
400	23.3	0.00170	0.04	0.00004	0	0.00807	0.19
420	33.0	0.02474	0.82	0.00073	0.02	0.11889	3.93
440	41.7	0.07944	3.31	0.00524	0.22	0.39846	16.62
460	50.0	0.06719	3.36	0.01387	0.69	0.38569	19.29
480	47.2	0.02222	1.05	0.03234	1.53	0.18908	8.93
500	36.5	0.00104	0.04	0.06797	2.48	0.05724	2.09
520	24.0	0.01151	0.27	0.12914	3.10	0.01423	0.34
540	13.5	0.05566	0.75	0.18285	2.47	0.00390	0.05
560	7.9	0.11751	0.93	0.19668	1.55	0.00078	0.01
580	6.0	0.16822	1.01	0.15972	0.96	0.00032	0
600	5.5	0.17885	0.99	0.10624	0.58	0.00014	0
620	6.0	0.14130	0.85	0.06301	0.38	0.00004	0
640	7.2	0.07381	0.53	0.02884	0.21	0	0
660	8.2	0.02720	0.22	0.01007	0.08	0	0
680	7.4	0.00737	0.05	0.00268	0.02	0	0
700	7.0	0.00164	0.01	0.00058	0	0	0
			Sum = X = 14.23		Sum = Y = 14.29		Sum = Z = 51.45

How to calculate tristimulus values from spectral distribution data. The products of the spectral energy distribution of the illuminant, E, and the tristimulus values of the spectrum, $\bar{x}$, $\bar{y}$, and $\bar{z}$, are tabulated in many books (Judd 1952, 1963; OSA 1953; Hardy 1936; Mackinney 1962, etc.) as they are here for CIE Illuminant C. Such tabulations must be adjusted so that the sum of $E\bar{y} = 1.000$ in order for the tristimulus values to be correct.

$$x = \frac{X}{X + Y + Z}$$

$$y = \frac{Y}{X + Y + Z}$$

$$z = \frac{Z}{X + Y + Z}$$

These equations define the CIE *chromaticity coordinates x, y,* and *z.* In some books, for example Hardy 1936, *x, y,* and *z* are known as the *trichromatic coefficients.*

chromaticity of the object, that is, the qualities of its color other than luminance (such as hue and chroma) by ratios of the tristimulus values to their sum. These ratios are known as the *chromaticity coordinates, x, y,* and *z.* Since the sum of the chromaticity coordinates is 1, they provide only two of the three coordinates needed to describe the color. One of the tristimulus values, usually Y, must also be specified.

Color as described in the CIE system can be plotted on a *chromaticity diagram,* usually a plot of the chromaticity coordinates x and y. Perhaps the most familiar feature of the chromaticity diagram is the horseshoe-shaped *spectrum locus,* the line connecting the points representing the chromaticities of the spectrum colors. The chromaticities of blackbody sources, as well as of CIE standard Sources A, B, and C, are also shown in the figure on this page. Locations corresponding to common color names are indicated in the similar diagram on page 43.

It is important to note that the CIE system is not associated with any particular set of physical samples. Only incidentally have sets of samples been produced to illustrate the system. Nor is the system based on steps of equal visual perception in any sense, although many modifications of the CIE system have been proposed as approaches to equal perception.

An alternative set of chromaticity coordinates, *dominant wavelength* and *purity,* correlate more nearly with the visual aspects of hue and chroma, although their steps and spacing are not visually uniform. The dominant wavelength of a color is the wavelength of the spectrum color whose chromaticity is on

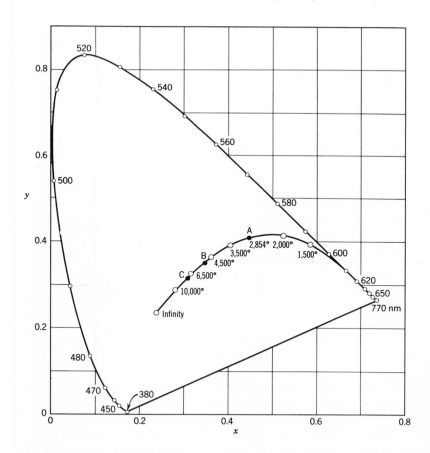

This is the famous CIE 1931 chromaticity diagram, showing the horseshoe-shaped spectrum locus with the spectrum colors identified by their wavelengths, the locus of blackbody light sources identified by their color temperatures in °K, and the locations of the CIE standard Sources A, B, and C.

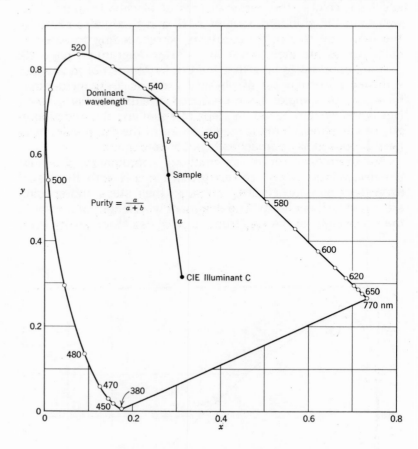

The definitions of dominant wavelength and purity are shown on this CIE chromaticity diagram.

the same straight line as the sample point and the illuminant point. Purity is the distance from illuminant to sample divided by that from illuminant to spectrum locus. Dominant wavelength and purity are readily obtained by reading them off large-scale graphs of the x, y chromaticity diagram found in A. C. Hardy's *Handbook of Colorimetry* (Hardy 1936). Computer programs have also been written for calculating dominant wavelength and purity (McCarley 1965).

The full three coordinates of the CIE system are usually plotted as on page 43 with the Y axis rising from the illuminant point of the chromaticity diagram. Only colors of very low luminance, such as spectrum colors, can lie as far away from the illuminant axis as the spectrum locus; all other colors have lower purity. The limits within which all colors having a given luminance must lie have been calculated (Rösch 1929, MacAdam 1935) and are shown projected onto the plane of the chromaticity diagram in the figures on page 44. They serve to outline the volume in x, y, Y space within which all real colors lie. Models (Nickerson 1943, Billmeyer 1953) show the shape of this volume.

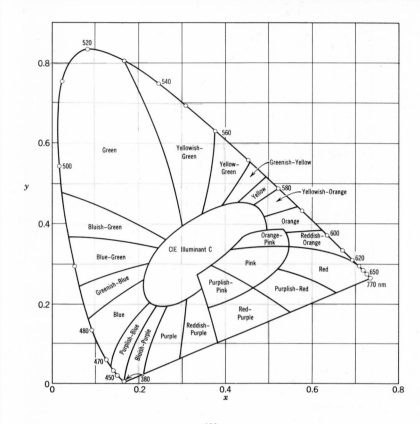

The names of various colors are shown on this CIE chromaticity diagram (Judd 1950, 1952).

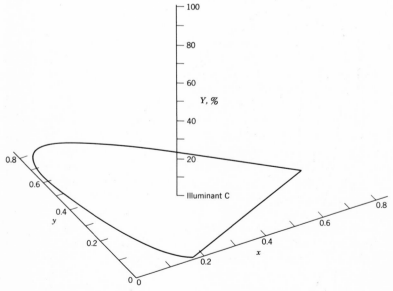

The third dimension of color is conveniently added to the CIE chromaticity diagram by thinking of the luminance or lightness axis rising up from it. Lighter colors lie in space at their proper level of Y and above the point representing their chromaticity x, y.

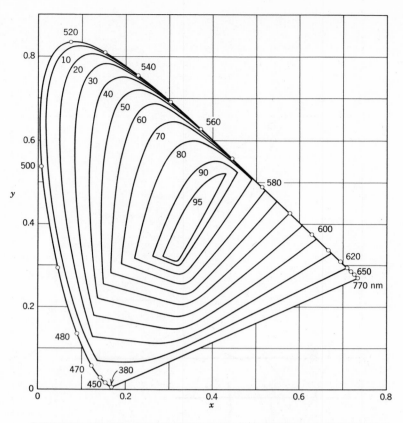

The lighter a color is, the more restricted the range of chromaticity it can have. This diagram shows the "MacAdam limits" of the chromaticity of real colors, viewed in daylight (CIE Source C), for different values of their luminance, Y.

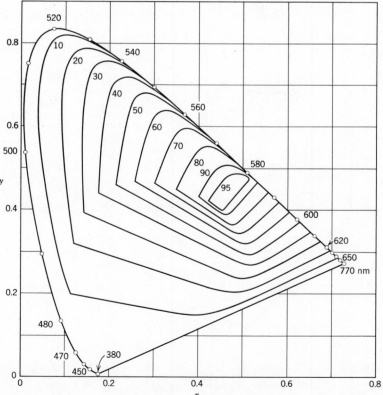

The MacAdam limits are shown here for colors viewed in tungsten light (CIE Source A).

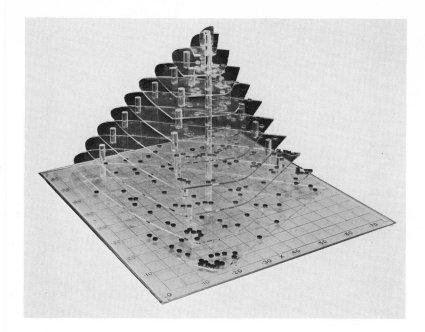

This photograph shows a model of the CIE system in three dimensions. The transparent plastic sheets are cut to the outlines of the MacAdam limits for Source C.

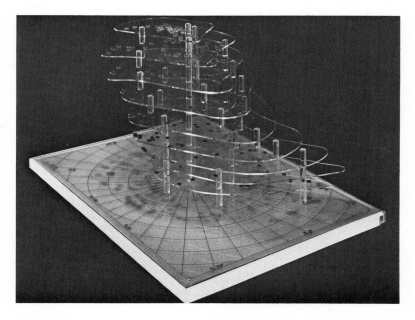

This model was built by converting the MacAdam limits into Munsell Hue, Value, and Chroma. It shows the boundaries in Munsell space within which all real colors must fall.

It is interesting to convert the MacAdam limits into the coordinates of the Munsell system. Models (Billmeyer 1953) built in this way show that the limits including all real colors in the equally-visually-spaced Munsell system form a very irregular solid.

C.   Uniform Chromaticity Systems

Transformations of the CIE System

Many transformations of the CIE system have been devised in attempts to produce ways of plotting in which pairs of colors,

A "linear transformation" results in the stretching or distortion of a familiar figure (Chamberlin 1955).

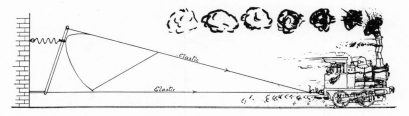

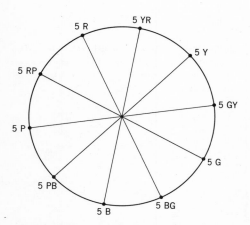

If equal distances represent equal differences in color, the ten Munsell colors with the hues shown in this figure (and value 5 and chroma 8) would lie, as shown, at equal distances from one another and equal distances from the center or neutral point, assuming that the Munsell System represents perfect visual spacing. In figures like this on the following pages, equality of visual spacing, compared to that of the Munsell System, can be judged by the amount of distortion of the circle.

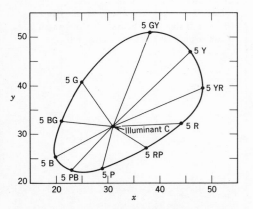

Equal visual spacing in the CIE system.

perceived as being equally different in visual perception, plot as being equally spaced. The success of these systems in portraying equal visual spacing can be assessed by plotting the positions of some of the Munsell colors in their coordinates (Burnham 1949). In the figures on this and the following pages, the locations of the Munsell colors are indicated for the 10 major hues at value 5 and chroma 8. For perfect agreement with Munsell visual spacing, these locations should lie on a circle centering at the illuminant point. Their locations in the CIE system are shown in the figure on this page.

One of the first transformations developed to improve the visual spacing of the CIE system was the Uniform Chromaticity Scale (UCS) system of Judd (1935). Later, a rectangular UCS or RUCS system was devised by Breckenridge (1939) for use in describing the colors of signal lights. MacAdam (1937) developed a system (u,v system) which in 1960 was tentatively recommended by the CIE as an approximation to uniform visual perception (see p. 140). Later, he developed (MacAdam 1943) another system, widely used for the calculation of small color differences, but it cannot be described by simple equations and is seldom used for plotting the entire chromaticity diagram. A system devised by Hunter (1942) is closely related to the readings of his color measuring instruments.

Other Perceptually Uniform Systems

Several systems have been developed in specific attempts to duplicate the uniform spacing of the Munsell System, either using transformation equations which are not too complex or adjusting the spacing in an empirical way. The DIN system (Richter 1955) makes use of coordinates similar to dominant wavelength, purity, and luminance. It is illustrated by physical samples arranged by a hue variable based on dominant wave-

$$r = \frac{2.7760x + 2.1543y - 0.1192}{-1.0000x + 6.3553y + 1.5405}$$

$$g = \frac{-2.9446x + 5.0323y + 0.8283}{-1.0000x + 6.3553y + 1.5405}$$

These equations show how the coordinates of the UCS system are calculated from those of the CIE system. Similar sets of equations are shown for other systems on the following pages.

$$x' = \frac{0.82303x + 0.82303y - 0.82303}{1.00000x - 7.05336y - 1.64023}$$

$$y' = \frac{3.69700x - 5.07713y - 1.36896}{1.00000x - 7.05336y - 1.64023}$$

$$x'' = 0.0750 - x'$$

$$y'' = y' - 0.5000$$

Equations for the RUCS system.

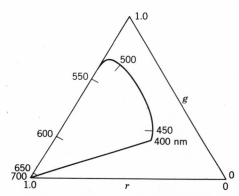

In Judd's UCS system, the horseshoe-shaped spectrum locus of the CIE system is transformed into this shape. Similar distortions are shown for other systems in figures like this on the following pages.

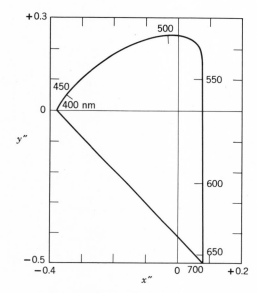

Spectrum locus in the RUCS system.

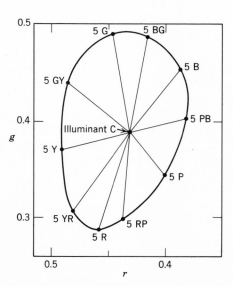

Equal visual spacing in the UCS system.

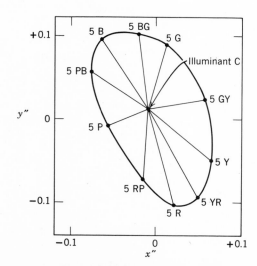

Equal visual spacing in the RUCS system.

$$u = \frac{4x}{-2x + 12y + 3}$$

$$v = \frac{6y}{-2x + 12y + 3}$$

Equations for the MacAdam system.

$$\alpha = \frac{2.4266x - 1.3631y - 0.3214}{1.0000x + 2.2633y + 1.1054}$$

$$\beta = \frac{0.5710x + 1.2447y - 0.5708}{1.0000x + 2.2633y + 1.1054}$$

Equations for the Hunter system.

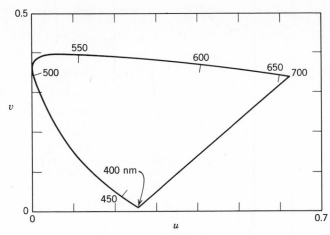

Spectrum locus in the MacAdam u,v system.

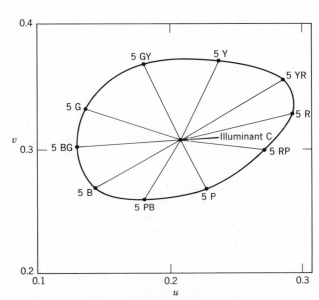

Equal visual spacing in the MacAdam system.

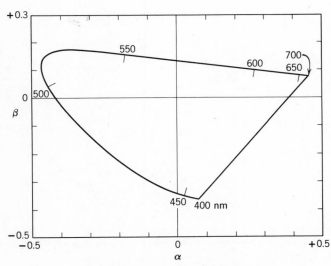

Spectrum locus in the Hunter system.

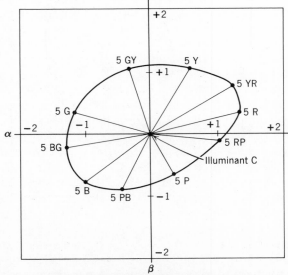

Equal visual spacing in the Hunter system.

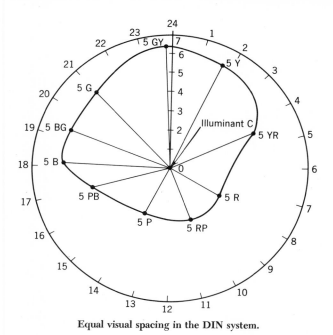

Equal visual spacing in the DIN system.

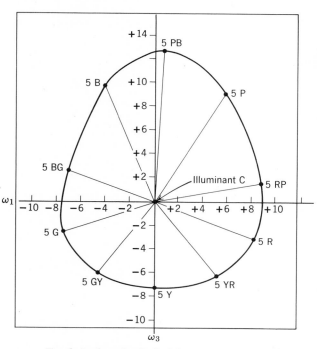

Equal visual spacing in the Moon-Spencer system.

length, a "darkness" scale approximating visual lightness perception, and a saturation scale similar in some ways to Munsell Chroma. Equality of visual spacing is not as good as that of the Munsell System. The Chromatic Value system of Adams (1942) is widely used for calculating small color differences. The Omega Space of Moon and Spencer (Moon 1943) introduced the effect of the surrounding field on the judgment of color differences in an attempt to improve the spacing. Among the more successful, but correspondingly more complex, systems of this sort is the Saunderson-Milner Zeta Space (Saunderson 1946). A system devised by Glasser (1958) is based on that of Adams and corresponds closely to colorimeter readings.

Few systems have departed from the assumption that the Munsell System is the ultimate in equal visual spacing. The Adjusted-Hue system (Billmeyer 1961) shows better conformity to visually perceived hue than the Munsell system; however, the two differ only in regions of color space beyond the highest chromas of the opaque *Munsell Book of Color* samples but accessible with transparent specimens.

By now it should be obvious that it is very difficult, if not truly impossible (Wright 1959), to calculate, from CIE coordinates or other results of instrumental color measurement, numbers which describe colors exactly as the normal eye sees them. Inevitably, the question arises as to why anyone should want to do this if it is so troublesome a task. This is a question we find a little hard to answer. Experience has shown that people can and

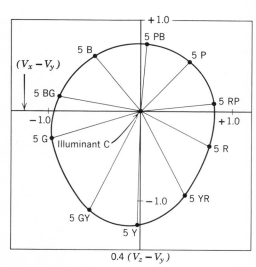

Equal visual spacing in the Adams chromatic value system.

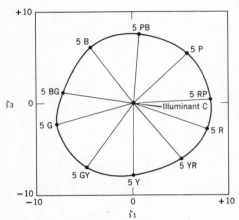

Equal visual spacing in the Saunderson-Milner system.

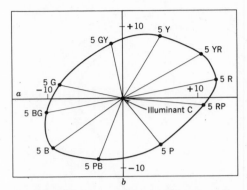

Equal visual spacing in Glasser's cube root system.

do get used to describing colors and color differences in many different systems, whether they are perceptually uniform or not. Sometimes we wonder exactly what a person would do, that he could not do otherwise, with a perfectly uniformly perceptual system if he had one.

D. Single-Number Color Scales

Many systems have been devised for describing the color of a series of related objects in terms of a single number. More often than not, these objects differ in a single respect, such as the amount of a colored component or impurity, and their color varies with this amount over a relatively narrow and well-defined range, for example from colorless through yellow to orange or red.

The assignment of a color number in such a case usually involves visual comparison of the test object to a series of standards. If the standards are selected to have color and spectral transmittance (or reflectance) curves similar to those of the test object, the comparison is not difficult and the position of the test object on the scale can be determined easily and precisely. In these cases, single-number scales are very useful and valuable.

However, the test sample may differ in color from the standards in some other way than that in which the standards differ among themselves. Then the test sample may neither look like any of the standards nor appear to fall between them, since the sample and standard form a metameric pair (Chapter 1D). In cases like this, it becomes difficult or impossible to make a reliable judgment of the position of the sample on the scale, and indeed it may well be said not to have such a position. Here, attempts to use a single-number scale may produce erroneous and misleading results. A common example is the estimation of the yellowness of a reddish or greenish sample, using a set of pure yellow standards: it cannot be done in a satisfactory way.

Lightness Scales

Since the lightness of an object is one of its most important color coordinates, much attention has been paid to devising scales of lightness corresponding to uniform visual perception in this variable. The early Munsell lightness scale (Priest 1920) assumed that lightness is just proportional to the square root of luminance. This is approximately correct when the samples of a gray scale are viewed on a white background. This scale was later adopted by Hunter (1942), who made his colorimeters direct-reading in lightness, L. If the samples are viewed against a background of middle gray, the equation must be modified (Godlove 1933, Munsell 1933) to take into account the reflectance of the background. A slight modification of this relation led to the Munsell Value scale (Newhall 1943), probably the most widely accepted lightness scale at the present time. Later, Glasser (1958) showed that a cube-root function is a good approximation to the Munsell Value equation for reflectances greater than 1%.

$$V = Y^{1/2}$$
$$\text{where } Y_{max} = 100$$

This equation (Priest 1920) and those following are approximate relations between CIE Y and Munsell Value. The Priest equation was later used by Hunter to define his lightness variable L.

$$V = (1.47Y - 0.474Y^2)^{1/2}$$
$$\text{where } Y_{max} = 100$$

The Munsell-Godlove approximation to the Munsell Value equation.

$$Y/Y_{\text{MgO}} = 1.2219V - 0.23111V^2 + 0.23951V^3 - 0.021009V^4 + 0.0008404V^5$$

The Munsell Value function as defined by Newhall (1943) in the Munsell Renotation System.

$$L = 25.29\,Y^{1/3} - 18.38$$
$$\text{where } Y_{max} = 100$$

The cube root lightness function defined by Glasser (1958).

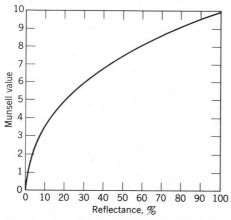

How the Munsell Value function varies with luminance (CIE Y).

Yellowness Scales

Since the presence of small amounts of yellowness in nearly white (or nearly colorless) samples is both common and, usually, objectionable, considerable attention has been paid to devising uniform yellowness scales. Some colorimeters (Hunter 1942, 1958b) are direct-reading in a yellowness coordinate, while with others a simple calculation gives a satisfactory measure of yellowness. The ASTM (ASTM D 1925) has adopted a yellowness scale derived (Billmeyer 1966b) by converting the formula based on colorimeter readings into one based on CIE color coordinates. These scales correlate with visual perception only for colors seen as yellow or blue; in the latter case, the yellowness index is a negative number. They should never be used to describe colors which are visibly reddish or greenish.

$$\text{Yellowness coordinate} = +b$$

On Hunter's colorimeters, the color coordinate b measures yellowness.

$$\text{Y. I.} = 100\,(R - B)/G$$

A yellowness index can be calculated from colorimeter readings (above). When converted into CIE coordinates, it has the form shown below (ASTM D 1925, Billmeyer 1966b).

$$\text{Y. I.} = (128X - 106Z)/Y$$

$$W = 4B - 3G$$

The ASTM equation for whiteness in terms of colorimeter readings (ASTM 1966).

$$W = 10\,(Y - 2p^2)^{1/2}$$
where $p = $ CIE per cent purity

The Chemstrand whiteness scale (Coppock 1965) for nonfluorescent materials.

$$W = 100 - [(100 - L)^2 + (a^2 + b^2)]^{\frac{1}{2}}$$

A whiteness scale based on Hunter's *L, a, b* coordinate system (Hunter 1942, 1958a,b).

Whiteness Scales

As with yellowness, whiteness is a subjective quality of surface colors whose quantitative measurement is very desirable. Unfortunately, there is even less agreement than with yellowness as to what constitutes a preferred white, resulting from differences of opinion among observers as well as with fashion and styling considerations. Nevertheless, several approaches to the definition of quantitative scales of whiteness have been made, as indicated by the equations on this page.

Other One-Dimensional Color Scales

Many scales have been devised in attempts to define the color of natural or commercial products (water, lubricating oils, rosin, paint vehicles, and other transparent materials) by single numbers. Some of these are described by Judd (1952, 1963). Correlations among them are under study by the Inter-Society Color Council; publication will follow completion of the work. These scales are very valuable when used with the proper precautions. If, however, the chromaticity or the spectral transmittance curves of the sample differ from those of the standards of the scale, it may be difficult or impossible to assign the sample a number on the scale, and ambiguous or misleading results may be obtained.

E.   Summary

This chapter has described a few of the ways in which colors may be classified and specified in an orderly fashion. What we have begun to do is assign numbers to the colors and the effects we described in Chapter 1. The next step in this process is to see how such numbers can be measured; this is the subject of Chapter 3.

CHAPTER 3

Color Measurement, Specification, and Tolerances

We have seen—several times by now—that three factors are needed for the production of color: a light source, an object to be illuminated, and an observer who both detects the light and converts the signal it detects into what the human brain recognizes as color. We have seen also that, for many reasons, it is useful to assign numbers to this response called color, so that it can be described accurately to someone else, somewhere else, at some other time. Now we come to the question of how this can be done, the subject of color measurement.

When we see the words "color measurement" most of us think of the use of instruments. But this is only one way to measure color, and probably not the most common nor the simplest way at that. The visual, rather than instrumental, examination and comparison of colored materials is just as much a measurement of color as that involving an elaborate and complex instrumental method. There is no need to consider the eye and an instrument as fundamentally different tools for measuring color.

A. Basic Principles of Measuring Color

Regardless of the techniques used, color measurement can be divided into two major steps: *examination* and *assessment*.

Examination

The step of examination of a color involves just the familiar triad which we have mentioned so many times:

a. A source of light which illuminates the sample and the standard.

b. The sample which is to be evaluated and the standard against which it is to be compared. In visual examination and in

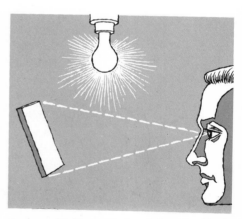

A source of light, an object, and the eye and brain

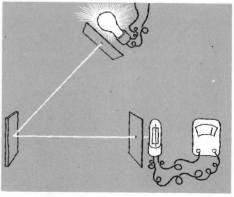

—or a source of light, an object, and a photo-electric detector and meter.

53

some instruments the standard and the sample are viewed at the same time. Viewing the sample and standard in succession is not good practice visually (Newhall 1957) but is commonly used in instrumental color measurement.

c. Some means of detecting the light which comes from the material being examined.

Assessment

The second step in color measurement is conveniently divided into the three operations necessary in order to make a decision as to whether the sample is or is not the same as the standard:

a. A statement must be made as to whether there is a difference between the sample and the standard. This statement may be in terms of instrument readings or in words, either thought, spoken, or written down.

b. Assuming a difference does exist, the statement about it must be expressed in terms which have the same meaning to all the people involved. These terms can be a standardized verbal description, using color terminology previously agreed upon, or the simple statement of the instrument readings themselves, or the coordinates of a point in some acceptable color-order system, to which the visual or instrumental data are converted.

c. The difference, however expressed, must be evaluated, and a decision must be made as to the acceptability of the sample. We have chosen to group these two steps together, although in practice they may be carried out separately, even by people other than those making the measurements.

It is this final step which is the most difficult in the whole procedure of color measurement and evaluation, but it is the one which fulfills the objective of the entire process.

THINK and LOOK

It is clear that people, rather than machines, must get involved in the final steps of the assessment procedure, if nowhere else. The reason for this is obvious: Machines can't think.

Many of us have seen, and perhaps been amused by, the signs prominently displayed by a large corporation that say THINK. If we have ever seen a machine, such as a large computer, turning out incorrect and useless data at an incredible rate, the signs get somewhat less amusing. They serve as a reminder that so far no machine, but only people (and perhaps not even all people) can do this. So our first word of advice in the measurement of color by any technique is THINK.

A second word of advice is an obvious one since we are dealing with a visual phenomenon: LOOK. This advice, also, is all too frequently ignored. No matter what methods of color examination are used, we cannot stress too strongly that the samples should be looked at. For, in the final analysis, the color match will eventually be judged by somebody looking at it.

We feel that, in every place where color is examined, the two words THINK and LOOK should be prominently displayed as a continuous reminder to all.

EXAMINATION
a. Light source
b. Sample and standard
c. Detector

ASSESSMENT
a. Difference or not
b. Description of difference
c. Acceptable or not

Statement of Difference
Standardized terminology: duller, yellower, darker

Instrument readings:

$$\frac{R_{\text{Standard}}}{R_{\text{Sample}}} = 98.0$$

$$\frac{G_{\text{Standard}}}{G_{\text{Sample}}} = 99.2$$

$$\frac{B_{\text{Standard}}}{B_{\text{Sample}}} = 99.1$$

Coordinates related to visual perception:

Directly from instrument:
$$\Delta L = -1.2, \Delta a = +0.7, \Delta b = -0.3$$
or

By calculation from instrumental readings:
$$\Delta C = 3.2, \Delta L = 1.5, \Delta E = 3.6$$

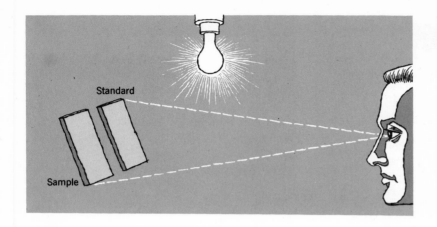

Standard

Sample

In the visual examination of colored objects, the sample and standard are usually placed side by side and viewed at the same time.

B.   The Sample

As we start our consideration of the steps involved in color measurement, we come first to the origin of the sample. We believe that this point should be considered in some detail.

Samples for Analysis

One thing that we in the business of coloring frequently forget is that color measurement is nothing more than a special technique of analysis. As such, it shares with all other analytical techniques the fundamental problem of obtaining a representative sample (Walton 1959). Care must be taken in the way in which the sample for analysis is selected, regardless of the means to be used for examining and evaluating the sample. If a decision is to be made on the basis of color measurement about a run of molded-plastic articles, painted parts, or bolts of dyed cloth, we must be certain that the sample to be examined truly represents the material being considered.

Our justification in mentioning this fact, which seems so obvious, lies in our experience that the question of sampling for color measurement is so often ignored. Laboratories in which standard products such as hydrochloric acid are carefully sampled according to statistical plans, and in which the results of replicate analyses must agree within previously stated tolerances, frequently make their color judgments on the basis of a single measurement on a single sample obtained in some fashion unknown to the analyst. Why should this be so we cannot say, except that there is a general aura of mystery and confusion surrounding the question of color measurement in many laboratories.

Form Suitable for Inspection

Whether a sample truly represents the material being examined is the first question to be asked before undertaking any color measurement, visual or instrumental. This question includes both selecting a sample and the further step of converting it into a form suitable for inspection. While there are a few cases where a finished article is already in a form suitable for either visual or instrumental examination after proper sampling, most materials require that the sample be handled in some special way. For example, a sample of fabric must be folded so that a standard number of layers is presented for examination, or a sample of paint or plastic molding powder must be converted to a colored object.

In the case of colorants, such as dyes or pigments, the problems are much more difficult, for it is not possible to make a suitable judgment of the performance of the colorant on the basis of its appearance as a dry powder. There is no substitute for the conversion of the colorant to the final form in which it is to be used, and it is difficult to get a technique, on a laboratory scale, which will duplicate results obtained in the plant with a given dye or pigment (Saltzman 1963a,b).

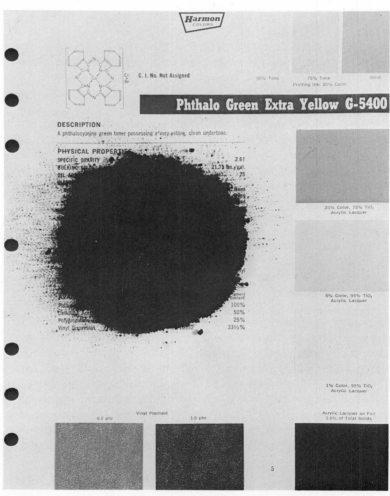

Munsell Renotation of Color Swatches

		H	V	C
Printing ink	50%	5.7G	8.4/3.2
	75%	6.0G	7.5/7.7
	Solid	4.9G	6.6/12.6
Acrylic lacquer	25%	6.0G	5.8/10.2
	5%	8.1G	7.5/7.2
	1%	9.7G	8.6/3.7
Acrylic lacquer on foil	1.6%	5.3G	4.3/10.4
Vinyl plastisol	1.0 PHR	3.7G	4.2/10.0
	0.2 PHR	4.3G	5.8/12.7
Pigment powder		4.4BG	4.3/6.3

Most colorants look quite different as raw materials (for example, the dry pigment powder sprinkled on the shade card) and as prepared in a form suitable for examination (for example, dispersed in a paint film or a plastic). The Munsell color coordinates of the sample are given in the left-hand column to illustrate the difference.

The conversion of any sample of colored material into a form suitable for examination requires a standardized procedure which is both repeatable (by the same person in the same laboratory) and reproducible (by different people in different laboratories at different times). It is only within the past few years that any amount of data has become available on the ability of the laboratory to produce replicate samples from the same colored materials (Peacock 1953, Billmeyer 1962, Johnston 1963, Saltzman 1965). Only after this ability is acquired and reliable data are available as to the repeatability of the test, can one begin to discuss a comparison of a batch of material with any accepted standard.

Again, LOOK

The question of converting a colorant into a form suitable for inspection assumes greater importance where the measurement of color is done by instruments. Reliance on the use of measurements by instruments in laboratories where a sample is simply "fed" to the machine and the results handed back to a central point, may lead to serious errors due to improperly prepared samples. When, for example, a paint panel is being looked at and compared with a standard, a trained observer will notice whether or not the sample and standard are in good condition. This is something which no machine, however complex, can do yet. Machines, though useful, cannot think. It is for this reason that we emphasize that the samples which are to be examined for color *must be looked at* before any evaluation is attempted, regardless of the techniques to be employed. This is especially true in large laboratories where sample preparation is done by someone other than the person who makes the examination.

C. Visual Color Measurement

For convenience in discussion, and not because of any fundamental differences, we choose to separate the subject of color measurement into discussions of wholly visual methods, techniques involving visual detectors in instruments, and entirely instrumental tests. In each section, the three subdivisions of the steps of examination and assessment remain all important. In purely visual examination, however, some of the steps in the assessment procedure may be combined. In many such examinations, the evaluation is a simple decision as to acceptability or non-acceptability (go/no-go type of judgment) without any attempt to describe the difference or express it in other than rough qualitative terms.

Sample and Single Standard

The visual examination and evaluation of color is the one most commonly used today. There are many standard methods for making this type of measurement (ASTM D 1535, D 1729). In the simplest form, the essential elements are the sample to be evaluated and a single standard, both viewed at the same time by an observer using a standardized light source. If agreement can be obtained between buyer and seller on the standard to be

EXAMINATION
a. Light source
b. Sample and standard
c. Detector

ASSESSMENT
a. Difference or not
b. Description of difference
c. Acceptable or not

used and the standard conditions of viewing (including the exact type of light or lights used), a great step forward has been made, even though the evaluation has been left to the eyes and brains of two different individuals.

For the determination of whether the color of two samples is or is not identical, the visual examination of the two samples, side by side, under standardized lighting conditions, is unsurpassed. In many cases, a single light source is not adequate for proper inspection and two or more standardized sources may be agreed upon. With the increased use of varied light sources, especially those which are quite different from daylight or tungsten lamps, it has become almost essential to use at least two (and in many cases three) standardized sources of illumination for the examination.

The related problem of variability in observers has not yet yielded to standardization in a like manner. Differences among observers, all with normal color vision by the usual tests, can lead to at least as great a variation in the judgment of what constitutes a match as can the use of different light sources (Brown 1957, Nimeroff 1962, Smith 1963). Unless observer differences are recognized and taken account of, for example by prior agreement, no amount of standardization of light sources can lead to satisfactory results.

Sample and Multiple Standards

The use of a single standard against which the sample is compared leads to difficulties immediately when the two are not identical. This stems from the fact that the single standard represents only one point in a three-dimensional world of color. If the sample does not match the standard, we would like both to describe the difference accurately and to say whether it falls within certain limits previously agreed upon. That is, we would like to know both *how* and by *how much* the sample and standard differ.

While the eye is an excellent judge of whether or not a color difference exists between two samples . . .

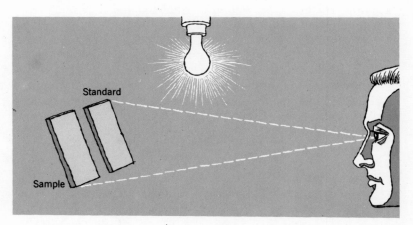

This brings us to an area of quantitative and analytical judgment in which the eye is less adept than it is at judging whether or not two materials are alike. To use the jargon of the world of instrumentation, the eye is an excellent *null detector*—that is, a detector of the point at which there is no difference. It is considerably less trustworthy in estimating how big a given difference is.

This limitation of the human eye can be compensated for by giving it more than one standard with which to make comparisons. If the observer has a second standard which is a known distance away from the first (in a given direction in color space), his judgment of whether the sample is closer to or farther away from the primary or *target standard* than is the second or *limit standard* (in the same direction, of course) is made much simpler.

Visual examination with the aid of one or more limit standards in addition to the target standard is becoming quite common. The number of limit standards as well as the degree of difference from the target will depend upon the level of color tolerance involved (Kelly 1962, 1965). Where necessary, fairly elaborate systems have been evolved, examples of which are the *Munsell Color Standards for Plastic Insulated Wire and Cable* (Munsell 1962) and the Color Packs prepared for purchase specifications by Sears, Roebuck and Co. In these systems, limit standards are set up in three directions from the target standard. In addition to the target standard, there are high and low limits for lightness and darkness (Munsell Value), hue (Munsell Hue), and saturation (Munsell Chroma). The use of a complete set of limits standards combined with standardized illuminants provides a very satisfactory procedure for plant control work. It is essential, of course, that these limit standards be prepared with the same colorants used in the products being inspected. This is not always the case with commercially available systems of this type, however.

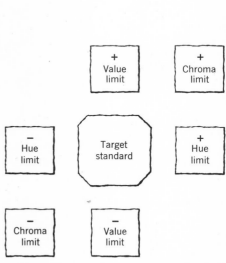

In this arrangement, the eye is presented with six standardized color differences (between the target standard and each limit standard). The difference between sample and target standard can be compared with one or more of these.

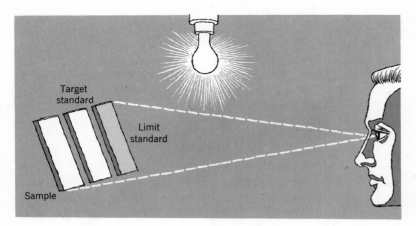

... it can estimate the *size* of such a difference (as between sample and target standard) much better in direct comparison with another color difference (as between limit standard and target standard) viewed at the same time.

It is important to remember that there is frequently a great difference between the conditions under which colored materials are examined and those under which they are used. The use of color-coded wire and cable is an excellent example. Here it is required that two different colored wires always look different when seen under field conditions. Color standards which will provide this assurance must be quite different from those needed to control the color of objects which must look exactly alike under viewing conditions which permit the slightest color difference to be perceived. Limit standards must be adapted to both the tolerance level involved (Kelly 1962, 1965) and the purpose for which color control is being sought (Halsey 1959a,b).

The procedure involving limit standards leads logically to the use of instruments. Since the limit standards define the range of acceptable materials, their measurement with an instrument of adequate sensitivity provides numerical values for these limits. The actual numbers obtained depend on the type of instrument and should only be used as previously agreed. This is discussed in Section E of this chapter.

The use of limit standards is quite common in the field of the measurement of the color of liquids or solids where the variation from a standard is primarily in a single dimension of the color solid. Where variation is in more than one direction but consistent for all materials being examined, these single number scales (Chapter 2D) have proved to be quite satisfactory in practical use.

Another type of visual comparison, using multidimensional standards of a type with which most people are still unfamiliar, is the United States Department of Agriculture Standards for the grading of cotton (Nickerson 1957). In this instance limit standards, carefully prepared for both color and degree of contamination, have been used for many years and are accepted in all parts of the world where cotton is graded.

D.   Instruments Using the Eye as Detector

In this section we bridge the gap between purely visual and purely instrumental techniques of color measurement by describing a series of methods in which the eye is used to detect the point at which the instrument is adjusted to achieve a color match. In these methods, the impressive sensitivity of the eye as a null detector is used to fullest advantage.

Disk Colorimetry

One of the simplest methods, in terms of equipment, for expressing color differences in numerical terms is that of disk colorimetry (Nickerson 1957). This method takes advantage of the ability of the eye and brain to see as a single color the combined effect of several different colors presented to it in rapid succession. This presentation is carried out by preparing a disk made up of sectors composed of different colors and spun rapidly by a small electric motor.

For control work, the sample is rotated and compared with a spinning disk consisting of sectors composed of the standard

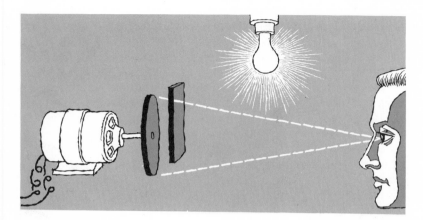

Disk colorimetry.

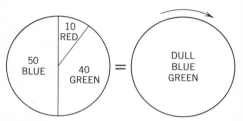

With a disk colorimeter, the statement on page 32 that a dull greenish blue test light is matched by 50 parts of the blue primary, 40 parts of the green, and 10 parts of the red, could be demonstrated in this experiment.

colorants used in the preparation of the sample. By varying the area of each standard colorant exposed, one can match the sample. It is possible with this procedure to obtain numerical data in terms of the area of each color used and to express the difference between a standard and the sample being examined. This technique, properly used, can be applied to materials of varying textures, such as deep embossings on vinyl plastic, or to printed materials where the printed area is only part of the pattern. Proper use of this method, combined with a knowledge of the colorants used, makes it possible to prepare disks so that a wide variety of application conditions may be simulated, and comparisons with finished materials made in a quantitative manner where no other method of color measurement can be used.

It is difficult to understand why such a basically sound technique has not been more widely employed. Perhaps, in this age of complex equipment, it has been ignored as being more complicated than straight visual comparison but not complicated enough to point at with pride when someone visits the laboratory.

Color Comparators for Liquids

In the examination of the color of liquids, a common technique is the use of tubes of standardized dimension (such as the Nessler tube). In using such devices, the amount of colorant viewed in the standard tube is varied until its color matches that of the sample. In cases where the colors under consideration are qualitatively identical, as in the determination of copper by the formation of a copper ammonia complex, or where the color of a dissolved dye varies in a simple fashion with its concentration, this technique is quite satisfactory. The visual assessment of the equality or nonequality of the color in the tubes, as a function of concentration, can also be performed in the common type of chemical colorimeter (this is a misnomer from the point of view of those of us who measure color, but it is a term widely used by chemists). In a typical comparator, one example of which is the Duboscq color comparator, the thickness of the layer of either

The Nessler-tube principle.

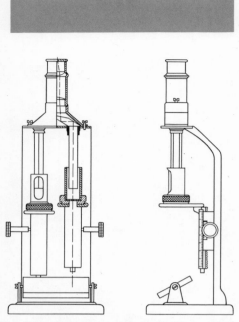

A typical color comparator for liquid samples.

The Lovibond Tintometer. (Courtesy Hayes G. Shimp, Inc.)

the standard or the sample can be varied and, provided the materials have similar chromaticities, a match can be made. The relative depth of solution required to make the match is an indication of the color difference.

It is very easy to see how, in this simple type of visual comparison, the substitution of a photodetector for the eye to judge the balance between the sample and the standard results in an instrumental method of analysis. Here it is quite clear that there is relatively little difference between a visual examination and a fully instrumental one. The one exception—and it is a very important one—is that, even in such a simple comparison, the trained observer can LOOK and see whether the variation between the standard and the sample is such that the balance made by adjustment of cell thickness is enough to bring about a color match. It will not be adequate if there is a difference in hue, if the sample contains suspended material, or if sample and standard differ in still other ways.

In the examination of transparent materials, the half-way point between a completely instrumental examination and a completely visual examination of the sample is exemplified by the Lovibond Tintometer in which carefully standardized Lovibond colored glasses (page 26) are combined to match a sample which is viewed at the same time. Since the glasses are standardized, it is possible, from the nature of the glasses used to make a match, to describe the sample in numerical terms. This method has been modified for use in the examination of opaque materials. A complete description of an idealized system of this type has been published by Judd (1962a,b).

More-Refined Instruments

In principle, almost any of the fully photoelectric instruments for measuring color described in Section E could be operated with the eye as a detector. A good many instruments of just such types have been built, particularly in the years before the photoelectric detectors of light were so highly developed. Only two instruments of this kind will be described.

The Koenig-Martens spectrometer (McNicholas 1928) is a very precise instrument, still used on occasion in referee laboratories such as that of the National Bureau of Standards, embodying all the essentials of the present-day spectrophotometers described in Section E. Its operation is like that of a simple color comparator in the way sample and standard are compared, except for the type of light source used. Originally designed to measure transmitting materials, it was modified by Priest (1935) to make reflectance measurements.

Another instrument using the eye as detector is the Donaldson colorimeter (Donaldson 1947). This device, called a six-stimulus additive colorimeter, mixes the light from as many as six different sources (usually different regions of the spectrum) and uses the mixture to illuminate a white reference standard. The amounts of the lights are varied until the color of the standard matches that of the sample, in essentially the same experiment as that described on page 31.

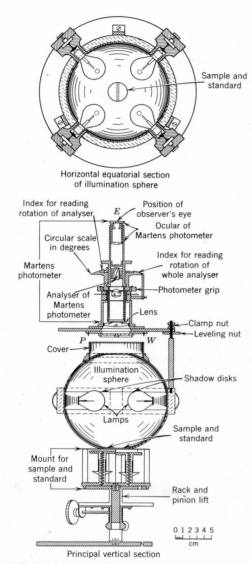

Horizontal equatorial section
of illumination sphere

The Priest-Lange reflectometer, a complex instrument using the eye as a detector (Judd in Mellon
1950, p. 548).

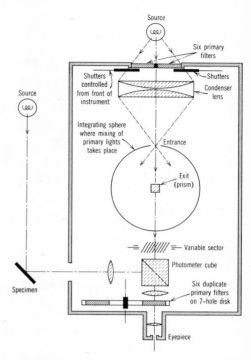

Sketch of the Donaldson six-stimulus additive
colorimeter. (Judd 1963)

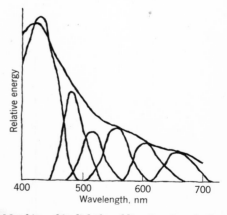

Matching white light by adding six primary colors
in the Donaldson colorimeter.

E.   Fully Instrumental Color Measurement

The problem of replacing the eye with an instrument for color
measurement can be looked upon as one in which a detector
which is very sensitive to qualitative differences—in short, one
which can THINK—is replaced with one that does not have this
remarkable ability but which instead has a much improved ability
to measure and remember in a quantitative way. In order to
obtain numbers, and the same numbers every time, we must
sacrifice the ability of the human observer to look at a sample in

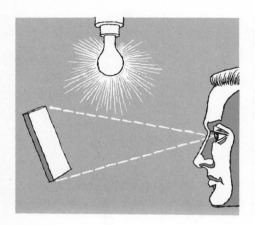

any reasonable sort of light and tell us its hue, lightness, saturation, and many other aspects of its appearance.

If the instrument is to have any value at all, we must build some of this discrimination into it, and this must be done at some place other than the detector, for the properties of available detectors are such that they cannot be changed drastically or readily.

Our well-studied triad of light source, object, and detector suggests how to do this. For a given object and an available detector, we must vary the nature of the light to introduce the ability of the instrument to recognize differences in color. Light is our probe, our surgeon's scalpel, and the nature and amount of information a color-measuring instrument gives depends on the manner and extent to which the light it uses is varied in viewing the sample. We are thus led to a classification of instrumental color-measurement techniques by the way in which the light is treated in the measurement process.

Classification of Methods

Unaltered Light. It is not quite trivial to consider the methods in which unaltered white light is used to illuminate the sample. This is, after all, the common situation where visual examination of colored materials is involved.

Subdividing further, we may note that it makes little difference what kind of light is used when color is not at all involved in the product. An example of a measurement of this kind is the densitometry of black-and-white photographic film: Almost any kind of light source or detector is suitable to measure the amount of blackening in such a system.

If, however, it is required that the instrument measure some one aspect of the appearance of colored objects, specifically their lightness or something related to it (reflectance, transmittance, haze, etc.), in a way which correlates with what the human observer sees, a little more care is needed. The requirement is

INSTRUMENTAL METHODS

a. Unaltered light
b. Three-colored lights
c. Monochromatic light

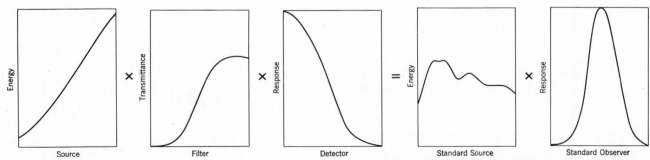

If an instrument is to measure lightness or a quantity related to it, in a way that correlates with visual observations, then the product of the spectral energy distribution of the instrument's light source and the spectral response of its detector must be adjusted, by the use of an appropriate light filter, to equal the product of the eye's spectral response and the spectral energy distribution of a standard light source, usually daylight.

that the spectral energy of the light source times the spectral response of the detector equal that for whatever standard source is desired (e.g., daylight) and the average human eye. Light filters are available which allow this requirement to be met for common light sources and detectors.

Three Colored Lights. The next step of refinement in using light as a probe to detect color developed from Grassmann's early observation (Grassmann 1853) that a wide variety of colors could be matched by mixing three colored lights. From this experiment the CIE system so widely used in color specification was developed, as described in Chapter 2B. It is possible to build instruments in which the sample is viewed in three different

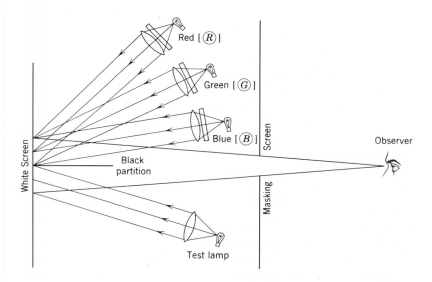

An arrangement for producing a large number of colors by mixing the light from three different colored lamps.

kinds of light so chosen that the instrument readings are in the form of three numbers which, with suitable standards, are either directly equal to the three CIE tristimulus values or are converted to them by simple calculation. These instruments are called *colorimeters* (in the correct sense of the word, not as it is sometimes used by the chemist). Colorimetry is described later in this section.

Monochromatic Light. The word monochromatic means one color, and monochromatic light is light containing only one color of the spectrum. A *monochromator* is a device, which may contain a prism like that first used by Newton (1730) (page 4), for producing such light by splitting white light into a spectrum and isolating one part of it at a time. A color-measuring instrument using monochromatic light can measure the spectral reflectance (or transmittance) curve of the sample. As we saw in Chapter 1B, this curve contains all the information needed to calculate the color of the sample for any source and observer. We shall see later in this section how this type of measurement, called *spectrophotometry*, is carried out and review how color coordinates are obtained from the spectrophotometric or spectral reflectance curve.

Monochromatic light is obtained by isolating light from a small region of the spectrum, as by the use of a slit to block out unwanted light.

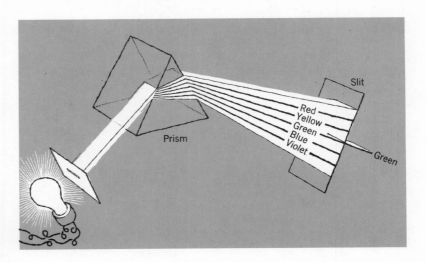

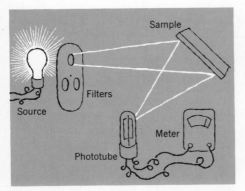

In a colorimeter, light from a source passes through colored filters onto the sample. The reflectance of the sample is measured as it is illuminated, in turn, by the light passing through each filter.

Colorimetry

In this section, we use the word colorimetry in a somewhat restricted sense. In general, it is taken to mean any technique for measuring color, but here we refer solely to color measurement with photoelectric instruments using three (or four) colored lights.

Source-Detector Response. In Chapter 2B we saw that the CIE tristimulus values of a sample, that set of three numbers representing its color, can be obtained by combining the sample's spectral reflectance curve with the spectral energy distribution of one of the standard CIE light sources and the response of the

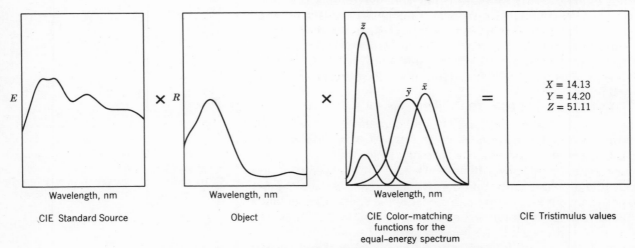

A reminder of the way in which the CIE tristimulus values (page 38) are obtained.

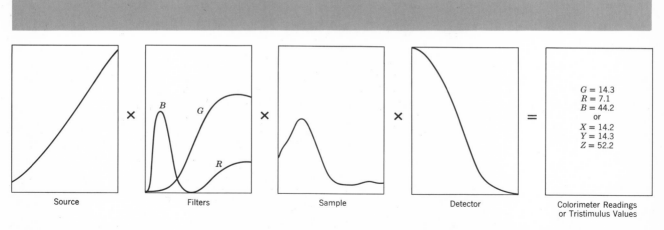

In *colorimetry*, the tristimulus values or numbers closely related to them are obtained from measurements with the instrument's response (light source times filter times detector) adjusted to that required by the CIE system and sketched in the figure just preceding this one. It is important to note, as discussed on pages 69–71, that it is difficult to do this with absolute accuracy.

CIE standard observer, in the form of the tristimulus values of the spectrum colors. If we wish to duplicate this same process in an instrument, we must make provision for adjusting the combined response of the source and detector used to equal that of the combination of one of the CIE standard sources (usually Source C, daylight) and the tristimulus values of the spectrum (Buchmann-Oisen 1950). It is usual for this purpose to use glass filters somewhere in the light beams in the instrument (whether before or after the sample makes little difference except for fluorescent materials, which should be illuminated directly by the source selected). The degree to which the instrument readings approximate the true CIE tristimulus values of samples depends on how well these curves are duplicated.

The curves to be duplicated are shown in the figures on page 68, with the actual response curves of a widely used set of filters (Hunter 1958b). One source of difficulty in duplicating the curves lies in the presence of two peaks in the curve for the X tristimulus value. In some instruments (Glasser 1952, 1955) the small X peak is taken to be identical in shape to the Z curve, but not as high. This procedure has limited accuracy, however (Van den Akker 1937), and other instruments (Hunter 1958b, Dearth 1963) use a separate filter to obtain this part of the X curve.

Sample Viewing. Two relatively well-standardized but quite different arrangements of light source, sample, and detector are in common use for color measurement. In one, called 0,45° viewing, the sample is illuminated by a source of light placed along the normal to its surface, and viewed at an angle of 45° from the normal, as indicated in the accompanying sketch. These viewing conditions or the equivalent reversed 45,0° conditions correspond closely to those most used in the visual examination of color. They are used in some commercially available colorimeters.

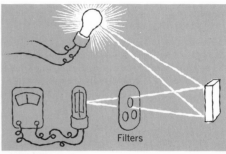

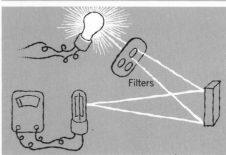

When fluorescent samples are to be measured, it is preferable to place the filters between the sample and the detector (above), rather than between the source and sample (below). Techniques for the color measurement of fluorescent samples have not yet, regrettably, been developed and standardized in a widely accepted way.

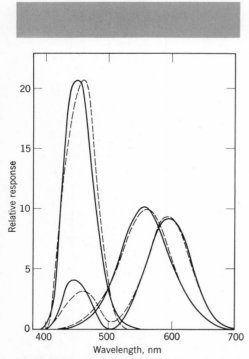

In this Figure, the solid curves are the CIE color-matching functions $\bar{x}$, $\bar{y}$, and $\bar{z}$. The dashed curves show the extent to which they can be duplicated in colorimeters using photocells as detectors (Hunter 1958b).

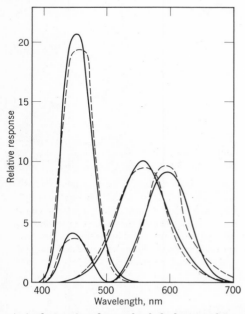

As in the previous figure, the dashed curves show how well the CIE functions are duplicated in colorimeters using phototubes as detectors (Hunter 1958b). (See also the figure on page 72.)

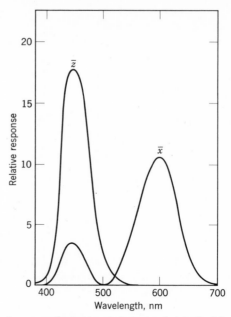

In some colorimeters, it is assumed that the left-hand peak of the X curve has the same shape and position as the Z curve. For the most precise work, this is not a good assumption.

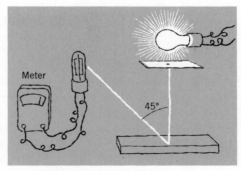

The 0,45° viewing geometry.

Reflectance measurement with an integrating sphere. The specular, or mirror, reflection can be excluded from the measured result by being absorbed in a light trap.

The other viewing conditions in common use involve an *integrating sphere*, a hollow metal sphere several inches in diameter painted white inside. An integrating sphere collects all the light reflected from the surface of a sample placed against an opening (called a port) in its side. Provision is usually made for including or excluding that part of the light reflected in the mirror, or specular, direction from a glossy sample. Either the detector or the light source is placed inside the sphere, the other viewing the sample through a second port.

The integrating sphere has a great advantage for measuring the transmittance of translucent samples, since virtually all the transmitted light is collected. For this purpose and for measuring haze and related quantities, these viewing conditions must be used. Unfortunately, the integrating sphere and 0,45° viewing conditions do not give identical results for the reflectance of some opaque samples (Middleton 1953).

Coordinate Scales. Colorimeter readings can be expressed in several different ways. Perhaps the simplest set of scales is that in which a pure white sample (for which freshly prepared magnesium oxide—MgO—is almost a universal standard, but see page 138) is taken to read 100 when viewed through each of the filters. These readings are often called G) for green, corresponding to CIE tristimulus value Y), R (for red, or sometimes A for amber, related to the large peak of the X curve), and B (for blue, related to Z). If a fourth filter is used corresponding to the small peak of the X curve, it might be called R'.

Approximate values of CIE X, Y, and Z can be calculated from these readings by adding a fraction of the B reading (three-filter instruments) or R' reading (four-filter instruments) to the R reading, and then multiplying the modified R, G, and B by the proper factors to give the tristimulus values for pure white. Since Y for MgO is 100, G and Y are identical by definition. Some four-filter colorimeters read X, Y, and Z more nearly directly.

Scales corresponding more nearly, but unfortunately not exactly, to equal visual perception are used on some colorimeters. A common set (Hunter 1958b) consists of L (lightness, related to Y), a (redness, if positive, or greenness, if negative), and b (yellowness, if positive, or blueness, if negative). These are calculated within the instrument by electrical means and read directly from its dials.

Instrument Metamerism. On page 20 we described a phenomenon known as *observer metamerism*, in which two objects look alike to one observer but not to another, as a result of differences in the spectral response curves of the observers. Exactly the same situation can exist with instruments, and it is a common and serious defect of colorimeters that they do indeed give different readings from instrument to instrument, even of the same make and model, for the same sample. These differences result from the fact that, with existing sources, filters, and detectors, it is very difficult to make the response curves of different colorimeters exactly alike.

The practical result of the individual differences in the response of colorimeters is that, when standardized in the usual

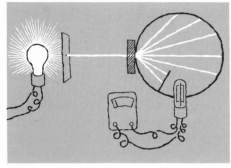

Measurement of diffuse transmittance with an integrating sphere. All the light transmitted or scattered in the forward direction by the sample is included in the measurement.

$$X = 0.98\,(0.8\,R + 0.2\,B\,)\,(3\text{ filters})$$
$$\text{or}$$
$$X = 0.98\,(0.8\,R + 0.2\,R')\,(4\text{ filters})$$

$$Y = G$$

$$Z = 1.18\,B$$

These equations relate the R (or A), G, and B readings to the tristimulus values by including the weighting factors to give the correct tristimulus values for the white standard MgO.

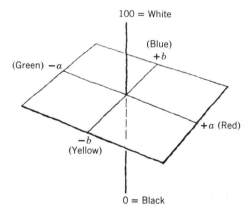

Hunter's L, a, and b coordinates are a common set of colorimeter readings corresponding approximately to equal visual perception. Their arrangement in three dimensions is shown above, and their relation to G, A (or R), and B is given in the equations below.

$$L = 10\,G^{\frac{1}{2}}$$

$$a = 70\,G^{\frac{1}{2}} \times \frac{A - G}{A + 2G + B}$$

$$b = 28\,G^{\frac{1}{2}} \times \frac{G - B}{A + 2G + B}$$

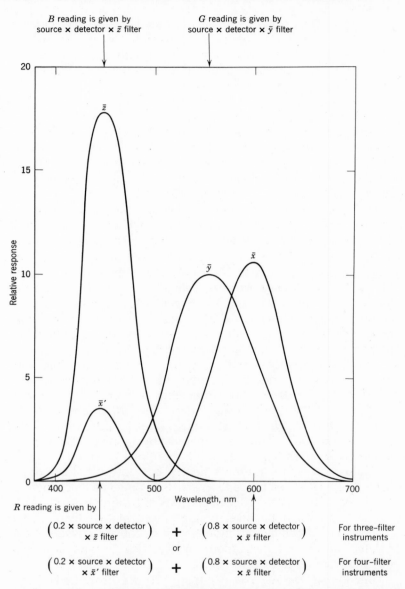

B reading is given by
source ✕ detector ✕ $\bar{z}$ filter

G reading is given by
source ✕ detector ✕ $\bar{y}$ filter

R reading is given by

$$\left(\begin{array}{c} 0.2 \times \text{source} \times \text{detector} \\ \times\ \bar{z}\ \text{filter} \end{array}\right) \quad + \quad \left(\begin{array}{c} 0.8 \times \text{source} \times \text{detector} \\ \times\ \bar{x}\ \text{filter} \end{array}\right) \qquad \text{For three–filter instruments}$$

or

$$\left(\begin{array}{c} 0.2 \times \text{source} \times \text{detector} \\ \times\ \bar{x}'\ \text{filter} \end{array}\right) \quad + \quad \left(\begin{array}{c} 0.8 \times \text{source} \times \text{detector} \\ \times\ \bar{x}\ \text{filter} \end{array}\right) \qquad \text{For four–filter instruments}$$

The *R* (or *A*), *G*, and *B* readings of colorimeters, proportional to the tristimulus values **X**, **Y**, and **Z**, are given by the source–filter–photocell combinations indicated in this figure.

way on a white sample, different colorimeters give different readings for the same colored samples (Billmeyer 1962, 1965b, 1966a). The differences are greater for darker and more highly saturated samples. For this reason, colorimeter readings obtained in this way *should never* be considered to have any "absolute" significance and *should never* be used for standardization, purchase specification, or the like.

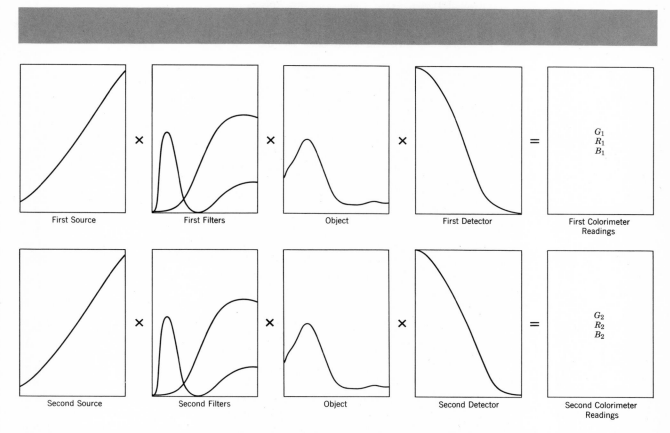

First Source × First Filters × Object × First Detector = First Colorimeter Readings

$$G_1 \\ R_1 \\ B_1$$

Second Source × Second Filters × Object × Second Detector = Second Colorimeter Readings

$$G_2 \\ R_2 \\ B_2$$

Instrument metamerism is exactly analogous to other types of metamerism (page 20): if two colorimeters have different response curves, they will in general give different sets of readings for a pair of samples which match but are a metameric pair. Most colorimeters suffer from this fault unless they have been individually calibrated for close conformance to one another and to the CIE system, as described on this page.

In recent years a great advance has been made in the production of commercially available colorimeters, whereby each individual instrument is custom-tailored to have response curves closely matching those of the CIE system. The readings of such colorimeters agree more closely, both among themselves and with CIE coordinates calculated in other ways, than do readings from instruments without this feature. The warnings of the preceding paragraph should still be heeded, however, and the best way to use these newer instruments is still for differential measurements as described below.

Standardization and Differential Use. Perhaps the greatest virtue of colorimeters is their extreme sensitivity in detecting and measuring small differences in color between two samples that are nearly alike. This *differential* measurement is highly reproducible from one properly adjusted colorimeter to another (Billmeyer 1962, 1965b) and represents the correct way to use these instruments.

The key to achieving this good reproducibility, and thereby extending the correct use of the colorimeter to other situations, lies in the principle of "local" calibration of the instrument. That is, a standard must be provided which has very nearly the same color and spectrophotometric curve shape as the samples to be measured. The smaller the color difference is between the samples and standard, the better will be the reproducibility of the measurements. The requirement of similar spectrophotometric curve shape in general implies that standard and sample must be made of the same material and colored with the same colorants. That is, they should not be metameric.

If the only measurement required is that of the color difference between samples, the standard may be one of the samples, and no absolute significance need be attached to its colorimeter readings. If, however, absolute values of the color coordinates of the samples are to be determined, then such absolute values must be obtained for the standard by some independent method of known accuracy, such as spectrophotometry. If the colorimeter is adjusted to read these values for the standard, it will read correct absolute values for samples with colors lying *within a small region of color space* surrounding the standard.

Typical Commercial Instruments. The following brief descriptions do not cover all the instruments on the market, but include only a few typical and popular models. Other instruments are described by Bassemir (1959), Judd (1963), Wurzburg (1963a,b), and Thurner (1965).

Hunter Associates Laboratories, Fairfax, Virginia, market several models of colorimeters. Their D25 Color and Color Difference Meter (Hunter 1958b) is a four-filter instrument available with either 0,45° or integrating sphere viewing. Individual calibration for close conformance to CIE coordinates is available. Scales of L, a, and b and X, Y, and Z are available. A series of calibration samples is supplied which allow instrument performance to be checked in detail. The Gardner Laboratories,

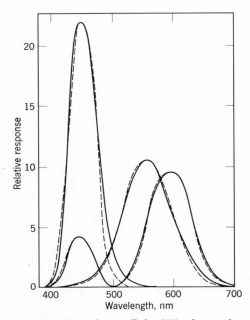

This figure shows how well the CIE color-matching functions (solid lines) are duplicated (dashed lines) in one colorimeter (IDL Signature model Color-Eye) specially calibrated for close conformance to the CIE system (compare with the figures on page 68).

Some colorimeters are equipped for the direct (simultaneous or sequential) comparison of sample and standard, and read directly the small difference in color between them by means of the ratios indicated in the figure.

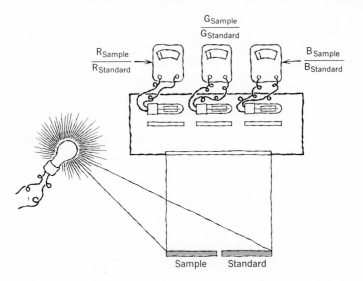

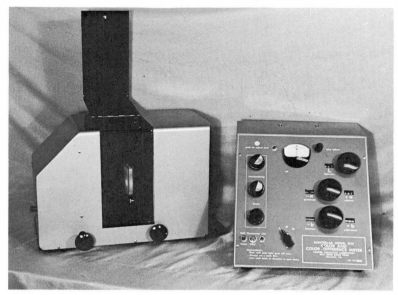

The Hunter D25 Color and Color Difference Meter, equipped with a measuring unit having integrating sphere geometry. (Courtesy Hunter Associates Laboratory, Inc.)

The Gardner AC-3 Automatic Color-Difference Meter. (Courtesy Gardner Laboratory, Inc.)

The Hunter D25 Color and Color Difference Meter, showing the 0,45° viewing arrangement. (Courtesy Hunter Associates Laboratory, Inc.)

The Gardner C4, a small and inexpensive three-filter color-difference meter. (Courtesy Gardner Laboratory, Inc.)

Bethesda, Maryland, market colorimeters made to earlier Hunter designs (Hunter 1942, 1958b; Huey 1956).

Instrument Development Laboratories, Attleboro, Massachusetts, market the Color-Eye, a four-filter integrating sphere-type colorimeter. Individual "signature" calibration of each instrument provides close conformance to CIE coordinates. An added feature of this instrument is a series of filters allowing its use as an abridged spectrophotometer, as described on page 75. Several IDL colorimeters are available, as illustrated in the accompanying photographs.

Manufacturers Engineering and Equipment Corp., Warrington, Pennsylvania, supply the Colormaster differential colorimeter (Glasser 1952, 1955; Tuttle 1956). This is an instrument of high sensitivity, well suited for the measurement of dark colors. It uses 0,45° viewing conditions and is a three-filter instrument with G, R, and B scales.

The IDL Model D-1 Color-Eye. (Courtesy Instrument Development Laboratories.)

The IDL Color-Rad, especially designed for measuring the color of light sources. (Courtesy Instrument Development Laboratories.)

The MEECO Colormaster.

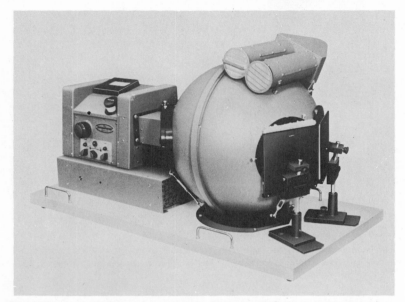

The IDL Model LS Color-Eye, equipped with an unusually large integrating sphere for the measurement of textured (rough-surfaced) samples. The direct illumination of the sphere with simulated daylight, including ultraviolet light, makes this instrument particularly well suited for measuring fluorescent samples. (Courtesy Instrument Development Laboratories.)

The Martin Sweets Company, Louisville, Kentucky, makes the Color-Brightness Tester, a four-filter colorimeter with individual calibration for close conformance to CIE coordinates. The instrument is sold only through the Institute of Paper Chemistry, Appleton, Wisconsin, as part of a "system" of color measurement including instruments, standards, and service for repair and periodic standardization (Dearth 1963).

Carl Zeiss, New York, markets the Elrepho, a three-filter integrating sphere colorimeter with provision for abridged spectrophotometry. Quite popular in Europe, the Elrepho is not yet widely used in this country.

Spectrophotometry

Spectrophotometry, the measurement of the spectral reflectance or transmittance curves of materials, has many uses besides color measurement. We shall describe only spectrophotometry in the visible region of the spectrum, which we saw on page 4 to be between about 380 and 750 nm, as carried out on instruments especially designed or adapted for color measurement.

Source of Spectrum. The white light from the source in a spectrophotometer, often a tungsten filament bulb, is spread out into a spectrum by means of a prism or a diffraction grating. A slit is used to select a small portion of the spectrum to illuminate the sample. This portion may be between a few tenths and 10 nm wide, depending on the instrument. The wavelength of the light passing through the slit is varied, either manually or by automatic scanning, to cover the entire visible spectrum.

Abridged spectrophotometry is a compromise between three- or four-filter colorimetry and true spectrophotometry. A series of 10–16 filters, transmitting bands of light 5–20 nm wide, is used to obtain as many points on the spectral reflectance curve. The system is available as an accessory on some commercial colorimeters.

Sample Viewing. Most of the spectrophotometers commonly used in this country for color measurement by reflected light are equipped with integrating spheres; only a few use 0,45° viewing conditions. A modification for the General Electric Recording Spectrophotometer which uses 0,45° geometry has been described (Brockes 1960).

The Martin-Sweets Automatic Color-Brightness Tester. (Courtesy The Martin Sweets Company, Inc.)

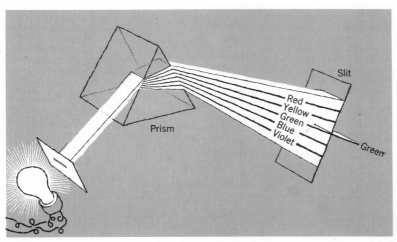

Dispersing white light into a spectrum by means of a *prism.*

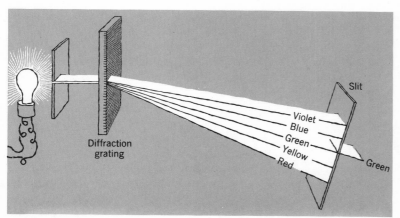

Dispersing white light into a spectrum by means of a *diffraction grating.*

The Zeiss Elrepho reflectance photometer. (Courtesy Carl Zeiss, Inc.)

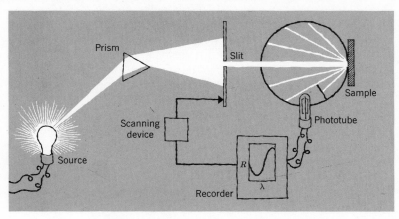

In a spectrophotometer, light is dispersed into a spectrum, made approximately monochromatic by means of a slit, and used to illuminate the sample (in this sketch, using integrating-sphere geometry). The reflectance of the sample is plotted against the wavelength of the light to give the sample's *spectrophotometric* (or spectral reflectance) curve.

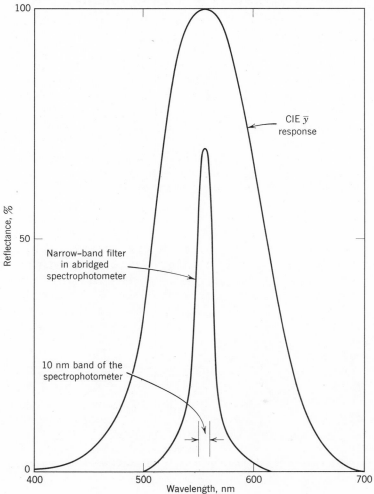

In this figure, the spectral response curve of the eye is compared with the spectral transmittance curve of a filter typical of those used in abridged spectrophotometry, and with the 10 nm band of wavelengths passed through the slit of a spectrophotometer widely used for color measurement.

Standardization and Accuracy. In contrast to colorimeters, which are properly used only for measuring small color differences between pairs of samples, spectrophotometers can be used to obtain the "absolute" values of the color coordinates for a single sample. (They can also be used differentially, of course.) A spectrophotometer in good working order need only be checked by measurement of one sample of known spectral reflectance at each wavelength, usually a white material. Magnesium oxide, MgO, whose reflectance is as high as or higher than that of any other commonly available substance, is the accepted standard for this purpose. Note, however, that the CIE has recommended that MgO be replaced by the "perfect diffuser" as the absolute standard of whiteness, as discussed on page 138.

Because of the difficulty of preparing and maintaining a fresh surface of MgO, this standard is gradually being replaced. Freshly smoked (NBS 1939) or pressed (ASTM E 259) MgO tends to yellow in a few days, while pressed barium sulfate ($BaSO_4$) (ASTM E 259), equally white and significantly more stable, is now widely accepted as a white standard. Other more durable materials such as opal glasses (Vitrolite, Carrara) are often used as "working standards" (Keegan 1944, Gabel 1949, Billmeyer 1956).

Other than the calibration with a standard white sample (or, for transmittance measurement, with no sample in place), no standardization is required for a spectrophotometer *in good working order.* Samples are available, however, and should be *used,* for insuring that the instrument *is* in good working order. Most laboratories measure some such standards periodically for checking the operation of their instruments (Keegan 1944, NBS 1955, Keegan 1962).

At the beginning of this discussion, we put the word absolute in quotation marks to emphasize the fact that, although spectrophotometry is the only practical way to obtain values of color coordinates (such as CIE tristimulus values) which are not dependent on calibrated color standards, the accuracy of existing instruments is only about one-tenth that which one would like to see (Wright 1959, 1964, Billmeyer 1960b, 1962, 1965a,b, 1966a, Keegan 1962). This is one of the most serious limitations in the measurement and specification of color at the present time.

Calculation of CIE Coordinates. As we have described elsewhere (page 38), the CIE tristimulus values are obtained from spectrophotometric data by multiplying together, wavelength by wavelength, the spectral reflectance of the sample, the relative spectral energy of the light source, and the tristimulus values of the spectrum colors. These products are then added up for all the wavelengths in the visible region of the spectrum. Tables are available (Hardy 1936, OSA 1953, Mackinney 1962) giving the products of the tristimulus values of the spectral colors and the source energy for the CIE Illuminants A, B, and C. Numerical examples of their use are given by Hardy and by Mackinney. These products are called weighting factors, and this method of calculating the CIE tristimulus values is known as the *weighted-ordinate* method.

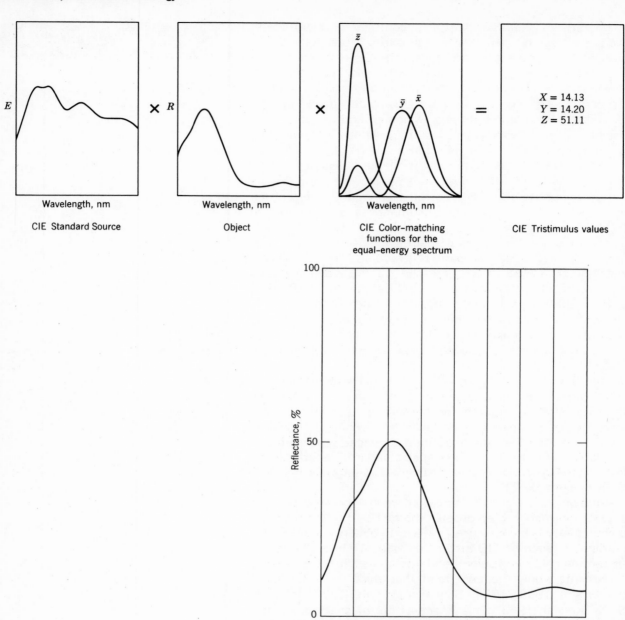

Wavelength, nm	Reflectance, R	Weighting Factor, $E_c\bar{y}$	Product, $E_cR\bar{y}$
380	10.0%	0.00004	0.0004
420	33.1	0.00153	0.0506
460	50.0	0.02786	1.393
500	36.8	0.13624	5.014
540	13.7	0.36646	5.021
580	6.0	0.32008	1.920
620	5.9	0.12632	0.745
660	8.2	0.02026	0.166
700	6.0	0.00121	0.007
		CIE Y, Ill. C, =	14.32%

An example of the use of the weighted-ordinate method for calculating CIE tristimulus value Y. See also the Table on page 40.

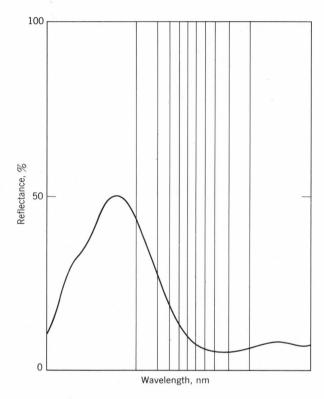

Ordinate number	Wavelength, nm	Reflectance (R), %
1	489.4	42.8%
2	515.1	26.9
3	529.8	18.4
4	541.4	13.1
5	551.8	9.6
6	561.9	7.3
7	572.5	6.3
8	584.8	5.8
9	600.8	5.6
10	627.3	6.3

$$\overline{142.1} \times 0.100 = 14.21$$

CIE Y, Ill. C = 14.21%

An example of the use of the selected-ordinate method for calculating CIE tristimulus value Y. X and Z are obtained similarly using the selected ordinates shown in the next figures.

The multiplication step at each wavelength can be avoided by choosing certain special wavelengths at which the spectral reflectance is measured and added up. This technique is called the *selected-ordinate* method, and tables of selected ordinates are given in the references cited above for the CIE and other sources. The selected-ordinate method is easier for hand calculation, since the multiplications are avoided, but it is less accurate by far than the weighted-ordinate method for the same number of wavelengths at which the reflectance is read (Nickerson 1935, De Kerf 1958). For example, the accuracy of the weighted-ordinate method at 10-nm intervals (31–38 readings) is not even equaled by the use of 100 selected ordinates each for X, Y, and Z (300 readings)!

Several automatic devices can be used as accessories to spectrophotometers for calculating tristimulus values. A mechanical analog computer (Davidson 1949), a digital computer (Franklin 1962), and a digital readout unit used in conjunction with a computer (Billmeyer 1960b) have been described in the literature. These and other devices are commercially available.

Typical Commercial Instruments. In principle, almost any spectrophotometer can be used for color measurement, but only a few are commercially available with provision for reflectance measurement. The following list is not complete, but covers

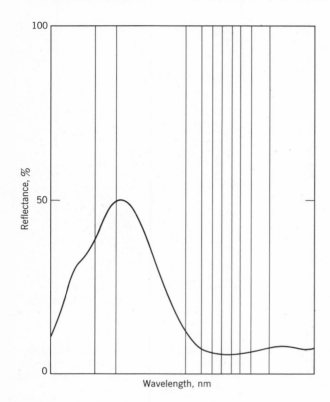

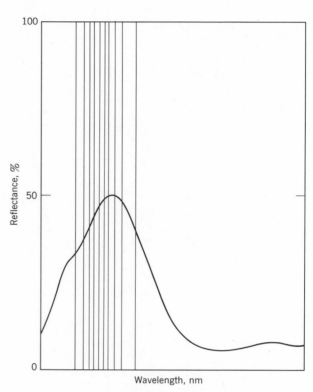

Ten selected ordinates for CIE X (left) and Z (right) for Illuminant C. The corresponding set for CIE Y was used in the preceding figure.

Ordinate number	Wave-length, nm	For CIE X Reflectance, (R), %	Wave-length, nm	For CIE Z Reflectance, (R), %
1	435.5	39.2	422.2	33.8
2	461.2	50.1	432.0	37.5
3	544.3	12.0	438.6	41.0
4	564.1	7.2	444.4	44.2
5	577.3	6.1	450.1	47.7
6	588.7	5.8	455.9	49.3
7	599.6	5.6	462.0	50.1
8	610.9	5.7	468.7	50.0
9	624.2	6.1	477.7	48.0
10	645.9	7.7	495.2	40.0
		$145.5 \times 0.098 = 14.26$		$441.6 \times 0.118 = 52.11$
		CIE X, Ill. C, = 14.26		CIE Z, Ill. C, = 52.11

some more widely used instruments. Other instruments are described by Bassemir (1959), Judd (1963), and Wurzburg (1963a,b).

Applied Physics Corp., Monrovia, California, makes several spectrophotometers with the trade name Cary, some of which can be fitted with integrating sphere and 0,45° accessories for color measurement.

Bausch & Lomb Co., Rochester, New York, makes the Spectronic 20, a small, relatively inexpensive instrument of limited

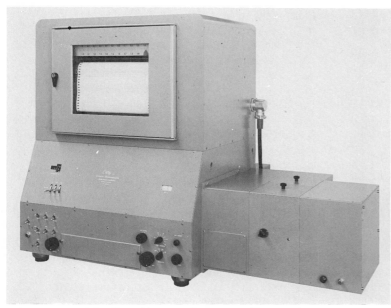

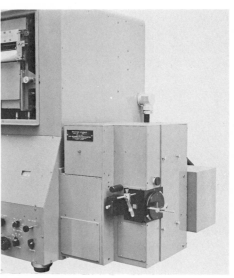

The Cary 14 spectrophotometer. (Courtesy Applied Physics Corp.)

Integrating sphere attachment for the Cary 14 spectrophotometer. (Courtesy Applied Physics Corp.)

The Beckman DK2 spectrophotometer with integrating sphere attachment. (Courtesy Beckman Instruments, Inc.)

The Bausch & Lomb Spectronic 505 spectrophotometer with integrating sphere attachment. (Courtesy Bausch & Lomb Co.)

**The old model General Electric recording spectro-
photometer. (Courtesy General Electric Co.)**

accuracy but suitable for approximate results in color measurement (Lange 1960). Their Spectronic 505 can be equipped with
an integrating sphere accessory for color measurement. To date,
only limited data are available on which to judge its performance
as a color-measuring instrument (Rood 1961).

Beckman Instruments, Inc., Fullerton, California, makes several spectrophotometers, some of which can be equipped with
integrating-sphere accessories for color measurement (Pugh
1956, Nill 1963).

General Electric Co., West Lynn, Massachusetts, makes the
General Electric Recording Spectrophotometer, long considered
the referee instrument for color measurement and probably
more widely used than any other for this purpose (Hardy 1935,
1938, Gibson 1938, Michaelson 1938, Pritchard 1955, Morse
1956, Billmeyer 1965a,b, 1966a). This is an automatic recording instrument especially built for color measurement. It uses
an integrating sphere with the detector in the sphere.

**The new model General Electric recording spec-
trophotometer. (Courtesy General Electric Co.)**

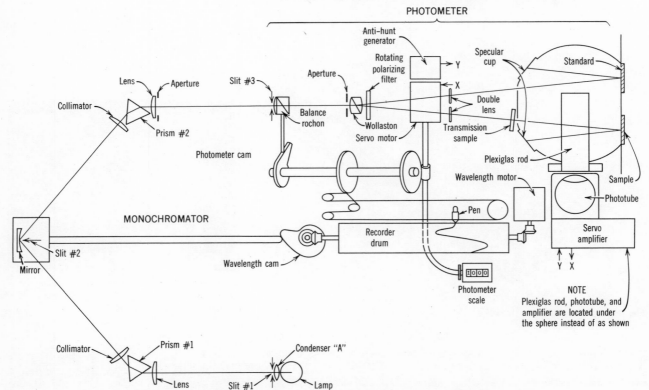

A sketch of the essential components of the General Electric recording spectrophotometer.

F.   The Use of Instruments in Color Assessment

In the beginning of this chapter we divided the subject of color measurement into *examination* and *assessment*. Since these two parts of the measurement process are usually carried out at the same time when the measurement is done visually, they were considered together in Section C. Since instruments cannot think, however, it is customary—and wise—to consider the problems of assessment separately from those of instrumental examination.

Assessment with Limit Standards

We have seen that the human eye and brain make an almost unsurpassed null detector. That is, it can tell precisely whether two samples are exactly alike or not. Once there is a perceptible difference between the standard and the sample, however, there is considerable variation in opinion, even among trained observers, as to both the nature and the magnitude of the difference. With untrained observers, this variation is a source of confusion and discouragement. One of the principal reasons instruments are useful is that they have proved quite valuable in reconciling some of these variations in opinion. With instruments, the description of the difference between the standard and the sample is unequivocal, even though its meaning in visual terms may be subject to interpretation (Thurner 1965).

The conversion of the description of the relationship between the standard and the sample into some language which is meaningful to all concerned, in terms of color as perceived, is not at all easy. With reliance on trained colorists and a standardized system, it is possible to describe the difference between the standard and the sample in such a way as to make it meaningful to another trained person. In actual practice, even this is not always done. Reliance may be placed on limit standards, and the final assessment may merely be a statement that the measured coordinates of the sample do or do not fall within the region defined by the coordinates of the limit samples as acceptable (Simon 1961).

This procedure, in which great reliance is placed upon instrumental measurements and limit standards, requires extreme caution in the standardization of the techniques employed. Since physical standards may change, it is important that their stability be checked before one uses conformity to these standards as a criterion for acceptability. It must be emphasized that limit standards, whether used only as visual aids or to set up numerical ranges of acceptability, must show the same color change (or lack of change) as the samples with a change of light source. The best way to set up proper limit standards is to select a large number of samples from actual production which show all the possible variations which may be expected from the process. These samples may be separated into acceptable and non-acceptable material by as many qualified observers as are involved in the problem. Measurement of these samples, already separated into categories, will provide the coordinates which define the region of acceptable material.

EXAMINATION
a. Light source
b. Sample and standard
c. Detector

ASSESSMENT
a. Difference or not
b. Description of difference
c. Acceptable or not

ΔE (Nickerson-Balinkin) =

$$\left[\left(\frac{2}{5}C\Delta H\right)^2 + (6\Delta V)^2 + \left(\frac{20}{\pi}\Delta C\right)^2\right]^{\frac{1}{2}}$$

where ΔH, ΔV, and ΔC are the differences in Munsell Hue, Value, and Chroma between samples.

The Nickerson-Balinkin color-difference formula.

ΔE (NBS) =

$$f_g\{[221Y^{\frac{1}{4}}(\overline{\Delta\alpha^2} + \overline{\Delta\beta^2})^{\frac{1}{2}}]^2 + [k\Delta(Y^{\frac{1}{2}})]^2\}^{\frac{1}{2}}$$

where f_g takes account of the masking influence of a glossy surface on the detection of color differences, k relates the lightness and chromaticity scales, and α and β are defined on page 48. The gloss factor $f_g = Y/(Y + K)$ where K is usually taken as 2.5 (Traub 1961), and k is usually taken as 10.

The color-difference formula for the National Bureau of Standards (NBS) unit.

$$\Delta E \text{ (Hunter)} = (\Delta L^2 + \Delta a^2 + \Delta b^2)^{\frac{1}{2}}$$

where ΔL, Δa, and Δb are the differences in Hunter's L, a, and b coordinates between samples.

The color-difference formula using directly the readings of Hunter and Gardner colorimeters.

ΔE (Adams Chromatic Value) =
$$40\{(0.23\Delta V_y)^2 + [\Delta(V_x - V_y)]^2 + [0.4\Delta(V_z - V_y)]^2\}^{\frac{1}{2}}$$

where V is the Munsell value function defined on page 51. The factor of 40 for the entire equation has been most frequently used to "normalize" the Adams Chromatic Value ΔE so that it conforms more closely to the NBS ΔE

The Adams chromatic-value color-difference formula.

All of the measurements are subject to instrumental errors and care must be taken that the instruments used are in proper operating condition. It may be self-evident, but the sum of all these errors must not exceed or even use any significant part of any tolerances (Johnston 1963). If these conditions are met, however, it results in a great saving of time and energy when the measurement, whether visual or instrumental, automatically classifies the material without any further calculation or discussion.

Assessment by Color Difference

Ideally, the end result of an instrumental color measurement should be a set of numbers describing the nature and magnitude of the difference in color between sample and standard in such a way that the numbers always have the same meaning in terms of visual perception. This has been the goal of the many workers devising the uniform-chromaticity color-order systems described in Chapter 2C. As we saw there, this goal has not been reached, and there is doubt in the minds of many experts that it can ever be reached (Wright 1959).

Nevertheless, there is considerable value in calculating a number representing the magnitude of a color difference, as long as one remembers that the numbers do not necessarily have the same meaning, in terms of visual perception, for different colors (Nickerson 1944, Davidson 1953). An additional problem arises, however, in that there are several different ways of calculating such color differences in common use, with some confusion among them, and that these various color-difference numbers do not agree even with one another, let alone with visual perception (Nickerson 1944, Davidson 1953, Ingle 1962, Little 1963).

The following brief descriptions of some of the most common color-difference calculations are not meant as instructions. An extensive discussion and comparison of different equations, with numerical examples, is given by Mackinney (1962).

Several color-difference formulas are based on the Munsell color-order system (page 26) (Nickerson 1936, Balinkin 1941), expressing color difference in terms of differences in Munsell hue, value, and chroma. Since these coordinates are usually determined by visual means, this color-difference calculation is most widely used to evaluate the results of visual rather than instrumental measurements of color.

A color-difference unit based on the uniform chromaticity scale of Hunter (1942) has been designated the National Bureau of Standards or NBS unit (alternatively, the *judd*, after Deane B. Judd). This system is only rarely used, but the term "NBS unit" is often erroneously applied to the results of other color-difference calculations. The availability of programs for digital computation of color differences may lead to the increased use of this unit (Ingle 1962).

Another, and quite different, unit of color difference is that derived simply and directly from colorimeter readings in Hunter's L, a, b coordinates (Hunter 1958b).

The Adams (1942) chromatic value system is widely used as the basis for a color-difference calculation (ASTM D 2244). The Adams unit is not the same as, and not to be confused with, the NBS unit defined in the previous paragraph. Tables of the Adams chromatic value functions are available (Nickerson 1950, Buc 1952, Judd 1952, 1963, Mackinney 1962, Billmeyer 1963a), making the hand calculation of color difference by this formula relatively simple.

The color space of MacAdam (1942) was used by him (MacAdam 1943) to define a color-difference calculation now

$$\Delta E \text{ (MacAdam)} =$$

$$\left[\frac{1}{K}(g_{11}\Delta x^2 + 2g_{12}\Delta x\Delta y + g_{22}\Delta y^2 + G\Delta Y^2) \right]^{1/2}$$

where g_{11}, $2g_{12}$, and g_{22} are constants whose value depends on x and y, and G and K are constants whose value depends on Y. The values of the constants are "built into" the Simon-Goodwin charts, and are tabulated for use with the CODIC.

The MacAdam color-difference formula, as modified for use with the Simon-Goodwin charts and the Davidson and Hemmendinger CODIC color-difference computer shown on p. 86.

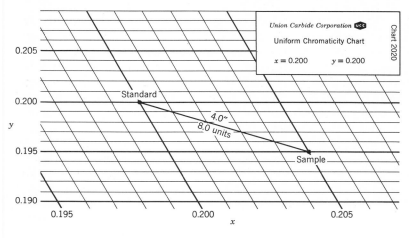

A section of a Simon-Goodwin color-difference chart, illustrating the calculation of the MacAdam color difference between a standard with $x = 0.200$, $y = 0.200$, $Y = 29.0\%$, and a sample with $x = 0.205$, $y = 0.195$, and $Y = 25.0\%$.

This chart, drawn according to the values of g_{11}, $2g_{12}$, and g_{22}, for x near 0.200 and y near 0.200, is used to find the "uncorrected" chromaticity difference between sample and standard. On the original chart, where ½ in. = 1 MacAdam unit, this difference was 8.0 MacAdam units for the test calculation. . . .

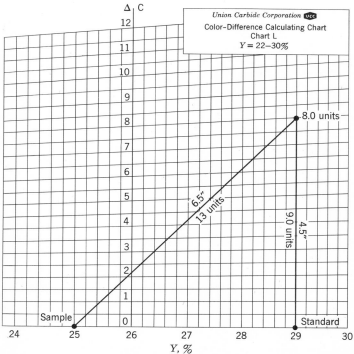

. . . The "uncorrected" chromaticity difference ΔC is now measured off at the lightness (Y) level of the *standard* on this chart. The "corrected" chromaticity difference is the distance between this point and the base line, here 9.0 MacAdam units. The total color difference is the slant distance shown, or 13 MacAdam units. (To clarify the test calculation, a rather large color difference was chosen. Note also that in the original Simon-Goodwin charts, Y is expressed as a decimal fraction—for example, 0.25 and 0.29—rather than in per cent as is our convention.)

The Davidson and Hemmendinger CODIC Color Difference Computer, for calculating MacAdam color differences. It is important to remember that the CODIC, the Simon-Goodwin charts, and the original MacAdam (1943) hand calculation will not give *exactly* the same answers for the same sets of data. (Courtesy Davidson and Hemmendinger, Inc.)

| Equation | Color difference for | | |
	Pair 1	Pair 2	Pair 3
Nickerson-Balinkin	5.6	6.1	4.8
NBS	6.4	6.1	5.0
Hunter	2.7	2.5	2.6
Adams Chromatic Value	3.6	5.6	4.4
MacAdam (Simon-Goodwin charts)	10.0	10.9	6.8

These data (Little 1963) illustrate the statement that no two color-difference equations give the same answers for the same sets of data. Therefore, *it is essential that the exact method of calculation be specified whenever color-difference numbers are used.*

These are the famous MacAdam (1942) ellipses. Ten MacAdam units in size, they show the areas in the CIE chromaticity diagram corresponding to equal visual perception of color differences.

widely used as modified by Davidson (1955b) and Simon (1958). The latter authors provide sets of charts making this calculation of color difference relatively simple. More recently MacAdam (1965) has modified and improved the calculation; see also page 141 and Blackwood 1966, Foster 1966a.

Several analog computers are commercially available, some as accessories to colorimeters, for the calculation of color difference in the MacAdam system or in other systems derived from colorimeter readings.

It must be emphasized that there is, in general, no agreement among the color-difference numbers calculated by any of the above methods. Comparisons of different methods (Nickerson 1944, Davidson 1953, Ingle 1962, Mackinney 1962, Little 1963) invariably show that the answers obtained are *not* the same, regardless of what "correction" or "adjustment" factors are applied. Therefore, it is *very* important to specify *exactly* how the calculation was made whenever color differences are used. As a rough rule-of-thumb, however, it is convenient to remember that the MacAdam unit is approximately a just-perceptible difference in color, while the NBS unit, representing approximately an average commercial tolerance, is three to four times as

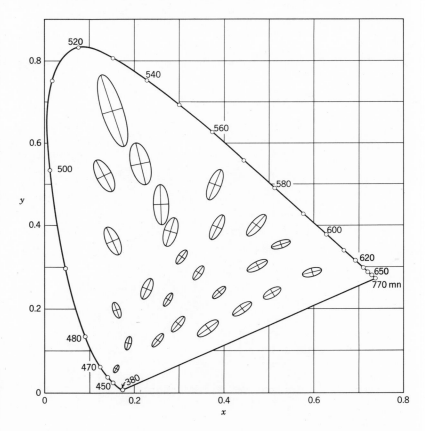

large as the MacAdam unit. The Adams and Hunter units are of the same order of magnitude as the NBS unit (Thurner 1965).

The calculation of small color differences falls into three classes: methods using digital computers and any of the aforementioned equations; those using analog computers, either as an accessory to a color-measuring instrument or separately; and those using numerical or graphical methods, an example of the latter being the charts for the Rapid Calculation of Small Color Differences available from the Union Carbide Corp., New York (Simon 1958). The choice among any of these techniques is one of facilities available and personal preference. But one must always specify *exactly* how the computations were made.

Perceptibility Versus Acceptability

Whether or not one has converted instrumental data to single color-difference numbers, heeding all the warnings, the final problem in color measurement is the evaluation of the color difference in terms of the *acceptability* of the sample as compared with the standard. If properly selected and prepared limit standards are used, this final step is made automatically.

If the limits of acceptability are expressed in terms of color-difference numbers, there is a real problem to be faced. Not only is it true that equal color-difference numbers, in any system of calculation so far devised, do not correspond to equal visually perceptible color differences, but it is also found that what constitutes an acceptable color difference is a statistical phenomenon (Davidson 1953). That is, not all people agree on what the size of a commercially acceptable color difference should be. Both individual differences in color perception and personal tastes undoubtedly become important here.

Perhaps the best procedure in cases where customer preference appears to be playing a part is to make color measurements over a sufficiently long period that an historical record is available. If the customer is at all consistent in the way he accepts or rejects material, it is possible in this way to reach agreement as to what constitutes an *acceptable* color difference, even if it bears little relation to what seem to be *perceptible* differences.

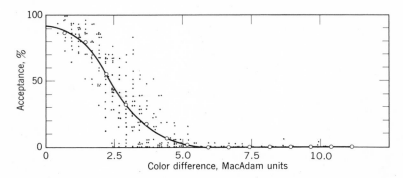

This figure (Davidson 1953) shows that, over a wide range of color differences (here, MacAdam units), some observers will consider a given color difference acceptable, while others will reject it. But the *average* acceptability (solid line) varies smoothly with the size of the color difference.

It is important to note here that the basic question of what is and what is not acceptable material must be settled in advance by agreement between the buyer and the seller. This is only sound business practice. If instrumental methods are to play a part, they must be defined exactly, including the techniques of measurement, converting the data, plotting or calculating, and evaluating the results. This agreement between buyer and seller is just as much a part of the usefulness of color measurement for purchase specification as are the instruments and computational techniques themselves.

Color Tolerances

In the final analysis, the sale and purchase of colored materials hinges upon the conformance of the samples to certain color-difference tolerances (Kelly 1962, 1965). Let us now consider how these tolerances should be set.

Color tolerances are, unfortunately, sometimes set in one of two quite undesirable ways. One is to make the tolerance as tight as possible so long as the vendor can supply satisfactory material. The other is to set the tolerance at the absolute limit of the ability of either the human observer or the instrument to detect a color difference. Both of these methods have a major defect in that they do not relate to what is required. If what is required does call for the utmost in control, then this is what must be furnished, but, to use an example from another industry, it would be foolish (to put it mildly) to order steel bars machined to a tolerance of a thousandth of an inch to be used as reinforcing rods for concrete. One reason this is not done, among others, is the fact that the tighter the tolerance, the higher the price. In this respect the situation in color measurement is unusual in that most requirements (until fairly recently) have called for "exact" matches. In recent years greater understanding on the part of all involved has resulted in some far more realistic tolerances, especially in the provision of limit standards in the several dimensions of color space. Where an "exact" match is needed, an "exact" match can usually be provided if one is willing to pay for it.

The use of instrumental color measurement as a threat or weapon in the buyer–seller relationship, through the measurement of very small color differences which have no significance in terms of function, is an abuse of instrumentation and one which will not contribute to its advance. On the other hand, where instrumentation is used in the measurement of color as an aid to a visual examination; where it is used to show the ability of a method to produce replicate samples which do not differ from each other; where it is used to determine the number of samples which need to be taken to obtain a reliable result; any of these will advance the cause of instrumentation (Johnston 1963, 1964a; Saltzman 1965). The use of instruments to determine the variables involved in the procedure for examining colored materials is an appropriate use of instruments and one which will serve to point up the variations which are due to techniques of measurement as compared with those due to techniques of sampling and sample preparation.

G. Summary

It is our belief that color measurement is the same whether the eye alone is used, or the eye and other instruments are used in combination. The instruments are aids to the eye. Their function, as can be seen from the methods used to convert data obtained from instruments, is to express the color of materials or color differences in terms of what the eye perceives. This does not make the instrument inferior in any way except that it is an aid and not an originator. It does not supersede the trained eye and the mind of the persons involved any more than the adding machine takes the place of the person who does the computations. However, like an adding machine, a properly working color-measuring instrument can be of great aid to colorists and in many cases a substitute for years of experience in the training period.

In emphasizing that there is no essential difference between color measurement as done by the eye and as done by other instruments, it is our feeling that increased proper use of instruments will resolve some of the problems of color measurement and comparison, especially where quantitative data are desired.

In addition, color measurement serves as a basis for "color memory." The unreliability of the memory, insofar as color is concerned, is well recognized (Bartleson 1960). The proper use of instruments gives to the manufacturer of colored materials a record of production, variation, and limits of acceptability which is independent of the memory of one or more observers. How long it will be before this historical record is accepted by most people in place of their faulty memory is a question best answered by the psychologists. In actual practice we have found that those most familiar with instrumentation are readily convinced by the historical record of instrumental readings on color.

Thus we conclude, and have tried to demonstrate, that there is no contradiction between color measurement with the eye and color measurement with instruments. Properly applied, the instrument can extend the usefulness of the eye. The eye is the final arbiter; the instrument, the aid.

CHAPTER **4**

Colorants

By now we have pointed out to our readers many times that the perceived color of an object depends on the combination of the spectral energy distribution of the light source, the spectral transmittance or reflectance of the object on which the light falls, and the spectral response curve of the eye. Yet we do not hesitate to do so again, for it is particularly important to keep in mind in this chapter the threefold nature of the production of what we call color, since this chapter is entirely concerned with only one of these factors. Here we consider the light source and the observer to be constant, and examine those substances used to modify the spectral reflectance or transmittance of an object.

Collectively, those substances which modify the perceived color of objects, or impart color to otherwise colorless objects, are called *colorants*. These are the *dyes* and *pigments* which are added to fabrics, coated on wood or metal with the aid of binders, or incorporated into a plastic mass, to change the original color. They are characterized by having selective absorption and scattering of light (that is, these quantities vary with the wavelength), so that they modify the spectral energy distribution of the light falling upon them. We have used the word *substance* in describing these coloring materials so as to exclude those color effects caused by the diffraction of light, such as the colors of feathers or the iridescence of certain insects.

A. Some Matters of Terminology

While *colorant* is the correct term for describing the materials used to impart color to objects, the word is still somewhat unfamiliar. Most people prefer to speak of dyes or pigments instead

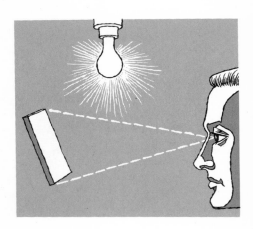

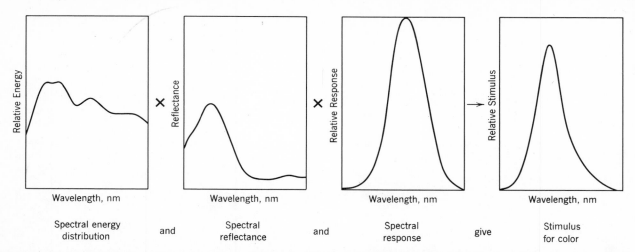

The perceived color of an object depends on the combination of the spectral curves shown here.

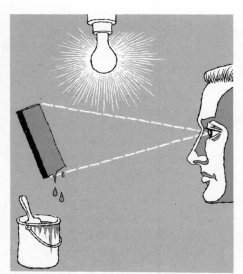

Colorants modify the spectral reflectance curve, and hence the color of an object.

of using the more general term. But the need to use two words to include all colorants, as well the confusion existing between dyes and pigments, described in Section B, is a strong argument for changing to the word colorant.

Even more confusing to those seeking precise definitions is the use of the word *color* in place of *colorant*. As it is used in this book, *color* means an effect perceived by an observer and determined by the interaction of the three components of light source, object, and observer. To speak of the manufacture or use of colors where colorants is meant is to take the part for the whole. This has been traditional, however, as evidenced by the existence of many companies with the word color in their corporate name. Since tradition dies hard, it will be a long time before the word color is no longer used to describe the materials which impart the effect of color.

The confusion between color and colorant, and between dye and pigment, is also found in foreign usage. In German, the word *Farbstoff* literally means colored material, but has become through usage to be synonymous with our word dye. In recent years the word *Pigment* has come to be used in German to distinguish the insoluble coloring matters from the broader class of *Farbstoffe*. In French, the words *matière colorante*, or colored material, are frequently used for all coloring matters. With a modifier, *colorant* can describe the type of coloring substance, as in *colorant pour cuve* for vat dye, *cuve* meaning vat, or even *colorant pigmentaire* meaning pigment. In addition the word *pigment* has come to be used in recent years, and the use of the term dyeing as synonymous with coloring has become less common.

In England, much as in the United States, the word *colour* has for many years been used to describe a colorant. This practice is disappearing, on the one hand, in favor of the use of the word dye with a modifier, such as vat dye, disperse dye, or even pigment dye, which in the terminology of this book is a contradiction. On the other hand, British references of a few years ago to "colours for printing ink" or "colours for paint" are largely replaced with phrases such as "pigments for paint" or "pigmentary colours."

U.S.A.		British		French		German	
Old	New or preferred	Old	New or preferred	Old	New or preferred	Old	New or preferred
Color	Colorant	Colour	Colour	Coleur	Matière colorante	Farbe	Farbstoff or Pigment
Pigment	Pigment	Colour	Pigmentary colour or pigment	Matière colorante	Colorant pigmentaire or pigment	Farbstoff	Pigment or Pigmentfarbstoff
Dyestuff	Dye (usually with a modifier as in *acid* dye or *wool* dye)	Dyestuff	Dye (usually with a modifier as in *reactive* dye, etc.)	Matière colorante	Matière colorante or the word colorant with a modifier as in *colorant pour cuve*	Farbstoff	Farbstoff or Farbe with modifier, e.g., *Kupenfarbstoff*

B. Dyes Versus Pigments

In the past, when things were relatively simple and uncomplicated, it was easy to distinguish between a dye and a pigment. A dye was a water-soluble substance used to color material from an aqueous solution, while a pigment was an insoluble material dispersed in the medium it was to color. Today, unfortunately, there are so many exceptions to this simple concept that new criteria must be sought to distinguish between dyes and pigments. As we shall see, no set of definitions is completely satisfactory, and a given substance can be either a dye or pigment— or both—almost irrespective of its chemical nature, solubility, method of application, or condition of use.

This confusion extends even to dictionary definitions. In the *Merriam-Webster Unabridged Dictionary* (both the second and third edition), the word dye is defined through its condition of use as a coloring matter used to alter the perceived color of an object by dyeing. The word pigment, on the other hand, is defined in close relationship to its original form and use, the latin *pingere*, meaning to paint. Pigments are thus limited, in this dictionary definition, to colorants used in painting. This is generally true, but as we use the word, pigments are used to color many other materials, including plastics, rubbers, spun-dyed fibers, and cement.

A word of warning is needed: In many industries the word pigment is used quite differently. In the rubber industry, for example, any material in the recipe other than the rubber itself is called a pigment, whereas in the paint industry many so-called "functional" or "structural" pigments are not used primarily to impart color to the paint.

In the following paragraphs we will examine some of the common criteria for distinguishing between dyes and pigments, and their exceptions.

Solubility

For many years it has been commonly stated that "dyes are soluble; pigments, insoluble." This is generally true: Most dyes are water soluble at some stage in their application to a fiber or fabric. But there are some exceptions, or at least borderline cases. Vat dyes, for example, are normally insoluble in water but are "solubilized" chemically during the dyeing operation. Disperse dyes for synthetic fibers are not truly in solution, but are so finely dispersed that it is almost academic to argue that they are fundamentally different from completely dissolved sub-

¹dye \'dī\ *n* -s [ME *dehe*, fr. OE *dēah*, *dēag*; akin to OE *dīegol* secret, hidden, OS *dōgalnussi* secret, hiding place, OHG *tugōn* to become variegated, *tougan* dark, hidden, secret, L *fumus* smoke — more at FUME] **1 :** color produced by dyeing **2 :** a natural or esp. a synthetic coloring matter whether soluble or insoluble that is used to color materials (as textiles, paper, leather, or plastics) usu. from a solution or fine dispersion and sometimes with the aid of a mordant — called also *dyestuff;* compare PIGMENT, STAIN, TINT; see DYE table — **of deepest dye** *or* **of the deepest dye :** of the worst kind ⟨a scoundrel *of the deepest dye*⟩ **:** of the most pronounced kind ⟨an intellectual *of the deepest dye*⟩

¹pig·ment \'pigmənt\ *n* -s [L *pigmentum* pigment, paint, fr. *pingere* to paint + *-mentum -ment* — more at PAINT] **1 a :** a natural or synthetic inorganic or organic substance that imparts a color including black or white to other materials; *esp* **:** a powder or easily powdered substance mixed with a liquid in which it is relatively insoluble and used in making paints, enamels, and other coating materials, inks, plastics, and rubber and also for imparting opacity and other desirable properties as well as color **b :** a compounding ingredient (as a filler or reinforcing agent) used in the manufacture of rubber or plastics — compare ¹DYE 2 **2 a :** any of various coloring matters in animals and plants; *esp* **:** solid or opaque coloring matter in a cell or tissue **b :** any of various related colorless substances (as various respiratory enzymes)

Although transparency or the lack of it is sometimes used to tell a dye from a pigment, this distinction does not always hold. Here, the same colorants are shown to have different transparency depending on their particle size and degree of dispersion.

As was described on page 11, a colorant must have its refractive index different from that of the material in which it is used in order to scatter light efficiently.

stances. And in *pigment padding*, an insoluble vat dye is incorporated into a *padding paste* and applied to the fabric. The dye is converted on the fiber to the soluble form, by various techniques which we will not discuss, and then back to the insoluble form which is "fixed" to the fabric. The other ingredients of the padding paste are not required to hold the dye to the fabric and do not remain on the fabric.

In contrast to dyes, pigments are always insoluble in the medium in which they are used: Any degree of solubility (called "bleed" in pigment-using industries) is considered a defect. We know of no exceptions to this. To put it another way, however, whenever a colorant normally used as an insoluble pigment is utilized in solution, it is simply called a dye!

Chemical Nature

Another traditional distinction between dyes and pigments is that dyes are organic, and pigments inorganic, substances. Again, the situation has changed with time. The number of inorganic dyes is almost zero, but the number of organic pigments has grown steadily since the rise of the organic chemical industry. Today the distinction works only one way: Most dyes are organic but it is not true that most pigments are inorganic. In terms of tonnage used, most pigments are inorganic but in terms of dollar value this is no longer the case.

Transparency

Still another distinction arose from the use of dyes and pigments to color resins such as paint vehicles or plastics. Colorants which dissolved in the resin and thus gave transparent mixtures were called dyes, in contrast to pigments which did not dissolve but scattered light and gave turbid, translucent, or opaque formulations. Except that solubility in an organic medium rather than in water is involved, the colorants usually thought of as dyes and pigments satisfy this criterion: If opacity is desired, pigments are used, whereas if one wants to color a transparent resin without spoiling its transparency, dyes soluble in the resin (generally classed as solvent-soluble or oil-soluble dyes) are used. This distinction still holds for the most part, but many organic pigments can be so well dispersed that the resulting resins are completely transparent. In many cases, it is impossible to tell from simple visual examination whether a resin is colored with a resin-soluble dye or a well-dispersed pigment.

To achieve this sort of transparency with insoluble pigments requires, in addition to a good dispersion, that the resin and pigment have similar indexes of refraction. This can be achieved with organic but not inorganic pigments. Most dyes can never be efficient opacifying colorants, even if they are insoluble in the resin (as, for example, are water-soluble dyes) because their refractive indexes are too close to that of the resin.

Presence of a Binder

A final distinction, to us the one with greatest validity and fewest exceptions, is based on the technique used to fix the colorant to a substrate, that is, on the need for a *binder* in the system. In this classification, which we make use of in this book, pigments are those colorants which are used with the aid of a binder (gum or resin) to fix them to the substrate. Dyes, on the other hand, become a part of the substrate without requiring a binder.

The application of this criterion to most systems is straight-forward. Dyes, whether vat, dispersed, solvent soluble, or other types, are dyes because a binder is not required to hold them to the material being dyed. (This is true even in pigment padding, but in resin-bonded pigment padding, they are pigments even if the identical colorants are used in the two cases.)

Pigments, on the other hand, are pigments because they must be incorporated into a binder in order to be attached to the substrate, as in a paint film attached to the wall of a house. In the case of a resin or plastic colored with an insoluble pigment, we hedge a little and call the plastic the binder, whereas we would call it the substrate when colored with a soluble dye.

Summary

It is obvious that the criteria we have discussed are all in agreement most of the time. By and large, the same colorants are likely to be soluble, organic, and transparent, and to require no binder in a given system. They deserve to be called dyes on all counts. In cases of disagreement, the choice of a name depends on how the colorant is used. If it is being used as a pigment by any of the accepted criteria, it should be called a pigment. The same colorant, if used as a dye, again by any of the accepted criteria, should be called a dye.

C.   Classification of Colorants

While colorants can be classified in at least as many ways as there are criteria to distinguish between dyes and pigments (Section B), we shall follow, in the present discussion, the system used in the standard work on the subject of dyes and pigments, the *Colour Index* (SDC and AATCC, 1956, 1963). (In the terminology we advocate in this book, of course, this five-volume, 4275-page work should be known as the *Colourant Index.*)

In the *Colour Index*, colorants are classified by method of use, and are designated by an application number, for example, C. I. Vat Red 13, C. I. Disperse Blue 1. Since users of the *Colour Index* are usually interested in the application properties of the colorants, this type of classification makes a great deal of sense. It is similar to the classification scheme used in the first edition of the *Colour Index* (1924, 1928) and in earlier German compilations of this type (Schultz 1931).

Examination of the *Colour Index* shows that, within a given class based on application, compounds of the same chemical type tend to predominate. There is no simple relation between chemical type and method of application, however, and in fact the *Colour Index* may list the same chemical in several application classes if it is widely used in each. An example is C. I. Vat Blue 14, which is also widely used as a pigment and listed as C. I. Pigment Blue 22.

The same colorant is called a dye when it is used to dye a fiber (above) and is called a pigment when it is dispersed in the fiber by spin-dying (below).

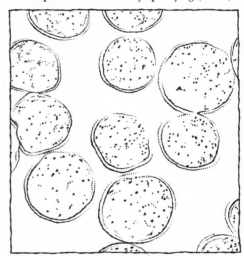

69810   C.I. Vat Blue 14
C.I. Pigment Blue 22

The same chemical compound can be used as either a dye or a pigment depending upon the method of application. The *Colour Index* recognizes this by applying the same five-digit number since the chemical compound is the same, but changing the application class numbers as illustrated.

37500 C.I. Azoic Coupling
Component 1

2-Naphthol

37035 C.I. Azoic Diazo
Component 37

NH$_2$

NO$_2$

p-Nitroaniline

Para Red
Colour Index No. 12070
C.I. Pigment Red No. 1

37550 C.I. Azoic Coupling
Component 12

5'-Chloro-3-hydroxy-2',4'-dimethoxy-
2-naphthanilide

37150 C.I. Azoic Diazo
Component 42

N',*N'*-Diethyl-4-methoxymetanilamide

Permanent Carmine
Colour Index No. 12490
C.I. Pigment Red No. 5

The *Colour Index* also assigns a number to the chemical constitution of each colorant, where this is known (the exact chemical natures of many colorants are trade secrets). This number is used for a given colorant regardless of the application class. Thus, the full *Colour Index* designations for the colorant mentioned above are C. I. Vat Blue 14, Colour Index 69810, and C. I. Pigment Blue 22, Colour Index 69810. There are 22 chemical categories in the classification of the *Colour Index*. Within each one, several application classes may be represented, although one may account for most of the colorants in that chemical category.

Up-to-date discussions of the chemistry of synthetic organic colorants are found in Venkantaraman (1952), Lubs (1955), and Gaertner (1963). Mattiello (1942) and Payne (1961) discussed the chemistry of inorganic colorants.

By and large, most of the materials listed by the *Colour Index* as dyes are used as such, and those which are listed as pigments are used in that way. There are some exceptions. Some vat dyes are, as we have seen, used as pigments. The same chemicals which are reacted to form azo dyes on the fiber (C. I. azoic diazo components and C. I. azoic coupling components) can also be reacted to form insoluble azo pigments. And there are many instances where a soluble dye is converted into an insoluble pigment by chemical treatment.

The *Colour Index* lists 17 classes of dyes according to method of application, including approximately 5000 dyes, plus many thousands more possible combinations of components leading to developed dyes, of which 400–500 are in use. Yet there is only one class of pigments, with only some 400 colorants listed. This disparity is an indication of the importance, to the user, of the method of application of the colorant. Pigments are always used with a binder, which plays an intermediary role between the colorant and the substrate on which it is placed. Changing the binder permits considerable flexibility in the application of pigments to the many substrates used. As a result, relatively few pigments are required for the many combinations of pigment, binder, and substrate which are in daily use. On the other hand, the many different fibers and dyeing conditions in use require different chemical properties as well as a wide variety of color effects. Thus, a relatively large number of dyes is needed in practice. Other factors important in determining the number of colorants needed in any given case are discussed in Chapter 6A.

Another case where the same chemical compound can be a dye or a pigment. In the examples shown, azoic coupling component 1 may be combined on the fiber with azoic diazzo component 37. The resulting compound is *Colour Index* (C.I.) 12070. When the same components are reacted and the resultant product isolated as a dry powder, it is called C.I. Pigment Red No. 1, the well-known Para Red. In a similar fashion, Permanent Carmine can be made on the fiber or as a powder. The combination on the fiber is called a naphthol dyeing; the powder product is called a pigment.

D. Selecting the Colorants to Use

The ability to select the appropriate colorants for a specific use is of considerably more importance to users of dyes and pigments than an understanding of their chemistry or other properties. To cover this subject would require a book many times the size of this one, written by people who are expert in far more areas than we. But the problem is far too important to be ignored. We shall, therefore, discuss, in part here and in part in Chapter 6A, some of the basic principles to be considered in the choice of a colorant, and indicate the sources of further information on this subject.

Sources of Information

We believe that there are three major sources of information on selecting colorants, valuable both for the beginner in the field of color technology and frequently for his more experienced colleagues.

Experienced Personnel. Perhaps the best source of information on choice of colorants is the senior, more experienced personnel in the laboratory or plant. Given a patient and knowledgeable master and a willing pupil, this source utilizes the best features of the apprentice system. If the knowledge, the time, and the patience are at hand, the information is likely to be the best because it is backed up with actual operating experience in the laboratory or plant concerned. But it is a situation which frequently can serve to perpetuate favorite myths which have grown up in that plant or in that group of people.

Suppliers of Colorants. A major source of information for most people is the supplier of colorants. Their information is available either through shade cards (pp. 98 and 99) and other published material furnished to the customer, or by personal contact between the customer and the supplier's technical representatives. While, admittedly, there may be some commercial bias in the information furnished, this can easily be recognized and discounted, and only a little experience is needed to ascertain which companies or representatives furnish reliable information.

Books and Periodicals. While there are relatively few books and periodicals relating to the *use* (in contrast to the *chemistry*) of dyes and pigments in specific industries, most of them are of very high quality (p. 100). Unfortunately, apart from the *Colour Index* and the AATCC *Technical Manual*, they contain largely the same information obtainable from the colorant suppliers: It would be most useful if the information were prepared more from the user's point of view. It must be said, however, that the published information differs from direct sales material in that it has been subjected to editing. As with all such published material (including books on the principles of color technology), the combination of the reputation of the writers and the standards of the publisher furnishes a clue to the reliability of the information presented.

The User's Experience. As the colorist gains in experience, his own knowledge will ultimately take precedence over any other information. This must be so since he alone is working under

A typical acid dye, C.I. Acid Orange 7 (Colour Index No. 15510)

$$NaO_3S \left\langle \bigcirc \right\rangle -N=N- \bigcirc^{HO}$$

is converted into the classical lake pigment Persian Orange, C.I. Pigment Orange 17

$$\frac{Ba}{2}O_3S \left\langle \bigcirc \right\rangle -N=N- \bigcirc^{HO}$$

$$+ Al_2O_3 \cdot nH_2O$$

by treatment with $BaCl_2$ (to form the barium salt of the acid dye) and $Al_2(SO_4)_3$ plus Na_2CO_3 (which yields aluminum hydrate, $Al_2O_3 \cdot nH_2O$).

A soluble dye is converted into an insoluble pigment by reacting it with a metallic salt and absorbing it onto aluminum hydrate.

Acid dyes
Mordant dyes
Basic dyes
Disperse dyes
Natural dyes
Food dyes
Leather dyes
Direct dyes
Sulfur dyes
Vat dyes
Ingrain dyes
Azoic dyes
Oxidation bases
Reactive dyes
Solvent dyes
Fluorescent brightening agents
Developers
Reducing agents

Dyes classified by use according to *Colour Index* —note that all pigments fall in only one use category.

C. I. Vat Orange 3
C. I. No. 59300

50% Tone   75% Tone   Solid
Printing Ink: 20% Color

Indofast Orange Toner OV-5964

DESCRIPTION
An alkali- and acid-resisting, light fast halogenated anthanthrone pigment.

PHYSICAL PROPERTIES
SPECIFIC GRAVITY	1.97
BULKING VALUE	16.41 lbs./gal.
OIL ABSORPTION	42

BLEEDING IN:

Xylol	Sl. Yellow	Oleic Acid	None
Lacquer Solvents	Sl. Yellow	Water	None
Ethanol	Sl. Yellow	5% Hydrochloric Acid	None
Aliphatic Petroleum		5% Soda Ash	None
Solvents	None	10% Caustic Soda	None

LIGHT FASTNESS: Reference: Official Digest, 31, December 1959, Part 2—Table 46.

Exterior Full Shade	Excellent
Exterior Tint Shade (95% TiO$_2$)	Excellent

25% Color, 75% TiO$_2$
Acrylic Lacquer

SUGGESTED USES
Alkyd Resin Enamels, Nitrocellulose Lacquers, Printing Inks, Rubber, Vinyl Products, Linoleum, Plastics and Emulsion Paints.

AVAILABLE FORMS

	Code	Pigment Content
Indofast Orange Toner	OV-5964	100%
Alumina Hydrate Lake	OV-6014	40%
Presscake	OV-5963	Approx. 25%
Water Dispersion	E-13415	16⅔%
Cellulose Acetate Dispersion	OV-6007	50%
Cellulose Acetate Butyrate Dispersion	E-16516	60%
Vinyl Dispersion	OV-5985	20%

5% Color, 95% TiO$_2$
Acrylic Lacquer

1% Color, 99% TiO$_2$
Acrylic Lacquer

Vinyl Plastisol

0.2 phr   1.0 phr

Acrylic Lacquer on Foil
1.5% of Total Solids

10

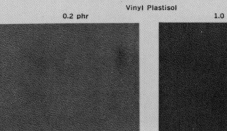

A typical pigment shade card. (Courtesy Allied Chemical Co.)

FASTNESS RATINGS ARE BASED ON THE PERCENTAGE DYEING INDICATED

	1.0% Chromolan Orange R
Solubility	5-4
Level Dyeing	4
Neutral Dyeing	4
Neutral Discharge	5
Effect of Chrome	2D
Effect of Metals — Monel	5
Copper	4D
Iron	3Y1D
Effect Threads — Acetate	2
Acrilan	7-8
Cotton	1
Dacron	1
Dynel	1
Nylon 6	9
Nylon 6.6	8-9
Orlon 42	1
Orlon 81	1
Silk	6
Viscose	1
Change in Artificial Light	3YBr
Light (Fade-Ometer) — Light Shade	5
Medium Shade	7
Heavy Shade	7
Urea-Formaldehyde Resin — Alteration	4W
Fade-Ometer	8-7
Melamine Resin — Alteration	5-4R
Fade-Ometer	8-7
Ethylene-Urea-Formaldehyde Resin — Alteration	5-4W
Fade-Ometer	8-7
Mill Washing Test #2 — Alteration	5-4R
Staining of Wool	4
Viscose	5
Silk	3
Nylon 6.6	3
Cotton	5
Acetate	5
Fulling Test #1 — Alteration	4WD
Staining of Wool	5-4
Viscose	5
Silk	3
Nylon 6.6	3
Cotton	5
Acetate	5
Lustering	3-2W
Steaming	5-4
Crocking (Rubbing) Dry	5-4
Wet	5-4

14

...NGS ARE ...PERCENT...DICATED

	1.0% Chromolan Orange R	1.0% Chromolan Orange GN
	5-4R	5
	5-4R	5-4Y
	5	4Y
	5-4R	5
	4WR	5-4R
	4D	5
Wool	5	5
Viscose	5	5
Silk	4	4
Nylon 6.6	4	4
Cotton	5	5
Acetate	5	5
	5	4Y
Wool	4-3	5
Viscose	5	5
Silk	4-3	5-4
Nylon 6.6	4-3	5
Cotton	5	5
Acetate	5	5
Wool	5	5
Viscose	5	5
Silk	5	4
Nylon 6.6	5	5
Cotton	5	5
Acetate	5	5
	4Y	4-3Y
Wool	5	4Y
Viscose	5	5
Silk	3	3
Nylon 6.6	5	5
Cotton	5	5
Acetate	5	5
...1 minute	4-3R	4R
...2 hours	4R	5-4R
...1 minute	3W	4W
...2 hours	5	5
Wool	5-4WR	4WY
Cotton	3	4
	5	5

14a

Chromolan Dyes on Wool

Chromolan Orange R

0.25%

1.0%

3.0%

Chromolan Orange GN

0.25%

1.0%

3.0%

15

A typical dye shade card. (Courtesy Allied Chemical Co.)

Books and articles relating to the *use* of colorants:

AATCC "Technical Manual,"
    annually
SDC and AATCC, *Colour Index*
    1956, 1963
Carr 1957
Cutter 1962
Lenoir 1959–1963
Moll 1960
Plant 1962
Simpson 1962–1963
Smith 1962
Vesce 1956, 1959

exactly the conditions which prevail in his plant. Again, as with all generalizations, we must insert a warning note: If the experience of a color technologist relative to a particular problem is contrary to the general experience which has been reported, the entire question should be reexamined. It may well be that something is not being done correctly, and frequently consultation with the dye or pigment supplier may be of great help. This is equally true when, as in many laboratory or plant procedures, the process is "followed exactly" but the results are different from those predicted by the supplier of the colorants involved. While it is perfectly normal and most often justified to take the operating experience in one's own plant as a guide, any serious difference between that experience and the general experience must always be open to question (Wegmann 1960, Smith 1962, Herzog 1965).

General Principles in Choosing Colorants

In the vast majority of cases, the class of colorant to be used is dictated by the nature of the material to be colored. Further, this is usually decided by someone other than the colorist in the laboratory. Each class of fabric, each type of plastic, and each kind of paint system has its particular requirements. Dye houses which do not have equipment for printing with resin-bonded pigments have already made the choice between direct dyeing of cotton and pigment printing.

One of the principal tasks of a color technologist in industry is to obtain sufficient information from his management or the sales force to make a rational selection of a coloring method in those cases where a choice is possible. Given the problem of coloring a specific material, recourse to the sources of information indicated above will generally give a colorist his preliminary answer. In those cases where there is a choice between dyes and pigments, the decision may be based upon economics, availability of equipment, or, as amplified in Chapter 6A, the engineering considerations involved.

It would appear, after this lengthy discussion of colorants and comparison of dyes and pigments, that in reality there is little to choose between them. There are indeed differences between them, but there are not many cases in which there is a choice of using one or the other of these two classes of colorants. Some cases where such a choice may be made are:

1. Using a soluble dye or a pigment or pigment dispersion in the preparation of flexographic inks.

2. Coloring a plastic article by molding it from colored stock or by dyeing or painting it after fabrication.

3. Using "spun-dyed" or "pigment-dyed" fiber, dyeing staple fiber, dyeing yarn, or dyeing the woven or knitted article.

E. Summary

While the dyes and pigments available to the color technologist may be different in many physical and chemical properties, they have one important point in common: Their absorption and scattering of light are intensively selective, so that their addition to other materials modifies the interaction of light with the latter and, hence, their perceived color. This much is basic; all the rest is a matter of added convenience in use, such as solubility in a given solvent, compatibility with a specific resin, or the ability to dye a particular fiber.

Colorants have little or no intrinsic value. They contribute to the value of a finished product, in the last analysis, by virtue of their properties of selective absorption and scattering of light. This is their reason for existence, the reason for the search for new colorants, and the reason for continuing the process, many thousands of years old, of selecting materials for the coloring of otherwise colorless substances. Because of the many new materials to be colored, as well as new techniques of coloring, the line of demarcation between dyes and pigments, while still a very strong one, is gradually being destroyed. It is therefore best to think of these materials from the point of view of their basic properties, and consider the fact that they are chiefly dyes or chiefly pigments part of the secondary characteristics of these light-modifying substances.

The Jay.   The Bay.

The Blue Jay, as we clearly see,
Is so much like the green Bay tree
That one might say the only clue.
Lies in their dif-fer-ence of hue,
And if you have a color sense,
You'll see at once this difference.

~R.W. Wood 1917

CHAPTER **5**

The Coloring of Materials in Industry

This chapter is concerned with the work of the industrial colorist, the man who is responsible for producing materials which are perceived as matching either a physical sample submitted to him or the verbal descriptions of a color effect stated by a designer or stylist. He recognizes (as by now our readers do) that the phenomenon of perceived color results from the combination of the spectral energy distribution curve of a light source, the spectral transmittance or reflectance curve of an object, and the spectral response curve of the eye of an observer. He knows, also, that his work deals almost entirely with the object, since he cannot alter the sensitivity of the human eye and since he is rarely afforded the opportunity of changing the light under which the material is seen. His business, then, is to use colorants, which were loosely classified in Chapter 4 as dyes or pigments, to modify the spectral transmittance or reflectance curve of a material until the desired color effect is achieved.

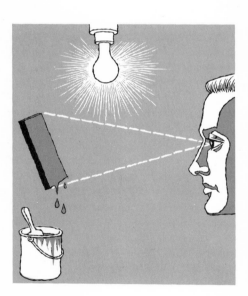

Our colorist must also be aware that he is changing *more* than the perceived color of the object. Many other properties of the material must be modified and controlled if the final article is to be functionally useful. Some of these are influenced by the colorants used, and this may result in limitations which must be recognized. These "engineering" aspects of the coloring process are discussed further in Chapter 6A.

A. Color-Mixing Laws

If color matching by mixing colorants is to work at all, and if the colorist is to make any sense out of the color effects he gets

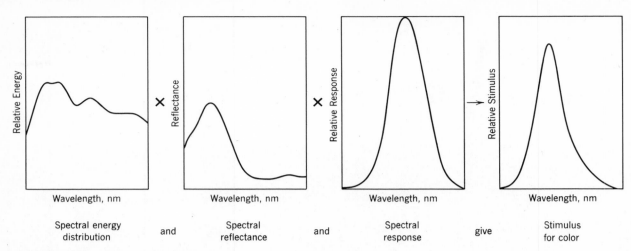

Spectral energy distribution **and** Spectral reflectance **and** Spectral response **give** Stimulus for color

The perceived color of an object depends on the combination of the spectral curves shown here.

as the result of such mixing, then it must be that certain laws of color mixing exist and are obeyed reasonably well. This is true, and although the laws are quite complex in some cases, they furnish both the qualitative basis for the traditional color matcher's skill developed by experience, and the quantitative bases for the calculation techniques which are beginning to aid him in many cases. We should look at these laws before considering the techniques of color matching in detail.

Additive Mixing

Perhaps the simplest kind of color mixing, in terms of physical actions, does not involve mixing colorants at all, but rather mixing colored lights. This can be done in several different ways. Colored lights from different lamps can be superimposed on a

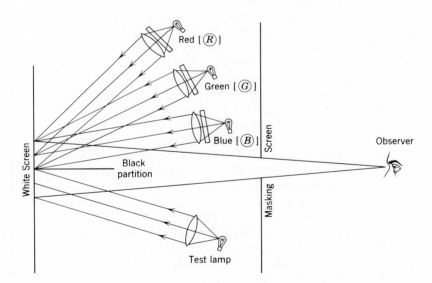

white screen, as described in Chapter 2B. Or, the light coming from different portions of a spinning disk can be caused to be seen as a single color, as discussed in Chapter 3D. (It makes no difference whether this light is reflected from an opaque disk or transmitted through a transparent disk.) Still another alternative is to place small colored areas close together and view them from a distance so great that the eye cannot distinguish the separate colored spots, as in a pointillist painting. In these last two cases, the adding of the colors takes place in the mind of the observer and must, therefore, be a physiological or psychological effect, but the result is the same as when the colored lights are directly added on a white screen.

As was described in Chapter 2B, a wide variety of colors can be made by additive mixing if the three lamps are chosen to have certain colors. For convenience, we call the most useful choice of colors for these lamps the *primary colors* for additive mixing, or the *additive primaries.* They are red, green, and blue. There is nothing magical or unique about them except that they happen to work best for this experiment. Mixtures of red and green give yellow lights, mixtures of green and blue give the blue-greens or cyans, and mixtures of blue and red give the purples or magentas. If the three primaries are properly chosen and mixed together in just the right proportions, they add up to give white or perhaps in the case of reflected-light colors, a light gray (see frontispiece).

Since it was shown in Chapter 2B that the CIE system was derived from experiments on the mixing of colored lights, it is not unexpected that the results of such mixing can be determined very easily with the aid of the CIE chromaticity diagram. Remembering that here we deal with the illuminant mode of viewing (p. 3), we can specify the color of a light by its chromaticity x and y and its luminance Y (pp. 38 and 40). Grassmann (1853) showed that the luminance of any additive mixture of lights is the sum of the luminances of each of them, regardless of their spec-

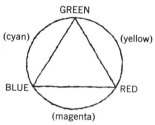

The usual choice of primary colors for additive mixing is shown in capital letters.

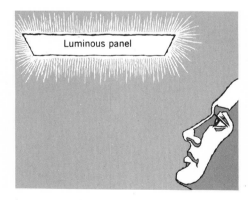

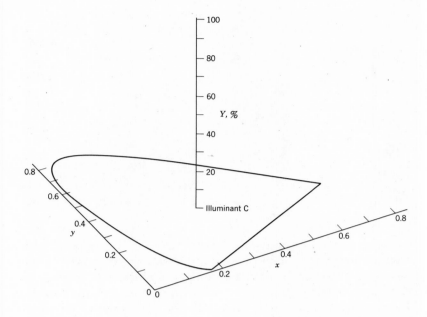

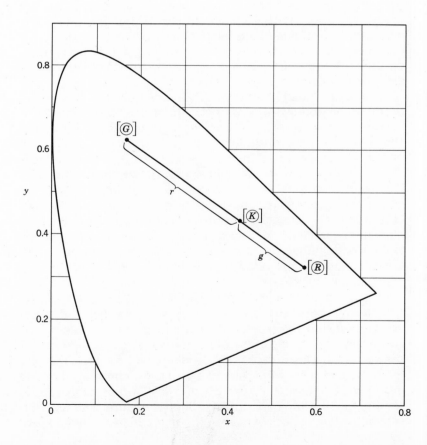

Grassman's laws of additive color mixing state that if ®️ units of light [®️] are added to ©️ units of light [©️], the luminance (CIE Y) of the resulting light [®️] is ®️ = ®️ + ©️ units. The chromaticity coordinates of [®️] lie on the line connecting [©️] and [®️], at the point which divides the line into segments g and r, such that $g/r = ©️/®️. \ldots$

tral energy distributions. Grassman's laws also allow the chromaticity of the mixture to be determined easily and quickly, as illustrated in the figures on this and the facing page.

The reason for the common choice of red, blue, and green as the additive primary colors now becomes clear—more colors can be matched by these primaries than by any other three.

The achievement of additive mixing by the pointillist painters suggests that this type of mixing might be found in some printing processes. This is not usually the case, however, since the colored areas usually overlap, and simple-subtractive mixing (see below) occurs. Color television sets, however, do operate by additive mixing (p. 108).

Simple-Subtractive Mixing

Just as the term additive mixing is descriptive of the process of adding colored lights, so subtractive mixing refers to the removal by an object of part of the light coming from a source. The ways in which this light can be removed (described on pp. 8–11) include absorption and scattering. The case of simple absorption without scattering, we call simple subtraction, and the mixing of colorants in this way we call *simple-subtractive mixing*. We call the more complex situation, where there is scattering as well as absorption, complex subtraction, and the mixing law *complex-subtractive mixing*. This is discussed beginning on page 111.

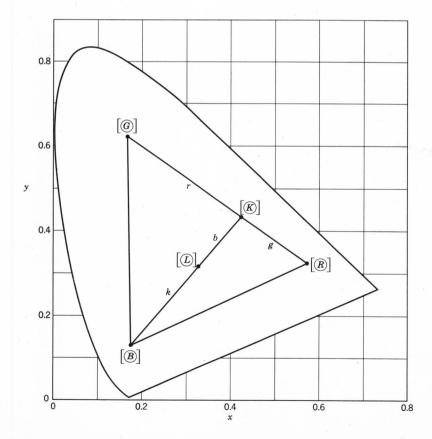

. . . This line of reasoning can easily be extended to the case where three (or more) lights are mixed, for example to find the location of light [Ⓛ], which has luminance Ⓛ = Ⓡ + Ⓖ + Ⓑ and chromaticity coordinates located so that $b/k = $ Ⓑ/Ⓚ.

In color television, three beams of electrons carry the information corresponding to the three additive primary colors. Kept on their courses by passing through holes in a mask, they strike phosphor dots of the correct primary colors on the face of the television tube. The additive effect of these tiny dots gives the desired color, just as colors are formed by additive mixing in a pointillist painting (Fink 1960).

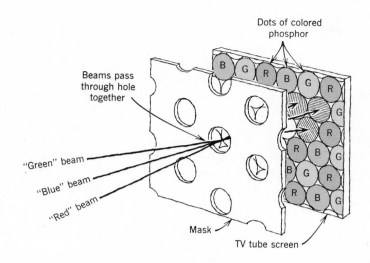

A red stop light lens subtracts out, by absorption, all of the components of white light except its own color, red.

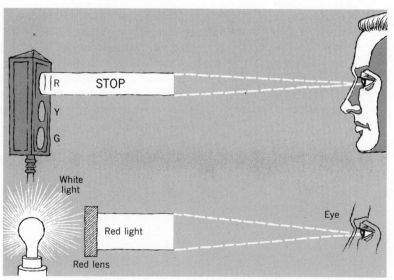

The usual choice of primary colors for simple-subtractive mixing is shown in capital letters.

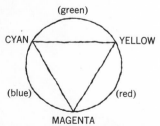

The most useful primaries for subtractive mixing are yellow, cyan (blue-green), and magenta. The action of these primaries is shown in the frontispiece. Greens result from mixing yellow and cyan; blues, from mixing cyan and magenta; and reds, from mixing magenta and yellow. The relations between additive and subtractive mixing are nicely illustrated by the familiar "color wheel" arrangement; each additive primary has a subtractive primary as its complementary color, lying directly across the wheel. When the subtractive primaries are balanced in color and amount, the result of putting all three together is to subtract all the light from the source, leaving, of course, black.

Simple-subtractive colorant mixing is widely used in color photography (Kodak 1962), in color printing by overprinting (Cooke 1955), and in the dyeing of transparent plastics (Billmeyer 1963b).

The prediction of the colors resulting from simple-subtractive colorant mixing is more complicated than for the case of additive mixing, for several reasons. First of all, the limitations of existing

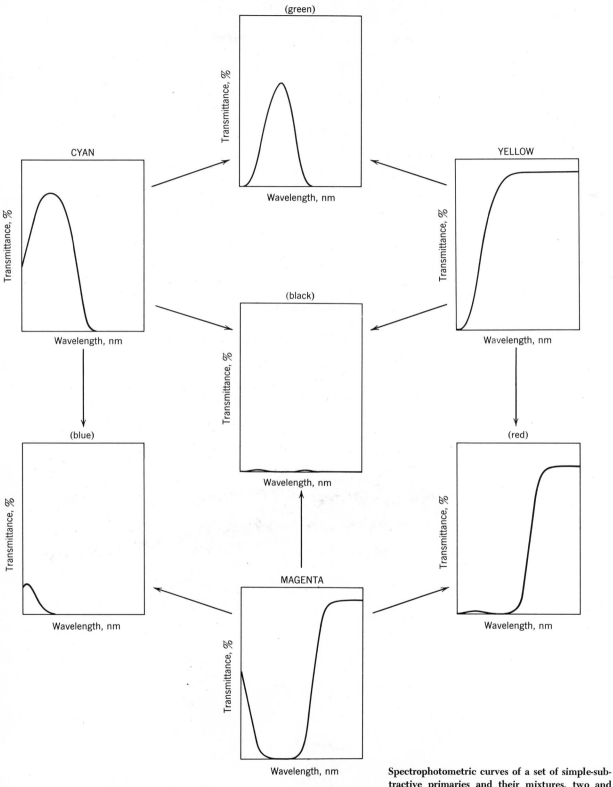

Spectrophotometric curves of a set of simple-subtractive primaries and their mixtures, two and three at a time, in a transparent acrylic plastic system.

$$\log T = -CA$$
$$\text{or} \qquad T = \exp(-CA)$$

For three colorants,

$$T = \exp(-C_1A_1 - C_2A_2 - C_3A_3)$$

Beer's law states that, at any wavelength, the logarithm of the transmittance T is given by multiplying the concentration C of colorant by its absorption coefficient, A. Alternately, T can be written as the *exponential* (here abbreviated exp) of C times A. If several colorants are mixed in the same sample, each contributes a separate (C times A) term.

$$X = \sum_\lambda E\bar{x} \exp(-C_1A_1 - C_2A_2 - C_3A_3)$$

$$Y = \sum_\lambda E\bar{y} \exp(-C_1A_1 - C_2A_2 - C_3A_3)$$

$$Z = \sum_\lambda E\bar{z} \exp(-C_1A_1 - C_2A_2 - C_3A_3)$$

To predict the colors resulting from simple-subtractive mixing, one has to perform the calculations described by these equations at many (30–65) wavelengths across the spectrum. The quantities E, $\bar{x}$, $\bar{y}$, $\bar{z}$, A_1, A_2, and A_3 all change with the wavelength.

colorants make them less than ideal as subtractive primaries. In additive mixing, on the other hand, the ideal spectrum colors can be obtained fairly easily with lights. Then, too, the fundamental law of simple-subtractive mixing, Beer's law (p. 10), is more complicated than Grassmann's law because Beer's law holds for only one wavelength at a time. To compute the colors resulting from simple-subtractive colorant mixing, one has to make Beer's law calculations at many wavelengths across the spectrum to obtain the spectral transmittance curves of the mixtures, and then obtain CIE coordinates by the integration techniques described in Chapter 3E. Unlike the situation in additive mixing, the spectral transmittance curves of the subtractive primaries do have an important influence on the colors resulting from subtractive mixing.

The Beer's law calculations and the subsequent integrations required to predict the colors resulting from simple-subtractive mixing are straightforward but cumbersome, and very little of this sort of work was done in industry before the invention of modern digital computers. Today, however, these calculations form the basis of the commercial formulation of transparent colors by computer techniques (Billmeyer 1960a).

The gamut of colors which can be made by simple-subtractive mixing is illustrated for a typical case in the figure on this page. Since the process is literally one of subtraction, the luminances of the mixtures are usually much lower than those of the primaries. Colors of relatively high purity can still be achieved.

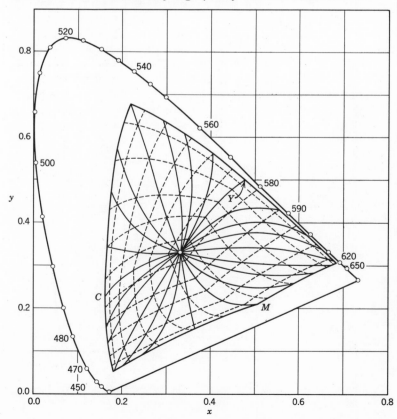

The gamut of chromaticities which can be made by mixing, two at a time, a cyan, a yellow, and a magenta dye used in a color photographic process. Points on solid lines locate mixtures in which the two dyes are taken in constant proportion, while points on dotted lines locate mixtures in which the concentration of one dye is kept constant (Evans 1948).

Complex-Subtractive Mixing

By far the most common and, unfortunately, the most complex type of color mixing we experience is that in which the colorants scatter as well as absorb light. This type of colorant mixing does not even have a satisfactory name. We choose to call it *complex-subtractive mixing*. Since complex-subtractive mixing involves the simultaneous absorption and scattering of light, both these quantities enter into the color-mixing laws for this case. These laws are correspondingly more complex than those for additive or simple-subtractive mixing. To write them down in exact form, as Beer's law for simple-subtractive mixing was written down on page 110, would give equations far too complicated for this book (Völz 1962, 1964; Beasley 1965). For most practical purposes, simplified equations, which are approximately correct, are commonly used to describe complex-subtractive mixing. The most widely used of these approximate equations were derived by Kubelka and Munk (Kubelka 1931, 1948, 1954), and may be found, in their most useful form, in Judd (1952, 1963).

Two of the assumptions in the Kubelka-Munk equations are: (*1*) The sample is illuminated and viewed by diffuse light (which does not correspond to the system used in any commercially available color measuring instrument) and (*2*) there is no change in refractive index at the sample's boundaries. The latter assumption is fulfilled for some cases, such as water-based paints in air, but not for most common pigmented mixtures. Saunderson (1942), however, modified the Kubelka-Munk equations empirically to include the effects of reflection losses accompanying a change in refractive index at the sample boundaries.

Despite these limitations, the Kubelka-Munk equations (though relatively complicated) are particularly useful for opaque systems. They have been applied for color-matching calculations both by hand or desk calculator methods (Duntley 1942, Saunderson 1942, Duncan 1949, 1962, Foster 1966b), somewhat simplified by the use of accessories for spectrophotometers (Pritchard 1952), and more recently with the aid of digital computers (Alderson 1961) and, with further simplifications, analog computers (Davidson 1963b). More complete equations for complex-subtractive mixing in translucent systems have been described by Völz (1962, 1964) and by Beasley (1965). They are so complicated that use of a digital computer is essential for their rapid solution. In addition, considerably more preparative work is required to obtain the data necessary for application of these equations.

The colors resulting from complex-subtractive mixing are determined, in a general way, by calculations similar to those for

$$R = \frac{1 - R_g \, (a - b \operatorname{ctgh} bSX)}{a - R_g + b \operatorname{ctgh} bSX}$$

$$T_i = b/(a \sinh bSX + b \cosh bSX)$$

where

R = reflectance
R_g = reflectance of material behind the translucent sample
T_i = transmittance within the sample
$a = (K + S)/S$
$b = \sqrt{a^2 - 1}$
K = absorption coefficient
S = scattering coefficient
X = sample thickness
ctgh = hyperbolic cotangent
sinh = hyperbolic sine
cosh = hyperbolic cosine

One form of the Kubelka-Munk equations. For others, conveniently summarized, see Judd 1963.

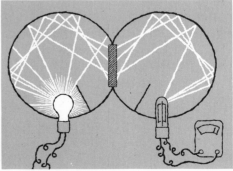

Diffuse illumination *and* viewing.

simple-subtractive mixing. Computations based on the Kubelka-Munk equations are made at many wavelengths across the spectrum to give a spectral reflectance curve, and are followed by integration to obtain the corresponding CIE coordinates. The additional complication of light scattering results in the need for four colorants rather than three as in additive or simple-subtractive mixing, to match a wide variety of colors at all luminance levels. One of the colorants is almost always a white pigment, chosen for high scattering power to impart opacity when used in relatively small quantities.

The gamut of colors obtainable through complex-subtractive mixing with a small number of colored pigments is more limited than that resulting from additive or simple-subtractive mixing. For example, brilliant oranges are obtained by the additive mixing of red and green lights and by the simple-subtractive mixing of yellow and magenta dyes, but result less often from complex-subtractive mixing of red and yellow pigments. For this reason, as well as for the "engineering" reasons discussed in Chapter 6A, a good many colored pigments are required to obtain a wide gamut of colors by complex-subtractive mixing, even though *any one* color requires the use of no more than three colored pigments plus white, or (with somewhat more flexibility) two chromatic pigments plus white and black (Davidson 1955a). In industrial practice, more pigments may be used for "engineering" reasons.

B.   Color Matching

The function of an industrial colorist is primarily to prepare colored material to meet the requirements of his industry, which may consist of meeting the demands of a stylist or of matching a competitive product. The colorist's job is to select the proper colorants and to adjust their amounts until a satisfactory result is obtained. He is concerned almost entirely with modifying the *object* in the triad of source, object, and observer.

In industrial practice, the process of determining the proper amounts of the chosen colorants is divided into two steps:

1. The preparation of an initial match, which in practice may include the selection of the colorants, and

2. The adjustment of a previously formulated match to conform to a standard process (for example, scaling up a laboratory development to plant size) or to maintain the uniformity of the colored product. This latter procedure is commonly known as shading (in the paint industry), tinting, or by one of several other terms varying from industry to industry.

Since the techniques as well as the objectives of initial formulation and adjustment differ somewhat, we shall consider them separately. Most of all we wish to emphasize the importance of the proper selection of colorants, a step which is far too often not given serious enough consideration.

Selecting the Colorants

In preparing a color match, the first question to be answered is whether or not the two samples are required to look alike to all

Minimum requirements for complex-subtractive mixing:
   two colored pigments
   black
   white

Steps in color matching:
   selecting the colorants
   making the initial match
   adjusting the match

observers and under all light sources. As we saw in Chapter 1D, this requires that the two objects have identical spectral reflectance curves. This type of match, we call an *invariant* match.

Invariant Matches. The requirement just stated, that two objects must have identical spectrophotometric curves to be an invariant match is a severe one, but we cannot overemphasize how true it is. It requires several things:

First of all, the match must be made with the identical colorants used in the sample to be matched. This leads directly to the subject of how to determine what these colorants are, as discussed in the next section.

Second, primarily because of limitations set by the properties of colorants, the same type of material must be colored. It is quite unlikely that a dyed fabric could be formulated to be an invariant match to a pigmented paint film. A *close* match can be obtained, but since it will be necessary to use different colorants in the two samples, and since the optical properties of the fabric and paint film are different, an invariant match cannot be achieved.

Third, the same or a very similar process of coloring must be used. This is especially important in complex-subtractive matching, where the color of a pigment depends on how well it is dispersed in the medium in which it is used. Other aspects of appearance, such as gloss, are also of great importance.

Finally, if instruments are to be used as aids in formulating invariant matches, spectrophotometers rather than colorimeters will be required.

Colorant Identification. If an invariant match is required, and the above conditions are met, the approach we have found most useful is to identify the principal dyes or pigments which have been used to color the submitted sample, and to use those colorants in formulating the match. This type of matching, known as *colorant* matching (Judd 1963, p. 406), is not used as much as we feel it should be, probably because it is not widely realized that the identification procedures are well worked out and relatively simple (Abbott 1944, Stearns 1944, Harkins 1959, Saltzman 1959). Briefly, they involve extracting the colorants from the sample and identifying them by simple chemical tests and by spectrophotometric curve shape. Examination of the spectral reflectance curves of the dyed or pigmented materials themselves, without extraction, is also useful for identifying colorants. Most laboratories engaged in color matching can easily use these techniques, or can have their colorant supplier use them, as an aid to color matching.

Conditional Matches. In the many cases where an invariant match cannot be made, it is necessary for the colorist to be content with making a close match under a limited set of illuminating and viewing conditions. We define this as a *conditional match*.

Some of the reasons why an invariant match cannot always be made have already been mentioned. If the same colorants that are in the sample to be matched cannot be used, a conditional match will almost inevitably result. This may be the case if different materials or different methods of coloring are involved.

An *invariant* match is one in which the two samples look alike to all observers and under all light sources.

A *conditional match* is one in which the two samples look alike to some observers or under some light sources, but do not look alike to other observers or under other light sources.

Even if the same materials and coloring methods are used, the customer may ask that the new samples have better light fastness, be less expensive, nonbleeding, or differ in some other property from the sample submitted. Here, too, the problem cannot easily be resolved. If the same colorants are to be used, an invariant match can be obtained, but it is very unlikely that the new sample will have better light fastness (unless a colorless stabilizer can be found) or be less expensive (unless someone is willing to cut the prices of the colorants). It is important to resolve the requirements of such a request at the very beginning to avoid a waste of time and effort.

Whenever it is agreed that a conditional match must be made, it is important to know under what conditions (e.g., preferred illuminant or illuminants) the match is to be judged, since the match must of necessity be metameric and will vary with the illuminant or the observer.

While in the case of conditional matches it is less important to identify the colorants used, this identification can be very useful, particularly if the materials and coloring methods are the same but an improvement in some property is desired. Here the colorist can unwittingly make an invariant match when this is not desired.

In many cases only a limited number of colorants can be used in the material in which the match is to be made. An example is the coloring of nylon and other plastics which must be processed at high temperatures. In these cases, identification of the colorant in the submitted sample is usually of little importance since the color match must be made with the limited palette available. It is very important to have it understood by all concerned that a conditional match will in general be obtained, and to determine in advance what the preferred conditions for judging the match are to be.

In making a match using colorants other than those used in the original material, we will obtain more than just a conditional match for color. Metamerism, by itself, is not the greatest defect of such a match. The more important consideration stems from the fact that such matches will not have the same fastness properties as an invariant match, or will differ in other important properties.

Summary. When a sample is submitted for color matching, it is essential to select from the following alternatives:

1. If the sample submitted is representative of the actual material and method of coloring to be used and contains colorants which are satisfactory for the intended use, an invariant match is possible and colorant identification is the proper starting point.

2. If the sample is not in the same material as that to be used, if different fastness, cost, or another property is required, or if a different coloring process is needed, then it must be recognized at the beginning that the match will be conditional, and the preferred conditions of judging must be specified.

The Initial Match

While the selection of the proper colorants is of major importance, especially in making invariant matches, it does not provide information on the correct amounts of colorants to use. These are traditionally determined by trial and error, relying on the skill of the visual color matcher, but more and more often, instrumental and computational methods are supplementing this skill.

Visual Matching. As with so many processes in an industry where there is so much art as well as science, the experience of the color matcher must never be underrated. There is simply no substitute for it, and it would be foolish for us to attempt to condense it to a few words. Very seldom, however, is this skill applied without the use of some aids, whether they be merely a careful written record of past experience, the use of the results of color measurement, or more sophisticated calculations. Since we strongly believe that these aids are extremely important, even frequently indispensable, we proceed to discuss them.

Instrumental Aids. The purpose of instrumentation and the chemical analysis of colorants is to reduce the amount of experi-

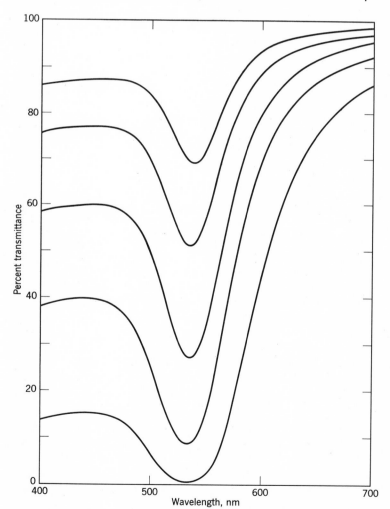

Special ways of presenting spectrophotometric data provide useful instrumental aids to color matching. On the following pages, two useful sets of curves are compared to the conventional plot shown here. These are transmittance curves (corrected for surface reflections) for a series of magenta Lovibond glasses with different colorant concentrations. (Similar curves would be obtained with glasses having thicknesses proportional to these concentrations, all made from the same material.)

ence required in the field of color matching, where it is becoming more and more difficult to obtain experienced personnel. In the last analysis, however, it is true that there is no substitute for experience, and the colorist must acquire some experience in the use of instruments and in the interpretation of their results before he finds them useful aids in the color-matching process. One major advantage does appear to favor the use of instruments: It is found (Johnston 1965b) that a previously unskilled person can learn to match colors with instrumental aids more rapidly than he can learn to do this by the time-honored visual method. Possibly because tradition dies hard, it is significantly more difficult for a skilled visual color matcher to adapt to the instrumental approach and derive the full benefits from it.

In discussing instrumental aids to color matching, we again find it useful to consider invariant matching and conditional

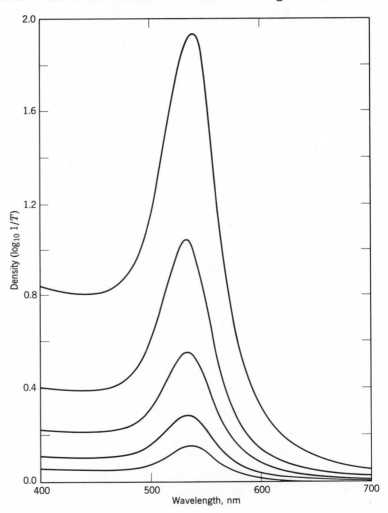

Density curves for the samples of the preceding figure. Linear distances on this plot are proportional to the Beer's-law absorption coefficients in the equations on page 110.

matching separately. Again we find the spectrophotometer the most useful instrument to assist in the process of formulating invariant matches. Much can be learned from the spectrophotometric curve shape about the amounts as well as the identity of the colorants used in a sample.

Two accessories available for some spectrophotometers are particularly useful in interpreting spectrophotometric curve shape. One is the log–density cam, which plots the curves in such a way that their shape is the same regardless of the amount of colorant present. This accessory is particularly useful in simple-subtractive colorant matching. The basic principle that makes the log–density cam useful is derived from Beer's law and states that, at any wavelength, vertical distances on the plot are proportional to the amounts of the colorants present, the contribution of each colorant adding independently to the total.

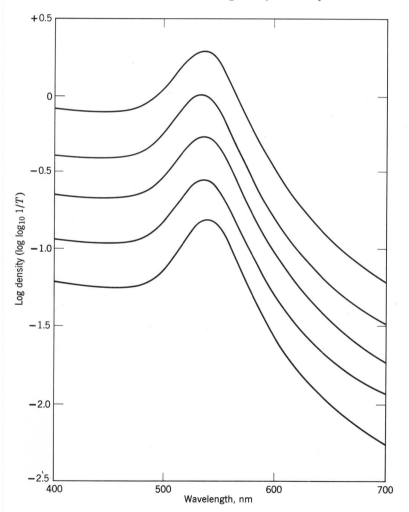

Log–density curves for the samples of the preceding figures. Linear distances on this plot are proportional to ratios of sample thicknesses or concentrations, and the shape of the curves is almost independent of thickness or concentration.

$$K/S = (1 - R)^2/2R$$

For a mixture of colorants,

$$(K/S)_{\text{mixture}} =$$

$$\frac{C_1K_1 + C_2K_2 + C_3K_3 + \cdots}{C_1S_1 + C_2S_2 + C_3S_3 + \cdots}$$

where C_1, C_2, C_3, $\cdots$ are the colorant concentrations.

The approximation to the Kubelka-Munk equations used for opaque samples. Note that in other books and articles, R is sometimes called β, and K/S is sometimes called θ.

A little arithmetic is all that is needed to calculate the concentrations of the various dyes needed for an initial match, once the dyes are identified.

For complex-subtractive mixing, Beer's law does not hold, but the more complicated Kubelka-Munk equations are frequently accurate enough to be useful. If one is working with completely opaque specimens, such as paint films pigmented to complete hiding, these equations simplify, and show that a function of the reflectance R exists which has the same property of being proportional to pigment concentration as does log–density in simple-subtractive mixing. The second useful accessory to the spectrophotometer is the "R-cam" (Pritchard 1952), which plots this function directly. Derby (1952) has described the use of this accessory as an aid in color matching in the textile industry.

The adage that one never gets something for nothing holds true here also. One must know the behavior of his individual colorants before distances on an R-cam or log–density cam chart can be converted into concentrations. Thus it is necessary that samples be made up, in a range of concentrations of one colorant at a time, and measured on the spectrophotometer to provide the data to calibrate the system. Once this is done, for a given substrate or medium and a given processing technique, all

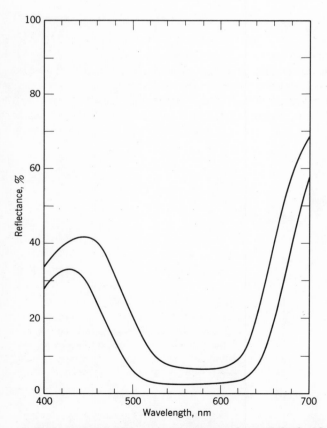

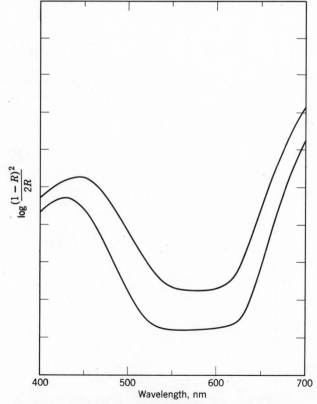

Reflectance (left) and "R-cam" (right) curves for wool dyed with C.I. Acid Violet 17, C.I. 42650. Linear distances on the "R-cam" plot are proportional to the logarithm of $K/S = (1-R)^2/2R$ (Courtesy Geigy Dyestuffs).

further samples made in the same way can be handled. The importance of this step cannot be overemphasized; see page 126 for further discussion.

Since all that we have said so far is based on duplicating the spectrophotometric curve of the sample to be matched, it applies only to the production of invariant matches. When the colorants to be used are different from those in the sample to be matched, and a conditional match is to be made, methods based on the spectrophotometric curve alone are of little value. Here one needs to work with the color coordinates of the samples. Although any coordinate system can be used, those related directly to instrument readings, such as the CIE Y, x, y or Hunter L,a,b systems are likely to be the most useful.

Since only the color coordinates rather than the spectrophotometric curves are required for instrumental aids to conditional matching, one might think that colorimeters could be used to advantage in this situation. However, a word of caution is required: As pointed out in Chapter 3E, colorimeters are basically suitable only for measuring small color differences between sample and standard when these are prepared with the same colorants. Their performance is poorest in the situation of conditional matching since different sets of colorants are involved.

Given the color coordinates of a sample to be matched and those of the individual colorants to be used at various concentrations, how can one formulate an initial conditional match? This is a serious problem, and one that has no easy answer. The problem can be solved in principle, and the computer techniques described later in this section have made the solution practicable in many cases, but without resort to these advanced methods the numerical calculations involved, analogous to those described for invariant matching, are formidable.

About the best that one can do, short of lengthy calculations, is to build up a history of experience and work from it. This is largely a matter of systematic record keeping. Every sample that is made should be measured, and its color coordinates plotted, for reference when a similarly colored sample is next encountered. Skills can be built up, and the memory assisted and refreshed in this way. This reference file will ultimately prove a highly valuable aid in predicting the initial formulation for a conditional *or* an invariant color match.

Computer Techniques. The basic problem in formulating an initial color match is to predict the correct concentrations of the colorants used to match the sample submitted, starting from its color coordinates or its spectrophotometric curve. The library of experience referred to in the preceding paragraph is a collection of solutions to the reverse problem: Given the colorant concentrations, what are the color coordinates of the sample? This can be solved directly by calculation as well as experiment, provided that the color-mixing laws for the system, and the necessary data on the individual colorants, are known. Again, the amount of calculation involved is so great that, before computers, very few colorists undertook this on a large scale.

Desired color-matching calculation:
  Given color coordinates, what concentrations of colorants are required to obtain them?

Direct color-matching calculation:
  Given colorant concentrations, to what color coordinates do they lead?

$$Z \qquad X \qquad Y$$

$$0.120\text{--}0.130 \; 0.170\text{--}0.180$$

$$0.150\text{--}0.160$$

0.7AG + 0.1LB + 0.25G

$$0.160\text{--}0.170$$

0.4MG + 0.3TA + 0.3TU

0.3MF + 0.5MG + 0.5TU

etc.

A small part of a typical page from a calculated catalog of colors. The letters AG, LB, SG, MG, etc. identify the colorants used, and the numbers preceding them, their concentrations. Tristimulus values X, Y, and Z are given as decimal fractions rather than per cent as is our custom (Miller 1963).

When computers became available, it was natural to inquire whether a calculated catalog of formulations, covering all color space and providing a "sample" close to anything that had to be matched, would be useful. The answer is only a qualified "yes." Such a catalog can be computed readily enough, but when it is big enough to contain all the data one would want, it is too big to be used easily. Although several such catalogs were computed, we know of none consisting only of formulas and color coordinates, with no actual samples, with any lasting utility.

It soon became apparent, however, that the step between calculating color coordinates from concentrations and the reverse computation was not a very big one. All that had to be done was to learn how to modify the concentrations to get a closer approximation than the first computed "trial" and then repeat the calculations. This can be done again and again until the calculated color coordinates are as close as one desires to those required. In mathematics, this technique is known as an iterative method, and each step closer to the desired goal is known as an iteration. The problem of correcting the colorant concentrations so that each iteration is closer to the desired formulation than the previous one can be solved in two ways: by trial and error or mathematically.

We must point out that what we have described is exactly the procedure followed by the visual color matcher operating in the traditional way. He makes a first trial based on what his experience and memory tells him are the correct colorant concentrations. From the result of this test, he corrects the concentrations by trial and error and makes a second iteration, and so on. There is just one important difference: The visual color matcher must make up each sample as he goes along, and then make estimates of the required change in concentrations based on his visual judgment and experience. The computer techniques, on the other hand, do not require that each sample be made up, and the corrections to the calculations are made more objectively in one of two ways: Either the corrections are computed mathematically according to color-mixing laws, or, if selected by trial and error, the result of applying them is seen instantaneously so that many changes can be made in rapid succession.

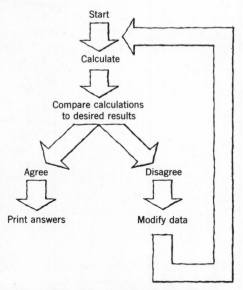

Start

Calculate

Compare calculations to desired results

Agree   Disagree

Print answers   Modify data

The essentials of the process called iteration.

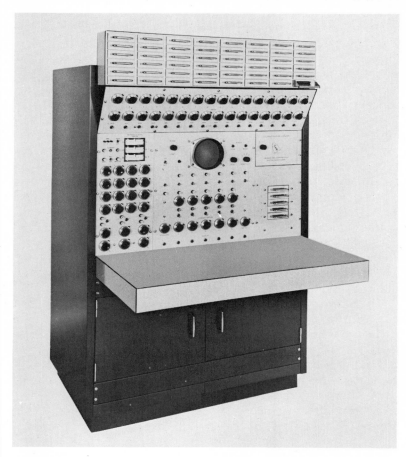

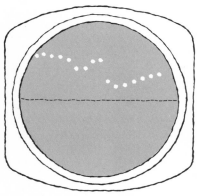

The Davidson and Hemmendinger COMIC Colorant Mixture Computer. The "plug-in" boxes referred to in the text are stored on top of the computer. (Courtesy Davidson and Hemmendinger, Inc.)

The oscilloscope face of COMIC shows the difference in K/S between standard and calculated match, at each of 16 wavelengths (dots). Here all the concentration dials are set to zero so only the K/S curve of the standard, turned upside down, is seen. . . .

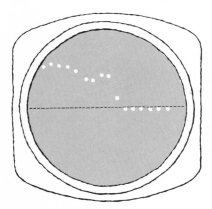

. . . Turning up the concentration dial for a blue colorant adds absorption at the long-wavelength red end of the spectrum, bringing the dots down to the line in that region. . . .

The latter technique, of displaying the results of a change in concentrations at once, works best with an analog computer. Here the numbers in the calculations are represented by electrical voltages and currents (their analogs), and the results of a calculation are displayed on a television-like screen or on a series of meters. A commercial COlorant MIxture Computer operating on this principle is the Davidson and Hemmendinger COMIC (Davidson 1963b). The COMIC is designed primarily for spectrophotometric matching, with the spectrophotometric curve of the sample (or equivalent information) displayed directly. Information on the spectral properties of the colorants is stored in "plug-in" electrical resistance boxes, which are selected and plugged into the computer as required. Dials control the "colorant concentrations," and as these are turned, the effect on the spectrophotometric curve can be seen at once. Usually, the spectrophotometric curve of the sample to be matched is also entered into the COMIC, and the computer is arranged to display the difference between the curves of the sample to be matched and the calculated formulation. When this difference is reduced to zero by adjustment of the concentration dials, the desired colorant concentrations can be read out.

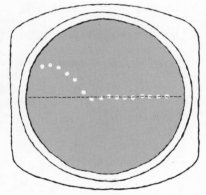

. . . Similarly, a red colorant brings down the middle portion . . .

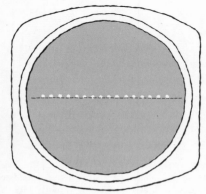

. . . and with the addition of a yellow to straighten the line at the left, the "match" is made. . . .

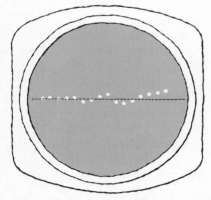

. . . If it is impossible to bring all the dots onto the line by any adjustment of the concentration dials, the wrong colorants have been chosen.

$$(K/S)_{\text{mixture}} =$$

$$\frac{aK_A + bK_B + cK_C + \cdots}{S_{\text{white}}}$$

The approximate equations of Kubelka and Munk for opaque samples (page 118) are still further simplified for use in the COMIC.

If the above-mentioned difference cannot be reduced to zero at all wavelengths, the computer predicts that a spectrophotometric match cannot be made. The operator then has the choice of selecting new colorants or making a conditional match. If the latter alternative is selected, an accessory known as the tristimulus difference computer (TDC) can be used to display on three meters the difference in color coordinates between the computed formulation and the sample to be matched. When these meters are brought to zero by further adjustment of the concentrations, the desired conditional match is achieved.

The COMIC is most widely used for complex-subtractive mixing of opaque colors. Even so, the Kubelka-Munk equations, most nearly applicable to this case, are further simplified for use in this analog computer. The simplifying assumption is that essentially all of the light scattering in the mixture comes from a single pigment, usually white. The COMIC therefore works best for pastels rather than dark colors, or for mixtures of dyes on a scattering substrate, as in dyed papers or some textile applications. Its usefulness is not, however, restricted to these cases, and in fact entirely different color-mixing laws, such as those of simple-subtractive mixing, can be used by proper adjustment of the instrument.

The alternative approach to computer colorant formulation, in which the concentrations are corrected by color-mixing law calculations, works best on digital computers because of the more lengthy calculations required. The basic principles of this technique (Park 1944) actually predate the availability of the computers that made it practical. More recently, applications to both simple-subtractive color mixing (Billmeyer 1960a) and complex-subtractive mixing (Alderson 1961, 1963, Gugerli 1963, Marsh 1964, Allen 1965, Preston 1965) have been described.

The greater calculating capacity and flexibility of the digital computer, plus the requirement that corrections to the colorant concentrations be calculated rather than estimated, make it usual to calculate matches based on color coordinates. If the colorants were chosen properly, these matches will be invariant matches. If colorants different from those in the standard were selected, then conditional matches are obtained. A distinct advantage of the digital technique over the analog is that more complicated color-mixing equations, such as the complete Kubelka-Munk equations or their more nearly exact modifications, can be used with a digital computer.

The usual operating procedure in calculating a color match with a digital computer, illustrated in the accompanying flow chart, is to supply the computer with data describing the illuminant in which the match is to be made, the colorants to be used, the color to be matched, and estimated colorant concentrations (which can be arbitrary if they are not known). The computer then calculates the color coordinates corresponding to the initial concentrations and the differences between them and those of the sample to be matched. These differences are then compared to the tolerance allowed in the final match. It is expected at this point that the differences will be large, so the next step is to correct the concentrations. This is done by computing quanti-

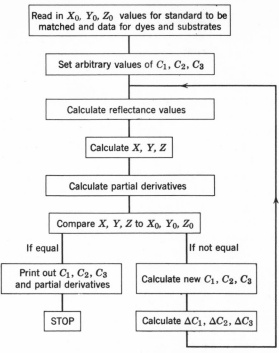

Flow chart for computer color matching (after Alderson 1961).

ties called partial derivatives which describe the changes in color coordinates when small changes are made in the concentrations. This information allows corrections to the concentrations to be calculated and applied. At this point the calculation of the color coordinates is repeated using the new concentrations, and the cycle of evaluation, correction, and recalculation continues until a formulation within the desired tolerance is reached.

Adjusting the Match

The dividing line between achieving an initial color match to a sample submitted and adjusting this match to conform to a plant (versus laboratory) process or to previous production is somewhat a matter of definition. There is, moreover, considerable overlap between adjustment and production control, which is further discussed in Section C of this chapter. Arbitrarily, we will consider here those aspects of adjustment in which the sample to be matched is that submitted from outside the color matcher's laboratory, and leave to Section C consideration of the case in which the sample to be matched is a laboratory or production standard, which is made with the same material, colorants, and process as the lots on which adjustment is required.

In this sense, the process of adjustment is, for the visual color matcher, identical to that of producing the initial match. He continues the process of repeated trials until, in his judgment, the match is close enough.

In both the digital and the analog computer techniques (and in some of the simpler applications of instrumental aids as well), it is convenient to consider the first formulation actually made up as the initial match, and any subsequent samples which must be prepared as the products of adjustment.

$$\partial X / \partial C_1 =$$
$$\Sigma E\bar{x}K_1 \exp\left(-C_1K_1 - C_2K_2 - C_3K_3\right)$$

$$\partial Y / \partial C_1 =$$
$$\Sigma E\bar{y}K_1 \exp\left(-C_1K_1 - C_2K_2 - C_3K_3\right)$$

$$\partial Z / \partial C_1 =$$
$$\Sigma E\bar{z}K_1 \exp\left(-C_1K_1 - C_2K_2 - C_3K_3\right)$$

plus a similar set of three equations for C_2 and a similar set of three equations for C_3

The partial derivatives. Here ∂ is the partial derivative sign and exp stands for the exponential function. The equations for simple-subtractive mixing are used.

If the computer techniques gave perfect results every time, there would be no need for adjustment. This is, of course, not the case. In all probability, the initial match will be close, but not close enough. The reasons for the difference include color measurement errors, batch-to-batch variation in sample preparation, data on the colorants which are nonrepresentative, and failure of the mixture to obey the color-mixing laws used.

For both types of computer techniques, the adjustment procedure involves calculating corrections to the concentrations used in the trial sample. The corrections required are those which will make its color coordinates the same as those of the standard. This is like the original calculation, except that a "local calibration" has been made in the region of color space of interest. This calibration can correct for such errors as nonrepresentative colorant data and failure to obey the mixing laws, but it *cannot* correct for color-measurement or sample-preparation error. In other words, *the process must be under good control before the adjustment procedure* (or, for that matter, *any* color-matching procedure) *can be successfully applied.*

It would be an oversimplification to credit instrumentation for all of the improvements which come from the introduction of a color-matching system using instrumental or computational aids. The discipline essential to the success of such a program requires that all of the steps in the coloring process be examined carefully. This exploration of the areas where trouble might be encountered and the corrective measures which might be used, in itself, invariably leads to an overall improvement in the process. Any steps which place a process under better control will result in improved performance (Peacock 1953).

In many cases, the second computed trial—or first adjustment on the computer—provides a satisfactory match to the sample submitted. This is probably an average situation. It is difficult to say how this compares with the average number of trials to make a satisfactory visual color match, but it is certainly true that a substantial reduction can be made in the number of trials required.

C. Color Control in Production

Just as color measurement is only a special form of analysis, so color control is but a special form of production control. The standard problems, such as sampling error, batch-to-batch variation in normal production, limits of acceptability, etc., all play their part. The only difference seems to lie in the aura of mystery with which some people tend to surround color.

As outlined in Chapter 3, two of the basic requirements of color measurement, whether or not an instrument is involved, are: (*1*) a description of the permitted tolerance in language acceptable to all concerned, and (*2*) a standardized procedure for determining the difference between sample and standard with sufficient reliability. In discussing color control in production, we assume that agreement has been reached on the nature of the variation in color that will be permitted and on the method of measuring this variability.

EXAMINATION
a. Light source
b. Sample and standard
c. Detector

ASSESSMENT
a. Difference or not
b. Description of difference
c. Acceptable or not

For the method of measurement, any of the techniques described in Chapter 3F is satisfactory. It makes little basic difference whether an instrument is used or not; the same rules must be followed. (The element of time may, of course, become quite important in production control.)

Monitoring

The Value of Instruments. It is in monitoring the production of colored items that the use of color-measuring instruments becomes particularly valuable. Instrumental data provide a running record of the nature of the item being produced and of its variation from the standard in quantitative terms. If the instrumentation and sampling are sensitive enough, small trends may be detected and corrected even before the process goes out of control and nonstandard material is produced.

While the eye is a superb instrument for deciding whether or not the sample and standard are identical, it is not a good one for determining the exact size and direction of a difference between sample and standard. This is especially true if more than one aspect of the sample's color differs from that of the standard. Used correctly, instruments can characterize such a color change very well. Without this information, a "corrective" measure might be applied which would do the opposite of what was needed. While the experienced colorist, who is familiar with his process and product, can tell what is happening and what to do about it with almost uncanny skill, the inexperienced man is frequently at a loss, and here the use of instruments can be of the greatest help. As in all control problems, however, the proper sampling and the proper use of the instruments are of the utmost importance.

The Effect of Process Variables. The final color of any item is usually determined not only by the colorant formulation used, but also by the effects of many other processing variables (Johnston 1964a). One of the jobs of the colorist is to determine as best he can the effects of such processing variables. It is far better to bring them under control than to attempt to compensate for their effects by changing the formulation. To do this may require considerable work, but the more that is known about the ability of a process to produce uniform-colored material, the better the colorist can advise the production department what to do about material which departs from standard.

More Than Measurement Alone. Good color measurement cannot only determine how the color of a product has changed, but, with enough preliminary work, can also help determine the reason for the variation. It cannot, however, control the uniformity of the color merely by furnishing measurements. This is where the understanding of the process must come in, so that the proper remedial action can be recognized and applied. In this respect, color measurement is, again, just like any other analytical procedure.

Adjusting

The main function of most colorists in industry is to maintain the uniformity of the color of a product once the formulation has

"If your product is colored, it may say to you,
'Color me red or color me blue
But color me the same whatever you do . . .'"

Bill Bednar

NO COLORANT OTHER THAN THOSE SPECIFIED IN THE FORMULATION MAY BE ADDED TO MAKE A MATCH

been established. That is, they work to reduce the difference in color between a production sample and the standard. Usually, the standard has been made with the same material, the same colorants, and the same coloring process as the production sample. (If it has not, it *should* be!)

Regardless of how well the process is controlled, there comes a time when the color of the product must be modified by altering the colorant formulation. Whether this is done by an experienced color matcher using only his skill and experience, or with the most complex system of color measurement and computers, there is one major point to be made about this type of adjustment: *No colorant other than those specified in the formulation may be added to make a match.*

This admonition ought to be displayed on a large permanent sign in every color-matching laboratory. Once the formulation has been established, no matter how simple or complex it is, no other dyes or pigments should be used in making adjustments to match the standard. Unless this rule is adhered to, so-called standard color matches will become metameric and distinctly nonstandard. In practice, it is amazing to see how many times "foreign" pigments appear in a finished formula. They have never "been added"; they just "show up."

One of the consequences of this rule is that, for any coloring operation, the colorants must be selected and standardized so that they always give the same result when used in the same way. A good color match cannot be made unless this is done. That is, the color match is no better than the quality of the colorants allows. By quality, we mean not only the colorimetric properties but also the working properties of the colorants—the rate of exhaustion in a dye bath, the ease of color development in a pigment, etc.

The comparison of a production sample to its standard is an ideal example of the kind of measurement for which colorimeters are best suited. The color differences involved are small and there are no problems of metamerism. (If these conditions are not met, the colorist is in real trouble!)

Colorimeters can be used both qualitatively and quantitatively to aid the colorist in this situation. In the qualitative sense, they can show in what way the sample differs from the standard. As indicated earlier in this section, the smaller the color difference, the more difficult it is for the visual color matcher to ascertain the direction of the difference, although he may have a very good idea of its magnitude.

It is very easy to use colorimeter measurements to give the colorist quantitative assistance as to how to change the formulation to bring the production sample "on standard." What he needs to know are the partial derivatives, described in Section B as obtained from computer formulation techniques, which tell how the color coordinates (in this case, colorimeter readings) of the sample change as the individual colorant concentrations are changed in the formulation. If these numbers are available from a previous computer calculation, good; if not, they can readily be determined.

$$X - X_0 = (X - X_1)\Delta C_1 + (X - X_2)\Delta C_2 + (X - X_3)\Delta C_3$$
$$Y - Y_0 = (Y - Y_1)\Delta C_1 + (Y - Y_2)\Delta C_2 + (Y - Y_3)\Delta C_3$$
$$Z - Z_0 = (Z - Z_1)\Delta C_1 + (Z - Z_2)\Delta C_2 + (Z - Z_3)\Delta C_3$$

As outlined in the accompanying figures, what one has to do is to make up a set of samples, in each of which one of the colorants in the formulation is varied by a known small amount, perhaps 10%. From the measurement of these samples, numbers equivalent to the partial derivatives can be calculated. The corrections to a formulation can then be calculated in a way simple enough to carry out on a desk calculator. Alternatively, simple graphical solutions can be used if the differences are small enough (Derby 1952, Berger 1964, MacAdam 1965).

While it may seem that this approach would not result in any savings, since several additional formulations are needed to get the necessary data (but it is most unlikely that the visual color matcher would have come "on standard" in the first trial), the situation improves steadily with experience. The partial derivatives do not change drastically between similar colors. The experience gained in formulating one color, carefully recorded and preserved, provides a starting point for the next similar color to be matched. This is true of all colorant formulation data, regard-

Let the tristimulus values of the standard be X_0, Y_0, Z_0, and those of the sample be X, Y, Z. Suppose that changing the concentration of colorant 1 by one unit (say, 10% of C_1) moves the sample to X_1, Y_1, Z_1; changing C_2 by one unit moves it to X_2, Y_2, Z_2; and changing C_3 by one unit moves it to X_3, Y_3, Z_3. Then the changes in concentrations required to adjust the match, ΔC_1, ΔC_2, ΔC_3, are found by solving these equations . . .

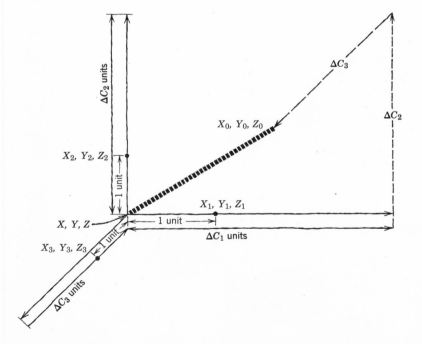

. . . and this figure illustrates the process.

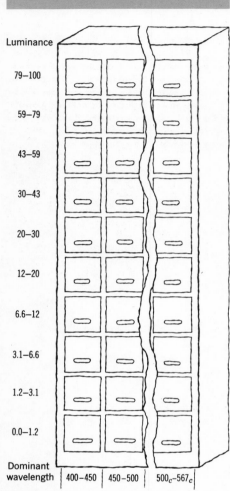

Luminance

79–100

59–79

43–59

30–43

20–30

12–20

6.6–12

3.1–6.6

1.2–3.1

0.0–1.2

Dominant
wavelength | 400–450 | 450–500 | 500$_c$–567$_c$ |

One way of storing samples and formulations is in a series of boxes or drawers according to luminance and dominant wavelength. Within each box, samples can be arranged by purity (Ingle 1947, Goodwin 1955).

less of how obtained. Systematic storage of this information, plus facilities for its retrieval, constitute an invaluable "memory" for the colorist (Ingle 1947, Goodwin 1955).

Controlling

The ultimate aim in applying any analytical procedure to a production situation is to develop a technique which will not only detect a variation but serve as a direct signal for corrective action. The same considerations apply also to color measurement. Here we have progressed to the point where continuous monitoring can be carried out on processes which are reliable and well controlled, but the transition to the next step, namely, what to do with the data obtained, is more difficult.

If the departure from normal color is known to be dependent entirely on a single process variable, such as an oven temperature, the result of a color measurement could well be used to generate a signal controlling the temperature in a predetermined way. On the other hand, if it is known that the variation in color is almost completely dependent on the colorant concentrations, continuous color measurement may give enough information to control the process, but some analog computation may be required to obtain the proper feedback signal.

This is an active area of research. Continuous color-monitoring equipment is available from several manufacturers, and complete automatic color control may well be a reality by the time you read this book.

D.   Those Other Aspects of Appearance

The colorist must keep in mind at all times that color is only one of several factors contributing to the appearance of an object. Variations in any of these other aspects of appearance— gloss, metallic reflex, haze, fluorescence—will inevitably affect the perception of the object's color. Thus, a change in gloss or a variation in surface texture may result in a product which appears to deviate from specifications for its color. Instruments, as well as the eye, can be fooled. The colorist must determine the cause of the variation before the necessary correction can be made. Hunter (1963a,b) has discussed aspects of appearance other than color in a readable and useful way.

CHAPTER 6

Color Technology—Present and Future

In previous chapters we have discussed our general concept of color and its application to the problems of color-order systems, color measurement, colorants, and the coloring of materials in industry. Here we shall in part review, reemphasize, and summarize what we have said, while considering the general problem of coloring as it affects and is affected by today's industrial technology.

A. Color as an Engineering Material

The Various Meanings of Color

Up to now we have emphasized only one of many meanings of the word color—that which is seen by you and me, the result of our brain's interpretation of the combination of the spectral distribution curves describing a light source, an object, and the response of the eye. At this point it is useful to consider some special ways in which the word color is used in present day technology.

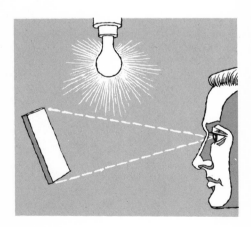

Let us start with the designer or stylist, since it is his concept which ultimately finds its way to the market place. The designer thinks of the effect that he conceives as being a new color: a new hue or shade added to a specific colored material. Of course, in the sense that we use the word, the *color* is not new at all, since all colors already exist. It may be a revival of a style of years gone by, however, or it may be new to the product involved as a result of new colorants or new coloring methods which make it possible for the first time.

129

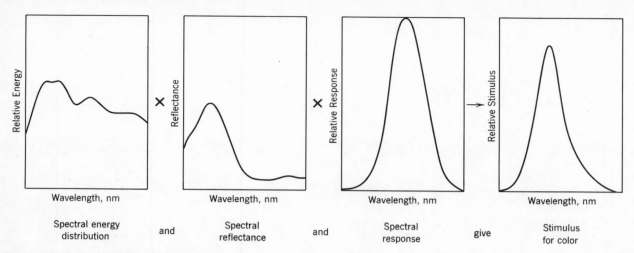

The perceived color of an object depends on the combination of the spectral curves shown here.

From the point of view of a designer, there is an infinite number of colors; certainly more colors than anyone would want to use at any one time, in a given range of commercial products. This almost infinite number of colors is only apparent, however, since it is not possible to produce all the colors which appear to the eye in the forms in which they can be used industrially. To simplify matters just a little, we will not consider the question of what has been called "appropriateness" of a color. If a designer decides that park benches should be changed from dark green to sky blue with pink polka dots, those who provide the raw materials and the finished products to give this color effect should not place themselves in the position of saying, "Nobody will sit on those benches." We must accept for the moment the designers' or stylists' (the customers') ideas as to what colors they wish to employ in decorating their products.

The manufacturer of colorants speaks of preparing a new color but in a completely different sense. What is meant here is either the preparation of a new chemical entity which can act as a coloring matter or a modification of an old chemical compound to do the same job, sometimes just by making it in a less expensive process. In both cases it is a substance which is new, in either chemical or physical form or both.

Finally, and most important in our discussion, is the colorist's concept of a new color. The colorist owes his existence to the need for having a technically trained and skilled person to carry out the designer's wishes, using the appropriate colorants and the best methods of coloring the material chosen. We would like to say that he uses color as an engineering material (Saltzman 1963a,b).

Of course, it is not strictly correct to speak of color, which is a distinctly nonmaterial phenomenon, as a special kind of material, much less an engineering material. What we really mean is the use of colorants and coloring methods in accord with the best engineering practice. Using the word engineering in the broadest sense—that is, the use of technically sound principles to carry out a certain operation in a profitable manner—we can consider the *use* of color from an engineering point of view.

Engineering Properties of Colorants

Let us consider the choices available to a designer who is called upon to specify the material and the colorants for a particular object to be colored. Ideally, he would like to have unlimited freedom to specify both materials of construction and color. This happy situation is seldom realized, however, and the colorist interpreting the stylist's demands immediately recognizes a series of limitations within the framework of which he must work. These limitations will no doubt include, but not be limited to, considerations of cost of colorants, methods of coloring, and fastness properties of the product. All of these constraints, to some extent, influence the choice of materials, colorants, and coloring methods, and ultimately limit the designer by restricting to some degree the color effects he can achieve.

The ability of a material to be colored is therefore one of its properties and is to be considered along with many others in its selection for a particular job. Naturally, the importance which can be placed on colorability varies widely from case to case. In many areas there is no choice of materials and the colorist must simply do the best he can. The selection of a fabric because of some aspect of its performance is an example. But if a man is asked to design a container to be used for displaying an object in a retail store, he may well give serious consideration to the question of the colorability of a particular material before making his choice.

Even if the choice of material to be used is dictated by factors other than colorability, the colorist frequently has freedom in the selection of the method of applying the color. It is almost axiomatic that the closer to the final consumer the choice of color is made, the more flexibility the producer has. On the other hand, the earlier in the manufacturing cycle that the color can be selected, the greater the control and uniformity that will result. Both extremes are practiced. Some industries have gone to the coloring of their materials in the earliest possible stage, as in the spin dyeing of synthetic fibers, while others have decided to color their product at the point of sale, as in the manufacture of house paint by the use of color additive systems in which the colorants are added to base paints at the time of purchase.

As with so many decisions in the industrial world, the choice of colorant and coloring method is usually a compromise between the wishes of the designer or stylist and the real world of available colorants and the economics which govern the coloring of the object in question. In an ideal world there would be no restriction as to cost, and there would be colorants available for every hue in every substrate at any desired level of fastness. It is quite evident that this state of affairs does not exist. For this reason, the colorist who is to transform the stylist's designs into the real world of industry must have, at the time the color is planned, a full list of the engineering properties which are needed.

Color Gamuts

Our consideration of colorability really begins at the level of practicability: Can the desires of the stylist be translated into a working material to provide a colored object which satisfies his aesthetic and commercial needs? When we consider this aspect of practicability, we then begin to concern ourselves with the problem of color "gamut," a convenient term used to describe the entire range of perceived color which may be obtained under stated conditions. There are several limitations to the available color effects at our command. These limitations can be discussed in terms of the CIE system (Chapter 2B). In order of increasing severity, they are:

1. The limits of all realizable colors, as indicated by the spectrum locus in the CIE chromaticity diagram.

2. The limits of all possible colors having a given luminance (CIE tristimulus value Y, the luminous reflectance or transmittance of the sample), as defined by the MacAdam limits (MacAdam 1935).

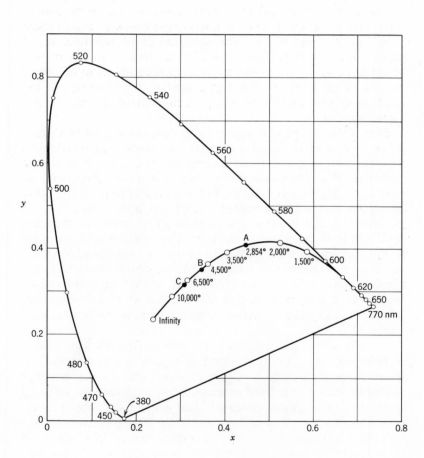

The spectrum locus is the limit of all realizable colors.

3. The further limitation to the gamut of surface colors obtainable, resulting from the fact that even the darkest colors reflect some light from the surface, independent of the degree of absorption. The amount of this reflectance varies with gloss and may vary from hue to hue. For moderately glossy surfaces, such as paint, this may amount to approximately 4% of the incident light. When this correction is applied, we get another series of maps of color space, reduced in area and somewhat displaced in position (Atherton 1955).

4. Limitations set by the working properties and reactivity of the substrate, and the performance requirements of the material after it is finished. (For a discussion of these factors for paint systems, see Moll 1960.) Consideration of these factors again reduces the gamut, but not in as readily calculable a way as in steps *1–3*.

5. Limits set by real colorants. We now begin to approach the practical problem of the selection of colorants to obtain a given color. Here we deal, not with theory, not with any system, but with physically realizable color effects based on existing coloring matters. Usually this results in a contour at any given level of lightness which is much smaller than the theoretically realizable

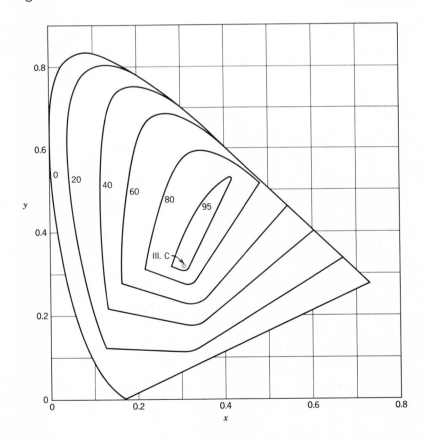

The MacAdam limits define all possible colors having a given luminance.

contour. In the accompanying figure, the inner line encloses the gamut of colors in the matte-surface *Munsell Book of Color* at value 6 ($Y = 30\%$), while the outer lines are copied from the preceding figures. The small circles show the locations of some newer colorants than those used in the Munsell Book (Saltzman 1963a).

6. Finally, limitations set by the fact that only certain colorants, from the ones available for each problem, are economically practical. If we could ignore this, it would indeed increase the number of coloring matters which could be used for any substance, but unfortunately economics cannot be ignored and the cost of obtaining a given color is important. This again cuts down the available number of colorants which can be used. To add the contours generated by the economic and engineering requirements to the figures would result in a completely different set of contours for each problem.

Taking some liberty with the solids which are generated by the considerations given above and considering these solids as

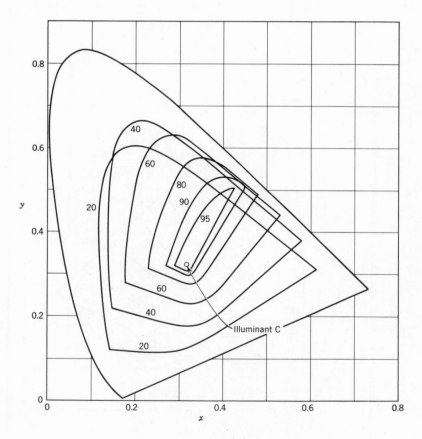

The Atherton and Peters limits (Atherton 1955) take account of surface reflections.

rough spheres or, at any rate, spheroid figures, we may consider that the limits of theoretical color space would encompass a beach ball (medium size), and the limits of MacAdam color space would be like a basketball. The Atherton color space (theoretical surface color space modified by surface reflection) might be represented by a soccer ball. If we then go into the field of real and realizable colors in any material without regard for economic considerations (limited only by available colorants), we come to a more irregular shape, probably something nearer that of a football. Going to the next step, that of colors which are realizable in a given system and pass stringent performance tests, we can have anything from an object the size of a football to something the size and shape of a beaten-up 50-cent baseball. Finally, we consider the cost. For some materials, this last limitation may reduce the choice of colorants so much that the realizable colors are represented by an extremely irregular solid, much like that of a small apple into which several tentative bites have been taken.

While each step reduces the number of available colorants, it by no means restricts us to a small number of colors, since, with colorants well spaced in the hue circle, we can derive a great number of colors even though the exact one desired may not be attainable.

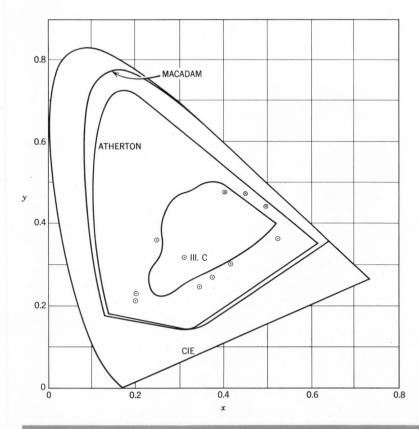

The properties of real colorants limit the gamut of possible colors still more (Saltzman 1963a).

While the color solid shrinks steadily from its theoretical limits to the physically realizable colors with existing colorants, there are many dyes and pigments in each hue category which may be used by the manufacturer to impart the desired color to his material. As with most things in our world, we do not get any property in a finished object except by paying for it. Therefore, a product using an inexpensive pigment will generally not have the fastness properties or the high chroma of one whose color has been obtained with a more expensive colorant of the same or similar hue (Vesce 1959). If bright hues are desired and processing conditions are severe, it is necessary to go to the more expensive pigments. Conversely, if cost is a primary consideration, one may be limited to less bright colors.

The Selection of Colorants

The selection of a colorant is always a compromise between the properties desired by the designer and the cost of imparting a given hue, value, and chroma to a particular material. There are very few colorants which are suitable for all materials, and those which are suitable for all systems seldom offer the best money value. It must be emphasized that all colorants are chemical materials and as such are more or less reactive with other chemicals. What may be a minor change from the point of view of an additive used (to impart drying, better flow, etc.) may be a major one so far as the colorant is concerned. A material suitable in one formulation, for example, may be completely unsuitable if another manufacturer's resin and catalysts are used. Some of these things are well known, but it is our feeling that these points cannot be overemphasized. It is essential to think automatically in terms of the entire colored system rather than of a specific colorant or a certain material. Anything added to the system may influence the behavior of the entire system. This fact is only beginning to be recognized. See Smith 1954; for applications in the paint industry, Vesce 1956, 1959; for plastics, Oehlcke 1954, Carr 1957, Simpson 1962–63.

It is not our intention in this book to provide a check list of what colorants can be used in any given application. Some of the sources of this information were given on page 97. What we do wish to emphasize is that the choice of colorants is invariably influenced by many factors, most of which depend upon and can only be evaluated for the system as a whole. Many examples could be given, encompassing the areas of colorant reactivity, fastness to light, washing, bleeding, and other treatments, stability at elevated temperatures, ease of incorporation or processing, and above all, economics. But these examples would be rather specific for the industry from which they were taken, and for that reason are best discussed elsewhere.

B.   Some Guesses About the Future

The scientific community has yet to become convinced that anyone can predict the future, and we do not claim to be expert practitioners with the crystal ball. But some trends are fairly clear to those closely associated with color and coloring. These

Books and articles relating to the *use* of colorants:

AATCC "Technical Manual," annually
SDC and AATCC, *Colour Index* 1956, 1963
Carr 1957
Cutter 1962
Lenoir 1959–1963
Moll 1960
Plant 1962
Simpson 1962–1963
Smith 1962
Vesce 1956, 1959

we will try to describe, and even venture a few guesses about where they may ultimately lead. We will take up these topics in about the same order as they occur in the main body of the book.

Colorimetry and the CIE System

As was discussed in Chapter 2B, the 1931 CIE x, y, system has been the foundation on which, almost without exception, the entire science of color measurement has been built. The fact that the system and all its components—the CIE standard observer, standard light Sources A, B and C, etc.—have had such lasting value does not preclude the possibility of future changes in the system. Committee E 1.3.1 on colorimetry of the CIE is an active international group, and continues to study the problems of color measurement and specification and to make recommendations designed to supplement and in some cases replace parts of the original CIE system. Some of these recommendations, likely to become of major importance in the near future, are:

New Illuminants. In 1965, Committee E 1.3.1 proposed that the CIE recommend a series of new illuminants to supplement Sources A, B, and C in the CIE system, based on recent definitive studies of the spectral energy distribution of natural daylight (Judd 1964). (The recommendation requires approval by the National Committees and the main body of the CIE before official adoption.)

The proposal recommends a series of illuminants representing daylight over the spectral range 300–830 nm and having

Source: A physically realizable light, whose spectral energy distribution can be experimentally determined. When the determination is made and specified, the source becomes a *standard source.*

Illuminant: A light defined by a spectral energy distribution, which may or may not be physically realizable as a *source.* If it is made available in physical form, it becomes a *standard source.*

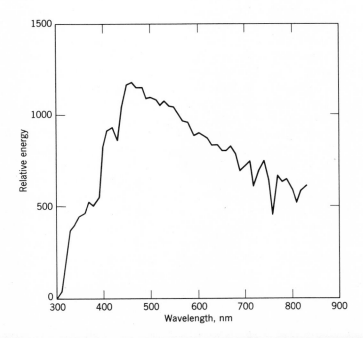

The proposed CIE Illuminant D_{6500}, based on average natural daylight (Judd 1964).

Wavelength, nm	E, (D$_{6500}$)	Wavelength, nm	E, (D$_{6500}$)
300	0.3	570	963
310	33	580	958
320	202	590	887
330	371		
340	400	600	900
		610	896
350	449	620	877
360	467	630	833
370	521	640	837
380	500		
390	547	650	800
		660	802
400	828	670	823
410	915	680	783
420	934	690	697
430	867		
440	1049	700	716
		710	743
450	1170	720	616
460	1178	730	699
470	1149	740	751
480	1159		
490	1088	750	636
		760	464
500	1094	770	668
510	1078	780	634
520	1048	790	643
530	1077		
540	1044	800	594
		810	520
550	1040	820	574
560	1000	830	603

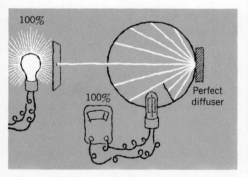

The perfect diffuser reflects 100% of the light incident on it. In addition, the relative amount of light reflected at each angle must follow a well-defined law. No real white substances are perfect diffusers.

correlated color temperatures (Chapter 1B) between 4000 and 25,000°K. The most important of these is D$_{6500}$, having a correlated color temperature of 6500°K, with illuminants at 5500 and 7500°K as alternates. The proposal states "For general use in colorimetry Illuminants A and D$_{6500}$ should suffice."

The proposal introduces illuminants with an ultraviolet light content similar to that of daylight and suitable for the colorimetry of fluorescent materials. Since Sources B and C are deficient in ultraviolet content, and are not representative of daylight, the proposal will lead to less use of B and C in the future.

New Reflectance Standards. In 1959 the CIE recommended the use of the theoretical perfect diffuser (the ideal white substance reflecting 100% of the energy incident on it in a perfectly diffuse way) as the reference standard for all reflectance measurements. That is, the use of magnesium oxide (MgO) (Chapter 3E) as the primary reference standard and the reporting of reflectances referred to MgO as 100% would be replaced by recalculating reflectances to "absolute" terms and reporting them with the perfect diffuser at 100%. This recommendation was very seldom used in the first few years after its adoption. It will be easier to put it into use as new white standards, better values for their absolute reflectances, and improved automatic calculation techniques become available.

New Supplementary Standard Observer. In 1963, the CIE recommended the use of new color-matching functions whenever more accurate correlation with visual color matching for large

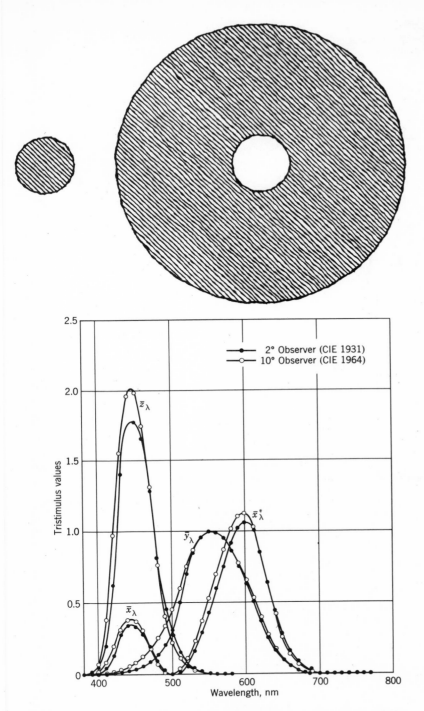

At a normal viewing distance of 18 in., the circle on the left represents the 2° field on which the 1931 CIE standard observer is based. The figure on the right is the 10° field.

The new CIE supplementary color-matching functions $\bar{x}_{10}$, $\bar{y}_{10}$, $\bar{z}_{10}$, compared to the 1931 CIE color-matching functions $\bar{x}$, $\bar{y}$, $\bar{z}$. (Judd 1963).

samples, covering an angle of more than 4° at the eye of the observer, is desired. The new functions, $\bar{x}_{10}$, $\bar{y}_{10}$, $\bar{z}_{10}$, were derived from color-matching experiments of the type described in Chapter 2B using a 10° area on the retina of the observer's eye with the central 2° spot obscured, while the 1931 CIE color-matching functions $\bar{x}$, $\bar{y}$, and $\bar{z}$ were based on experiments using just the central 2° of the eye. Differences in the structure of the central and surrounding parts of the retina, which we need not

Wavelength, nm	$\bar{u}$	$\bar{v}$	$\bar{w}$
380	0.0009	0.0000	0.0025
390	0.0028	0.0001	0.0081
400	0.0095	0.0004	0.0274
410	0.0290	0.0012	0.0837
420	0.0896	0.0040	0.2616
430	0.1894	0.0116	0.5682
440	0.2323	0.0230	0.7339
450	0.2242	0.0380	0.7749
460	0.1940	0.0600	0.7792
470	0.1303	0.0910	0.6826
480	0.0638	0.1390	0.5672
490	0.0213	0.2080	0.5286
500	0.0033	0.3230	0.6180
510	0.0062	0.5030	0.8289
520	0.0422	0.7100	1.0724
530	0.1104	0.8620	1.2313
540	0.1937	0.9540	1.2959
550	0.2891	0.9950	1.2801
560	0.3965	0.9950	1.1972
570	0.5083	0.9520	1.0480
580	0.6112	0.8700	0.8477
590	0.6845	0.7570	0.6229
600	0.7085	0.6310	0.4158
610	0.6687	0.5030	0.2533
620	0.5699	0.3810	0.1444
630	0.4285	0.2650	0.0763
640	0.2987	0.1750	0.0385
650	0.1891	0.1070	0.0187
660	0.1100	0.0610	0.0090
670	0.0583	0.0320	0.0043
680	0.0312	0.0170	0.0021
690	0.0151	0.0082	0.0009
700	0.0076	0.0041	0.0004
710	0.0039	0.0021	0.0002
720	0.0019	0.0010	0.0000
730	0.0009	0.0005	0.0000
740	0.0005	0.0003	0.0000
750	0.0002	0.0001	0.0000
760	0.0001	0.0001	0.0000
770	0.0001	0.0000	0.0000

The color-matching functions $\bar{u}$, $\bar{v}$, $\bar{w}$, for the 1960 CIE u,v coordinate system. The 1931 CIE standard observer is used here, but Nimeroff (1964b) also gives results using the 1964 CIE supplementary observer.

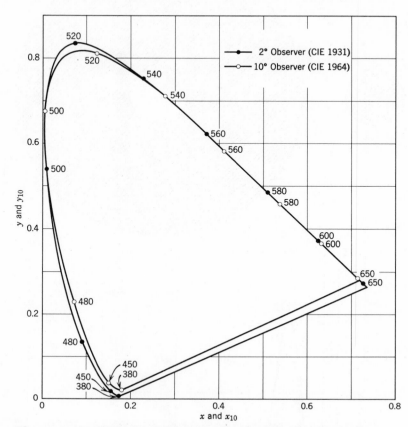

The x_{10}, y_{10} chromaticity diagram based on the ten-degree color-matching functions, compared to the 1931 x,y chromaticity diagram (Judd 1963).

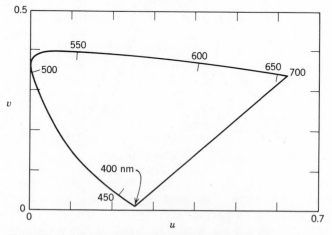

The 1960 CIE u,v chromaticity diagram, showing the spectrum locus.

describe further, lead to differences in the eye's average color-matching characteristics for the two sets of conditions. The 10° color-matching functions were recommended for field trial (Nimeroff 1964a) to supplement, but not replace, the 1931 CIE standard observer.

Uniform Chromaticity System. In 1959 the CIE recommended the use of the MacAdam (1937) u, v system described in Chapter 2C whenever a chromaticity diagram with more nearly uniform spacing in terms of the visual perception of color is required (MacAdam 1965). Little immediate use has been made of the u, v system, but some basic data on it are available (Nimeroff 1964b). With the proposed extension described below, the system may well be considerably more widely used.

$$u = \frac{4X}{X + 15Y + 3Z} = \frac{4x}{-2x + 12y + 3}$$

$$v = \frac{6Y}{X + 15Y + 3Z} = \frac{6y}{-2x + 12y + 3}$$

$$w = 1 - u - v$$

Equations for the 1960 CIE chromaticity coordinates u and v in terms of 1931 CIE tristimulus values and chromaticity coordinates.

New Color-Difference Formulas. In 1963 the CIE recommended the use of the U^*, V^*, W^* extension (Wyszecki 1963) of the MacAdam system described here, whenever a three-dimensional color-order system more uniform in terms of visual perception than the 1931 CIE X,Y,Z system is required. The recommendation is tentative, recognizing that a still better system may later be recommended. The U^*, V^*, W^* system allows calculation of color differences by a formula which early tests (Wyszecki 1965) indicate should give results in good agreement with visual observation.

In a recent review on color measurement and tolerances, MacAdam (1965) has refined his 1943 color-difference calculation. The new formula permits the computation of color differences in units approximately equivalent to 1943 MacAdam units, from CIE tristimulus values without the need for special charts or tables. A digital computer is conveniently used (Blackwood 1966). While the new 1965 MacAdam unit is approximately equal to the old, they are not interchangeable, and we repeat our previous warning that one must always state explicitly how a color-difference calculation has been made.

Foster (1966a) has prepared charts, based on a simplification of the 1943 MacAdam equations, which permit the very rapid calculation of *small* color differences from colorimeter readings in the form of sample/standard ratios.

$$W^* = 25\, Y^{1/3} - 17$$
$$\text{where } Y_{max} = 100$$

$$U^* = 13\, W^*(u - u_0)$$

$$V^* = 13\, W^*(v - v_0)$$

where u_0 and v_0 are the chromaticity coordinates of the light source. For CIE Source C, $u_0 = 0.2009$; $v_0 = 0.3073$.

Equations for the tristimulus values of the 1964 CIE U^*, V^*, W^* coordinate system.

$$\Delta E = [(\Delta U^*)^2 + (\Delta V^*)^2 + (\Delta W^*)^2]^{1/2}$$

The color-difference equation in the U^*, V^*, W^* system. One unit of color difference is *approximately* equivalent to the NBS unit (but see page 86).

Instrumentation

Recent studies (Billmeyer 1965a,b) have made it abundantly clear that, even under the best conditions, the precision and accuracy of industrial color measurement is currently barely adequate to meet the demands placed on it. There seems little doubt, however, that significant improvements can and will be made.

The evidence already in hand indicates that substantial improvements can be effected by the development and adoption of improved procedures and material standards for the calibration, standardization, and operation of existing spectrophotometers and colorimeters. Research is active in this area.

Beyond this, a new generation of color-measuring instruments will be required, and we can attempt to outline their specifications in a general way. An important first point is that they should be designed specifically for color measurement. The requirements for analytical spectrophotometry are essentially different, for example, than those for colorimetric spectrophotometry (Johnston 1965a). It is no accident that the General Electric spectrophotometer, designed specifically for color measurement by A. C. Hardy over 30 years ago (Hardy 1935), remains the referee instrument in the field despite the availability of several excellent analytical spectrophotometers of much more recent design.

A major requirement for future spectrophotometers and colorimeters is flexibility in illuminating and viewing conditions, including at least integrating sphere geometry, the 0,45° conditions recommended by the CIE, and some type of ability to measure reflectance as the illuminating and viewing angles are varied.

New spectrophotometers should have modest increases in wavelength resolution, to the point where further increases will have no effect on CIE coordinates. Major improvements will be required in photometric precision and accuracy, however, especially in the low reflectance region. New tristimulus integrators should be of the digital type for maximum accuracy. The spectrophotometer-integrator combination should be designed as a unit for complete compatibility. High accuracy digital indication of wavelength and photometric scale readings will be required, accuracy of the recorder chart then being non-essential.

A major consideration for improved colorimeters will be the achievement of even closer correspondence to the CIE system. Compatibility between colorimeters and spectrophotometers with respect to illuminating and viewing geometry will be essential. Simplicity of operation and immediate and automatic presentation of results in their final and most useful form, for example, CIE chromaticity coordinates or some standard color difference units, will be important.

Colorants

It seems certain that the dyes and pigments available to the designer and the colorist will continue to change and improve just as will other areas of color technology. There appear to be two major incentives for this improvement.

The first compelling reason for research on improved colorants is an economic one. As the technology of the chemical industry advances, new manufacturing methods become available to reduce the cost of old products and to allow the manufacture of new ones at a reasonable price. In addition, the synthesis of entirely new dyes and pigments proceeds at an ever-increasing rate despite the complexity of the chemistry involved (Gaertner 1963, Pugin 1965).

This research is not haphazard by any means. The greatest attention is given to the areas of poorest current performance, with the objective of upgrading them so as to approach a constant level of performance through out the gamut of hues, in all important properties such as brightness of shade, fastness to light and other treatments, ease of processing and application and, of course, cost.

The second challenge to the makers of colorants comes in the form of new materials for which they are asked to supply their products. Each of these new applications brings new requirements on the colorants, and in many cases this means more research and new products. For example, the need for coloring high-temperature plastics and synthetic fibers led to the development of entirely new families of colorants. In addition, older products are continually reviewed for new applications, while new raw materials produced elsewhere in the chemical industry are examined for their possible use in colorant production.

The history of the colorant industry, like that of so many others, is a mixture of sudden dramatic advances and slow, painstaking improvement by small steps (White 1960, Rattee 1965). Predicting the major breakthroughs is about like forecasting the next big earthquake, but their possibility should never be overlooked.

Color Matching

There is no doubt that the trend in color-matching techniques is strongly toward the use of the instrumental and computational aids to the color matcher described in Chapter 5B. The number of publications in this field is increasing rapidly (for example, Allen 1965, Atherton 1965, Bunkall 1965, Preston 1965) and all indications are that this trend will continue. Several features of this adoption of modern techniques are worth noting:

First, the wider application of computer color matching is taking place in several ways. The techniques are being applied independently by individual laboratories, often using analog computers because of their lower initial cost. In addition, large companies are in some instances carrying out the initial steps of formulation under computer control at a central laboratory, with a number of plants at various locations making final adjustments by means of small analog computers. Finally, several major colorant producers are offering, as a service, computer color matching for purchasers of their colorants (Alderson 1963, Atherton 1965, Preston 1965, Allen 1965, and others). Large digital computers are almost invariably used in these applications because of their speed and flexibility.

Secondly, the Kubelka-Munk equations or simplifications of them are still the most widely used for computer color matching. The application of the more complete equations described recently (Völz 1962, 1964, Beasley 1965) has not yet been noted in the literature, although it is clear that they should ultimately prove to give much more accurate descriptions of the optical properties of colored materials.

Despite the importance of these more complete equations, the experience of those active in the field indicates that computer techniques are being pushed empirically far beyond the ranges where their simpler equations are known to hold accurately, and yet with considerable success. It seems as if the computer's repetitive or iterative techniques are so powerful that, properly applied, they almost invariably "zero in" on an acceptable match.

On the other hand, the optical properties of metallic or "pearlescent" colorants, and of several other unusual systems, are not described well by existing color-mixing laws, and attempts to apply simple computer techniques to these systems in an empirical way have not yet met with great success. Clearly, more theoretical work and the development of appropriate instrumentation is needed in these areas, and will undoubtedly be forthcoming.

Education

One final trend which seems to be appearing—very late—in the field of color technology, is that of formal education at the university level in the United States. For many years there have been very few colleges or universities in this country with staff members interested in any of the aspects of color technology described in this book. Even related fields such as dye chemistry and optics have steadily diminished in popularity.

This trend seems now to have reversed with the establishment of programs of research and instruction in color technology in at least one major academic institution. A color measurements laboratory has been established, students are active in research at the postgraduate level, and special lectures and conferences are held. A particularly interesting feature of this trend has been the establishment of summer courses in the principles of color technology, open to participants from industry. The overwhelming response to these courses is strong evidence of the need for formal education in this field. Similar courses have been offered in the past by a few manufacturers of color-measuring and computing equipment.

It is our feeling that the science of color is properly considered a branch of analytical chemistry. The discussions of Chapters 3A and 3B in this book contain very little beyond a discourse on sound analytical chemical techniques. It is refreshing indeed to be able to predict that more opportunities for formal education in color technology will become available in the years to come. Analytical chemists with this type of formal training will provide industry with a new kind of color technologist. The combination of training in color theory and practical experience should give the colorant-using industries a sound basis for expanding their complex programs of colorant formulation and production control.

CHAPTER 7

Annotated Bibliography

Entries in the Annotated Bibliography have been selected on the basis of importance in the literature of color technology and availability to the reader, in that order.

In our opinion, anyone who is seriously interested in color technology should own some of the books and articles annotated in this chapter. The particular entries which we feel should be on each serious reader's bookshelf are indicated by the use of **boldface type.**

No references in foreign languages have been annotated. The interested reader who is proficient in French, German, or Russian will have no difficulty in locating material in these languages among the references in this book and in other works in the Bibliography.

The items in the Bibliography are arranged as follows: first, books and general works; second, journals in which papers on color appear most frequently; and, finally, references according to subject matter in the same order as in this book. With the aid of the cross references, the reader should be able to find an annotated reference to almost any subject mentioned in the text.

A. Books

BERGER 1964

Anni Berger and Andreas Brockes, with N. Dalal as co-author of the English version, *Color Measurement in Textile Industry.* **Bayer Farben Revue, Special Edition No. 3, USA. Leverkusen: Farbenfabriken Bayer A. G., 1964. 63 pp.** (Available in the U.S.A. from Verona Dyestuffs, P.O. Box 385, Union, New Jersey 07083.)

A beautifully illustrated and technically sound introduction to the fundamentals of color measurement. Although, by title, it is addressed to the textile industry, it is basic enough to apply to all fields. Only in some specific areas is it limited to textiles. Especially noteworthy are the numerical examples of the calculations involved in color matching and obtaining color differences. A few minor errors do not detract from the usefulness of this beautifully prepared booklet. A rare example of clear, concise information on color measurement. Brief coverage (with bibliography) of measurement technique, description of instruments, colorant formulation, and color-difference calculation.

BROWN 1958

Margaret Wise Brown, *The Color Kittens.* New York: Golden Press, 1958. Unpaged.

An engaging book for children showing (in color) how colors are mixed on the artist's palette (complex-subtractive mixture). Plenty of sense for the grown-ups, too.

BURNHAM 1963

Robert W. Burnham, Randall M. Hanes, and C. James Bartleson, *Color: A Guide to Basic Facts and Concepts.* New York: Wiley, 1963. xi + 249 pp.

A collection of basic facts and concepts dealing extensively with color vision and perception but not with the coloring of materials. The text is written in outline form, with each statement selfcontained. As a result, the thread of development from one statement to the next is very tenuous and the book does not lend itself to being read through. Excellent color plates. A report of the ISCC Subcommittee for Problem 20: Basic Elements of Color Education.

EVANS 1948

Ralph M. Evans, *An Introduction to Color.* **New York: Wiley, 1948. x + 340 pp.**

A highly authoritative, highly readable book. Un-surpassed in its treatment of the perception of color. The text is enhanced by illustrations, in color, of the effects of illumination and mode of viewing on perception. Much excellent material on the interaction of color and the visual process.

GODLOVE 1957

I. H. Godlove, *Bibliography on Color.* **Cleveland, Ohio: Inter-Society Color Council (c/o Braden Sutphin Ink Co.), 1957. v + 357 pp.**

An extensive bibliography of books and articles on color and related fields, collected by I. H. Godlove for the ISCC News Letter from 1936–1954 and arranged, by subject, by Mrs. Godlove after his death. The only collection of its kind known to us, albeit somewhat difficult to search thoroughly. Listings in the ISCC News Letter continue to the present time.

HARDY 1936

Arthur C. Hardy (Director), *Handbook of Colorimetry.* **Cambridge, Massachusetts: The Technology Press, 1936. 87 pp.**

The "bible" for the determination of CIE tristimulus values and related color coordinates from spectrophotometric data. Extensive tables of data and conversion charts providing the only convenient way of finding dominant wavelength and purity.

IES 1966

Illuminating Engineering Society, *IES Lighting Handbook.* New York: Illuminating Engineering Society, 4th Edition, 1966. viii + 780 pp.

Primarily concerned with the design and practice of lighting installations for all types of applications —industry, residences, public buildings, sports, transportation, and many others. Extensive sections on light sources and lighting calculations.

JACOBSON 1948

Egbert Jacobson, *Basic Color: An Interpretation of the Ostwald Color System.* Chicago: P. Theobald, 1948. 207 pp.

As the subtitle indicates, this is an interpretation of the Ostwald system of color harmony. It is well written and beautifully illustrated by an experienced advocate of the Ostwald theory. Required reading for anyone interested in this type of colorant mixture system. For the Munsell system, see Munsell 1963 (Sec. A).

JENKINS 1957

F. A. Jenkins and H. E. White, *Fundamentals of Optics*. New York: McGraw-Hill, 3rd Edition, 1957. vii + 637 pp.

One of the better standard textbooks on physical optics.

JUDD 1963

Deane B. Judd and Günter Wyszecki, *Color in Business, Science, and Industry*. New York: Wiley, 2nd Edition, 1963. x + 500 pp.

Authoritative and complete. Excellent treatment of color-order systems, color scales, and color standards. The beginner will find, however, that careful reading and re-reading is required. Some sections presuppose a knowledge of mathematics beyond the calculus.

KELLY 1955

Kenneth L. Kelly and Deane B. Judd, *The ISCC–NBS Method of Designating Colors and a Dictionary of Color Names*. Washington, D.C.: U.S. Government Printing Office, National Bureau of Standards Circular 553, 1955. v + 158 pp.

A description of a logical system of designating the names of colors, and a dictionary of 7500 color names indexed to the ISCC–NBS system. An excellent description of how the Munsell system is actually used. Good historical background material as well. If you want to know what color is meant by Intimate Mood, Wafted Feather, Kitten's Ear, or Griseo-Viridis, you can find out here. See NBS 1965.

KODAK 1962

Kodak Publication No. E-74, *Color As Seen and Photographed*. Rochester, New York: Eastman Kodak Co., 1962. 68 pp.

While originally intended to provide background information for color photography, the book provides an excellent treatment of the basic concepts and is a fine introduction to the field. Only half of its pages are directly concerned with photography (and much of this is of general interest), the rest being devoted to well-illustrated descriptions of light and color, color and its characteristics, and psychophysical attributes of color.

LE GRAND 1957

Yves Le Grand, *Light, Colour and Vision*. (Translated by R. W. G. Hunt, J. W. T. Walsh, and F. R. W. Hunt.) New York: Wiley, 1957. xiii + 512 pp.

An excellent discussion of "the ways in which the optics of the eye and the retina provide us with our perception of the universe: form, colour, depth, and movement." Complete and detailed, but quite readable. Unfortunately, out of print (1966).

LUBS 1955

H. A. Lubs, editor, *The Chemistry of Synthetic Dyes and Pigments*. New York: Reinhold, 1955. xiv + 734 pp.

An American Chemical Society monograph describing the chemistry of dyes, organic pigments, and dyestuff intermediates. For the advanced organic chemist.

MACKINNEY 1962

Gordon Mackinney and Angela C. Little, *Color of Foods*. Westport, Conn.: The AVI Publishing Co., 1962. xii + 308 pp.

Despite its title, this book is more concerned with general problems of color than specifically with the color of foods. It deals with color-order systems, color measurement, color tolerances, and color differences. While the examples are drawn from the food industry, they are applicable to any colored material. The many detailed calculations associated with color measurement and color tolerances are very useful for the beginner.

MELLON 1950

M. G. Mellon, editor, *Analytical Absorption Spectroscopy—Absorptimetry and Colorimetry*. New York: Wiley, 1950. vii + 618 pp.

An authoritative handbook on the application of color measurement as a tool and technique for the analytical chemist. Contains an excellent chapter on colorimetry by Judd and a fine article by Stearns on the many analytical uses of the spectrophotometer. Unfortunately, out of print (1966).

MUNSELL 1963

A. H. Munsell, *A Color Notation*. Baltimore: Munsell Color Co., 1936–1963. 67 pp.

Description of the origins and the workings of the Munsell color-order system. For the Ostwald system see Jacobson 1948 (Sec. A).

NEWTON 1730

Sir Isaac Newton, *OPTICKS: or A Treatise of the Reflections, Refractions, Inflections & Colours*

of Light. **New York: Dover Publications, 1952. (Reprint based on the 4th Edition, London 1730.) cxvi + 406 pp.**

It is amazing and illuminating to see how many of the basic facts of color were first discovered by this remarkable scientist. Not eminently readable, in 18th Century English, but well worth the effort.

OSA 1953

Optical Society of America, Committee on Colorimetry, *The Science of Color.* **New York: Thomas Y. Crowell Co., 1953. xii + 385 pp.**

Perhaps the most authoritative of all existing books on the general subject of color. An advanced treatise and a true source book for the expert. Reprinted by the Optical Society of America in 1963.

PEACOCK 1953

William H. Peacock, *The Practical Art of Color Matching.* New Jersey: American Cyanamid Co., Calco Chemical Division, 1953. 111 pp.

A practical guide to color matching, covering both the techniques for manipulating colorants to approach a color match and the factors influencing the visual judgment of the match.

SOUTHALL 1937

James P. C. Southall, *Introduction to Physiological Optics.* New York: Dover Publications, Inc., 1961. x + 426 pp.

A sound and well-regarded study of the eye and the process of vision. An unabridged and corrected republication of the 1937 edition (University Press, Oxford).

TEEVAN 1961

R. C. Teevan and R. C. Birney, editors, *Color Vision (An Enduring Problem in Psychology: Selected Readings).* New York: Van Nostrand Co. (Insight Books), 1961. viii + 214 pp.

A small well-written book on a subject we do not cover. Contains selections from outstanding original articles.

THURNER 1965

Karl Thurner, *Colorimetry in Textile Dyeing-Theory and Practice.* **Ludwigshafen am Rhein: Badische Anilin- & Soda-Fabrik, 1965. 150 pp. (Available in the U.S.A. from BASF Colors and Chemicals, Inc., P. O. Box 8467, Charlotte, North Carolina 28208.)**

Another beautifully illustrated and technically

sound introduction to the fundamentals of color measurement. Like Berger 1964, it is addressed by title to the textile industry, but is basic enough to apply to all fields. This booklet is distinguished for its discussion of the difference between visual and instrumental color evaluation. Many examples, both qualitative and quantitative, are presented to indicate the value of objective methods. An extensive section is included describing instruments and their use in color matching.

WRIGHT 1964

W. D. Wright, *The Measurement of Colour.* New York: Van Nostrand, 3rd Edition, 1964. x + 291 pp.

An authoritative, precisely written book "concerned with the principles, methods, and applications of the trichromatic system of colour measurement" by the British expert whose own contributions add to the soundness of his opinions.

B.   Journals, Yearbooks, and Other Serials

AATCC (W. H. Cady, editor), *Technical Manual of the American Association of Textile Chemists and Colorists.* New York: Howes Publishing Co., annually. Approx. 550 pp.

Contains information on the AATCC, its Committee reports, a compilation of its test methods, a bibliography of books and articles relating to textiles, extensive lists of American dyes and textile chemical specialties, and a buyer's guide. Valuable for the user of dyes.

American Dyestuff Reporter. New York: Howes Publishing Co., Inc., biweekly. (Includes Proceedings of the American Association of Textile Chemists & Colorists.)

A leading journal of the American textile industry. Contains many good articles on color as related to dyeing and textiles.

Color Engineering. New York: Chromatic Publishing Co., Inc., irregular.

A new journal which intends to cover all aspects of the field of color from physics through aesthetics. Too new to tell, but off to a good start.

Inter-Society Color Council (ISCC) News Letter. **Rochester, New York: Inter-Society Color Council (c/o Mr. Ralph M. Evans, Color Technology Division, Eastman Kodak Co., Rochester, New York 14650). Irregular.**

The publication of the ISCC whose member bodies encompass the world of color. Small in size but concentrated. Many items on color appear in the

News Letter which can be found in no other source in English.

Journal of Paint Technology. (Formerly *Official Digest,* Federation of Societies for Paint Technology; *Official Digest,* Federation of Paint & Varnish Production Clubs.) Philadelphia: Federation of Societies for Paint Technology, monthly.

The outstanding American journal of the paint industry. Contains many excellent and important articles on color.

Journal of the Oil and Colour Chemists' Association. London, England: The Oil & Colour Chemists' Association, Gresham St., London E. C. 2, monthly.

The publication of the British counterpart of the Federation of Societies for Paint Technology. Contains regular information and occasional articles on color and colorants. And every once in a while a magnificent one [see Gaertner 1963 (Sec. G)].

Journal of the Optical Society of America. New York: American Institute of Physics (AIP), monthly.

As this bibliography suggests, the *JOSA* probably contains more important articles on color than any other in the world. By editorial policy (at least through 1966), articles on color appear here and not in its newer sister journal, *Applied Optics.*

Journal of the Society of Dyers and Colourists. Yorkshire, England: The Society of Dyers and Colourists, Dean House, 19 Picadilly, Bradford 1, England, monthly.

One of the best journals in the world for people interested in color. Well edited with a good balance between theory and practice. Publishes excellent abstracts of literature relating to the field.

NPVLA (F. Scofield, editor), *Raw Materials Index.* Washington, D.C.: National Paint, Varnish and Lacquer Association, Inc., 1955. (Looseleaf, supplemented at irregular intervals.) Approx. 300 pp.

A compilation of information on and sources of pigments and other raw materials for the paint industry. Of considerable value to the colorant purchaser.

Review of Current Literature on the Paint & Allied Industries. Teddington, Middlesex: Paint Research Station, The Research Association of British Paint, Colour & Varnish Manufacturers.

The single most complete abstract journal in the field. Although it is not as current as some abstract journals, its coverage is by far the best for the paint and related industries.

SDC 1956

Colour Index. Yorkshire, England: Society of Dyers and Colourists, and Lowell, Mass.: American Association of Textile Chemists and Colorists. 2nd Edition, 1956. xviii + 3152 pp. Supplement, 1963. xix + 1123 pp.

An extensive and international compilation of the structure and properties of dyes and pigments, as well as a system of numbering these materials. Unfortunately, there is some duplication in the assignment of different CI dye class numbers to the same chemical structure. Regular (quarterly) additions and amendments keep this monumental work up to date and will, in time, eliminate errors.

C.   Color Perception and Appearance*

BARTLESON 1960

C. J. Bartleson, "Memory Colors of Familiar Objects," *J. Opt. Soc. Am.,* **50,** 73–77 (1960).

Colors as remembered seem more saturated and shifted in hue towards their most impressive color characteristic. An explanation of "why the grass is always greener."

BURNHAM 1959

Robert W. Burnham, "Predictions of Shifts in Color Appearance with a Change from Daylight to Tungsten Adaptation," *J. Opt. Soc. Am.,* **49,** 254–263 (1959).

Equations and charts are given which allow one to predict how a color will change in appearance when the illuminant is changed from daylight to tungsten light.

BURNHAM 1960

R. W. Burnham and R. J. Malach, "Color Appearance Specification with Adaptation to Daylight and Tungsten Illumination," *J. Opt. Soc. Am.,* **50,** 1071–1074 (1960).

The authors conclude that color-order systems based on daylight as the illuminant are likely to be unsuitable for describing colors as seen with another illuminant, such as tungsten light.

*See also Evans 1948 (Sec. A).

HELSON 1956

Harry Helson, Deane B. Judd, and Martha Wilson, "Color Rendition with Fluorescent Sources of Illumination," *Illuminating Engr.,* **51, 329–346 (1956).**

An excellent presentation, with striking illustrations in color, of the effect of illumination on the appearance of colored objects.

HUNTER 1963a

Richard S. Hunter, "Measurements of the Appearance of Paint Finishes," *Official Digest,* **35, 350–366 (1963); see also Hunter 1963b.**

Excellent description of the origin and measurement of all the variables determining the appearance of objects, including color, various kinds of gloss, and various degrees of transparency.

NEWHALL 1957

S. M. Newhall, R. W. Burnham, and Joyce R. Clark, "Comparison of Successive with Simultaneous Color Matching," *J. Opt. Soc. Am.,* **47,** 43–56 (1957).

As one might expect, color matching in which the two samples are viewed one at a time in succession rather than simultaneously side by side, gave more variable results. The article shows how variable and describes other systematic differences.

NICKERSON 1960

Dorothy Nickerson, "Light Sources and Color Rendering," *J. Opt. Soc. Am.,* **50, 57–69 (1960).**

A thorough discussion of the effect of the spectral energy distribution of light sources on the way colors appear when illuminated by them. Contains spectral energy distribution data for many widely used sources.

STILES 1962

W. S. Stiles and G. Wyszecki, "Field Trials of Color-Mixture Functions," *J. Opt. Soc. Am.,* **52,** 58–75 (1962).

Modifications of the CIE system have been proposed to establish a new standard observer for color matching with large samples. Some of the proposals were tested, but none was found completely satisfactory.

D.   Color-Order Systems*

ADAMS 1942

Elliot Q. Adams, "X–Z Planes in the 1931 ICI

*See also Kelly 1955 (Sec. A); MacAdam 1965 (Sec. I); Tilleard 1964 (Sec. F).

[CIE] System of Colorimetry," *J. Opt. Soc. Am.,* **32,** 168–173 (1942).

The paper defining the Adams chromatic value system widely used in color difference calculations.

ASTM D 1535

Method for Specifying Color by the Munsell System. **ASTM Designation: D 1535, 35 pp. Philadelphia: American Society for Testing and Materials.**

A method for determining the Munsell coordinates of a sample, either by visual comparison to the samples of the *Munsell Book of Color* [Munsell 1929 (Sec. D)] or from CIE data. Tables and graphs facilitating the latter conversion are included.

BURNHAM 1949

Robert W. Burnham, "Comparison of Color Systems with Respect to Uniform Visual Spacing," *J. Opt. Soc. Am.,* **39,** 387–392 (1949).

Diagrams like those on pp. 46–50 are computed and presented comparing ten color-order systems to the Munsell Renotation system for uniformity of visual spacing. Numerical ratings were assigned to the various systems tested.

CHAMBERLIN 1955

G. J. Chamberlin, *The C.I.E. International Colour System Explained,* 2nd Edition. Salisbury, England: The Tintometer Ltd., 1955. 34 pp.

"A simple explanation of the [CIE] system for the description of colour, written for the nontechnical reader and showing its value for colour specification in industry." Tied fairly closely to the promotion of the Lovibond system [Schofield 1939, Judd 1962a,b (Sec. D)].

CONTAINER CORPORATION OF AMERICA 1958

Color Harmony Manual, Chicago: Color Standards Department, Container Corporation of America. Editions of 1942, 1946, and 1948 no longer available. 4th edition, 1958.

A collection of about 1000 samples in the form of painted transparent plastic. Both glossy and dull surfaces available on each sample. Based approximately on the Ostwald color-order system. See discussion on p. 30.

DAVIDSON 1958

H. R. Davidson and H. Hemmendinger, "Comparison of Munsell and MacAdam Color Space," *J. Opt. Soc. Am.,* **48,** 606–608 (1958).

The MacAdam color-order system used for color difference calculations [MacAdam 1943 (Sec. F)] is compared in considerable detail with the Munsell Renotation system. The two are far from identical, but no conclusions were drawn as to which, if either, is in good accord with visual perception.

GRANVILLE 1944

Walter C. Granville and Egbert Jacobson, "Colorimetric Specification of the *Color Harmony Manual* from Spectrophotometric Measurements," *J. Opt. Soc. Am.*, **34**, 382–395 (1944).

One of several papers grouped together in the *J. Opt. Soc. Am.*, attempting to define the Ostwald system in numerical terms. Not so useful as those concerned with the Munsell system [Newhall 1943 (Sec. D)] since the Ostwald system is neither defined independent of colorants nor capable of describing all possible colors (see p. 31). The Granville paper refers only to the first (1942) edition of the *Manual*.

IPI 1962

IPI Color Finder, New York: Printing Ink Division, Interchemical Corporation, 1962.

A collection of over 400 lithographed samples, printed with combinations of not more than four out of a total of ten commercially available inks. The ink formula is given for each sample. Prepared on both coated and uncoated paper.

JUDD 1962b

Deane B. Judd, G. J. Chamberlin, and Geraldine W. Haupt, "Ideal Lovibond Color System," *J. Opt. Soc. Am.*, **56**, 813–819 (1962); See also Judd 1962a.

The glass samples defining the Lovibond color-order system were measured and specified in terms of the CIE system.

KELLY 1962

K. L. Kelly, *Coordinated Color Identifications for Industry*. Washington, D.C.: U.S. Government Printing Office, NBS Technical Note #152, pp. 1–9, 1962.

Five levels of precision are defined for classifying colors by name for identification purposes. At the first or least precise level, the color is designated by one of 13 hue names such as red or blue. Higher levels subdivide the classification into 29, 267 [ISCC–NBS system, Kelly 1955 (Sec. A)],

about 1000 [*Munsell Book of Color*, Munsell 1929 (Sec. D)], and a very large number (from color measurement) of possible designations.

KORNERUP 1962

A. Kornerup and J. H. Wanscher, *Reinhold Color Atlas*. New York: Reinhold, 1962. 226 pp.

A collection of 1440 lithographed samples, arranged roughly by hue and by the admixture of white and black. Considerably less useful than the other collections listed in this section because of poor spacing, awkward and nonstandard nomenclature, and the lack of formulas for the inks used. A dictionary of color names is included, but this cannot be compared for completeness with Kelly 1955 (Sec. A). (Published in the United Kingdom as the *Methuen Color Atlas*.)

MACADAM 1957

D. L. MacAdam, "Analytical Approximations for Color Metric Coefficients," *J. Opt. Soc. Am.*, **47**, 268–274 (1957).

This paper shows that no simple transformation of CIE color space can yield a system in which all pairs of colors, perceived as being equally different in visual perception, plot as being equally spaced. That is, such a perceptually uniform color-order system, if indeed it exists, cannot be related to the CIE system by simple mathematical equations. See also MacAdam 1965 (Sec. I).

MUNSELL 1929

Munsell Book of Color. Baltimore, Maryland: Munsell Color Co., 1929–1966.

Collections of painted samples based on the Munsell color-order system. Both matte and glossy finish collections are available in various sizes and numbers of samples, up to about 1000.

MUNSELL 1962

Munsell Color Standards for Plastic Insulated Wire and Cable. Baltimore, Maryland: Munsell Color Co., 1962. 2nd Edition, looseleaf, approx. 16 pp.

A series of charts for specifying the color of the plastic insulation used on electrical wire and cable. A typical chart consists of a target standard or centroid, six acceptable limit standards (varying from the centroid in both directions in Munsell Hue, Value, and Chroma) and six unacceptable limit standards. Typical of several systems for the visual examination of color.

NEWHALL 1943

Sidney M. Newhall, Dorothy Nickerson, and Deane B. Judd, "Final Report of the O.S.A. Subcommittee on the Spacing of the Munsell Colors," *J. Opt. Soc. Am.*, **33**, 385–418 (1943).

This paper defines the Munsell Renotation System in numerical terms by giving the CIE coordinates corresponding to whole-number Munsell renotations. See also Nickerson 1940 and the following papers in that symposium, Munsell 1929 (Sec. D), and Munsell 1963 (Sec. A). The Newhall paper is one of several in that issue of *J. Opt. Soc. Am.* describing color measurements on the Munsell samples.

SAUNDERSON 1946

J. L. Saunderson and B. I. Milner, "Modified Chromatic Value Color Space," *J. Opt. Soc. Am.*, **36**, 36–42 (1946).

The defining paper for the Saunderson-Milner Zeta Space, the color-order system which seems to approach equal visual perception more closely than any other amenable to calculations (see for example pages 46–50). Conversion from CIE to zeta coordinates is tedious, but digital computers can be used (Carroll 1963).

TILLEARD 1963a

D. L. Tilleard, "Colour Systems and Atlases," *Rev. Current Lit.*, **36**, 931–940 (1963).

A well-written review paper. 78 references.

E.   Color Measurement*

ADAMS 1961

J. M. Adams, "Control and Specifications of Fluorescent Whites and Colours," *J. Soc. Dyers Colourists*, **77**, 670–677 (1961).

The limitations of colorimeters for color measurement are discussed in general and particularly with respect to fluorescent samples. The conditions necessary for both visual and instrumental measurement of the color of fluorescent samples are outlined and discussed.

ASTM E 308

Recommended Practice for Spectrophotometry and Description of Color in CIE 1931 System, ASTM Designation: E 308, 21 pp. Philadelphia: American Society for Testing and Materials.

*See also Hardy 1936 (Sec. A); Hunter 1963a (Sec. C); Johnston 1963 (Sec. I); MacAdam 1965 (Sec. I).

Methods and procedures for color measurement with a spectrophotometer and the calculation of CIE color coordinates.

BILLMEYER 1960b

Fred W. Billmeyer, Jr., "Use of a Digital Readout Unit in Converting Spectrophotometric Data to Color Coordinates," *J. Opt. Soc. Am.*, **50**, 137–143 (1960).

Describes a device for automatically recording spectrophotometric data on punched cards or tape and the use of a digital computer to obtain CIE color coordinates. Perhaps the most important part of the paper is the data which are presented on the precision and accuracy of the spectrophotometer and readout system for color measurement.

BILLMEYER 1962

Fred W. Billmeyer, Jr., "Caution Required in Absolute Color Measurement with Colorimeters," *Official Digest*, **34**, 1333–1342 (1962).

The precision and accuracy of color measurement is determined for spectrophotometers and for differential colorimeters. It is shown that colorimeters should be used only for the measurement of small color differences between pairs of almost identical samples.

BILLMEYER 1965a

Fred W. Billmeyer, Jr., "Precision of Color Measurement with the G. E. Spectrophotometer. I. Routine Industrial Performance," *J. Opt. Soc. Am.*, **55**, 707–717 (1965).

Although the precision found was "shockingly" poor, the results of the round-robin study clearly showed that the G. E. Spectrophotometer, suitably calibrated and operated, is still the referee instrument for accurate color measurement. But few laboratories take the necessary care in the essential but time-consuming calibration steps.

DAVIDSON 1950

H. R. Davidson and I. H. Godlove, "Applications of the Automatic Tristimulus Integrator to Textile Mill Practice," *Am. Dyestuff Reptr.*, **39**, 78–84 (1950).

Application of spectrophotometry to color matching and control in the textile industry. Correlates dyer's brightness and strength with CIE coordinates [see also Alderson 1961 (Sec. H)].

DE KERF 1958

J. L. F. De Kerf, "Accuracy of Tristimulus Computations," *J. Opt. Soc. Am.*, **48**, 334–338 (1958); **49**, 109 (1959).

Various methods of converting spectrophotometric data to CIE color coordinates were compared for accuracy. The 5-nm weighted-ordinate method was preferred [see OSA 1953 (Sec. A) for a description of this and other common methods].

FOOTE 1964

P. V. Foote, "Measurement of Colour and Colour Difference," *Rev. Current Lit.*, **37**, 1–10 (1964).

A well-written review article on color measurement (but not the calculation of color differences, despite its title). 155 references.

GIBSON 1949

Kasson S. Gibson, *Spectrophotometry (200–1000 Millimicrons)*. Washington, D.C.: U.S. Government Printing Office, National Bureau of Standards Circular 484, 1949. 48 pp.

Thorough discussion of the principles, techniques, and errors of spectrophotometric measurements. Despite its age, required reading for all who use a spectrophotometer.

HUNTER 1942

Richard S. Hunter, *Photoelectric Tristimulus Colorimetry With Three Filters*. Washington, D.C.: U.S. Government Printing Office, National Bureau of Standards Circular C 429, 1942. 46 pp. Reprinted in *J. Opt. Soc. Am.*, **32**, 509–538 (1942).

A thorough discussion of the principles of construction and operation of colorimeters, their inherent errors and limitations, and their use for the measurement of color and color difference. Defines the NBS unit of color difference and the Hunter α, β color-order system. Despite its age, still required reading.

HUNTER 1958a

Richard S. Hunter, "Description and Measurement of White Surfaces," *J. Opt. Soc. Am.*, **48**, 597–605 (1958).

The concept of whiteness and how to measure it. (See also Allen 1959.)

HUNTER 1958b

Richard S. Hunter, "Photoelectric Color Difference Meter," *J. Opt. Soc. Am.*, **48**, 985–995 (1958).

Design and construction of the Gardner and Hunterlab colorimeters. Good discussion of the selection of source–filter–phototube characteristics to match the CIE standard observer. An example typical of papers describing other photoelectric colorimeters.

JUDD 1950

Deane B. Judd, *Colorimetry*. Washington, D.C.: U.S. Government Printing Office, National Bureau of Standards Circular 478, 1950. 56 pp.

Discussion of the CIE system, small-difference colorimetry, material standards for color, one-dimensional color scales, and instrumental methods. Much of the material is covered in Judd 1963 (Sec. A), but is conveniently summarized here.

MIDDLETON 1953

W. E. Knowles Middleton, "Comparison of Colorimetric Results from a Normal-Diffuse Spectrophotometer with Those from a 45-Degree-Normal Colorimeter for Semiglossy Specimens," *J. Opt. Soc. Am.*, **43**, 1141–1143 (1953).

It is shown that the integrating-sphere geometry used in most spectrophotometers can lead to results seriously in error for semiglossy samples, since the specular (mirror) reflection from the surface is not handled properly.

NICKERSON 1957

Dorothy Nickerson, *Color Measurement and its Application to the Grading of Agricultural Products: A Handbook on the Method of Disk Colorimetry*. Washington, D.C.: U.S. Government Printing Office, U.S. Department of Agriculture, Misc. Publ. #580, 1957. 62 pp.

A thorough discussion (and almost the only one available) of disk colorimetry, of the Munsell System, and of their application to agricultural products. Required reading for all those seriously concerned with production control of color.

ROBERTSON 1965

A. R. Robertson and W. D. Wright, "An International Comparison of Working Standards for Colorimetry," *J. Opt. Soc. Am.*, **55**, 694–706 (1965); see also Johnson 1963.

A comparison of color measurement of white, gray, and near-black ceramic tiles, involving various types of spectrophotometers and a few colorimeters. As in Billmeyer 1965a (Sec. E), the spread among all the measurements was quite wide, but here differences in viewing and illuminating geometry could account for part of it.

WRIGHT 1961

W. D. Wright, "Colour and its Measurement; Instrumental Methods of Colour Measurement; Colour Theory and Measurement Applied to the Textile and Dyeing Industries; Bibliography," *CIBA Rev.* 1961/2, 2–24, 25–28, 29–32, 33–34 (1961).

A beautifully illustrated, concise discussion of both visual and instrumental aspects of color measurement. The practical applications are considered as they apply to the textile industry. Contains a choice (though not annotated) bibliography of 43 entries. The intensive treatment of so many aspects of the problem makes for difficult reading, but reading which richly rewards the effort expended by the reader.

WURZBURG 1963a

F. L. Wurzburg, Jr., "Survey of Instruments for Color Specification," *Tappi*, **46**, No. 7, 115A–159A (1963); see also Wurzburg 1963b.

Includes a brief description of the various color-measuring instruments currently available in the United States, listing various operating features, price, accuracy, and accessories available.

F.   Color Difference*

ASTM D 1729

Recommended Practice for Visual Evaluation of Color Differences of Opaque Materials. ASTM Designation: D 1729, 6 pp. Philadelphia: American Society for Testing and Materials.

"This method covers the spectral, photometric, and geometric characteristics of light sources, illuminating and viewing conditions, sizes of specimens, and general procedures to be used in the visual evaluation of color differences of opaque materials."

ASTM 1952

ASTM Committee E-12 on Appearance, *Symposium on Color Difference Specification.* Philadel-

*See also Adams 1942 (Sec. D), MacAdam 1965 (Sec. I).

phia: American Society for Testing and Materials, 1952. 56 pp.

An excellent series of papers summarizing the status of color difference specification in 1952. Surprisingly little seems to have changed over the last decade. These papers and the discussion that follows should be read by everyone concerned with evaluating small color differences.

BALINKIN 1941

Isay A. Balinkin, "Measurement and Designation of Small Color Differences," *Bull. Am. Ceramic Soc.*, **20**, 392–402 (1941).

A detailed study of the principles of color-difference specification, and a comparison of color differences calculated in several different ways with visual estimates.

BROWN 1949

W. R. J. Brown and D. L. MacAdam, "Visual Sensitivities to Combined Chromaticity and Luminance Differences," *J. Opt. Soc. Am.*, **39**, 808–834 (1949).

A classic paper extending the well-known studies of MacAdam (1942, 1943) (Sec. F) to cases where luminance as well as chromaticity differences are involved. One of the most thorough studies ever made of the visual perception of small color differences.

DAVIDSON 1955b

Hugh R. Davidson and J. J. Hanlon, "Use of Charts for Rapid Calculation of Color Difference," *J. Opt. Soc. Am.*, **45**, 617–620 (1955).

Describes the use of a set of charts for the rapid calculation of color difference by the MacAdam formula [MacAdam 1943 (Sec. F)].

INGLE 1962

George W. Ingle, Frederick D. Stockton, and Henry Hemmendinger, "Analytic Comparison of Color-Difference Equations," *J. Opt. Soc. Am.*, **52**, 1075–1077 (1962).

Color differences (calculated by digital computer) were compared for the MacAdam 1943 (Sec. F), Adams 1942 (Sec. D) and NBS (Hunter 1942) (Sec. E) equations, using a large number of samples. As observed by Little (1963) (Sec. F), it is *not* possible to adjust any one formula so that it gives a good correlation with any other.

LITTLE 1963

Angela C. Little, "Evaluation of Single-Number

Expressions of Color Difference," *J. Opt. Soc. Am.*, **53**, 293–296 (1963).

Color differences, calculated for the same pairs of samples by eleven different equations, were compared. When the equations were adjusted so that the color-difference numbers were all the same for one pair of samples, the numbers differed by more than a factor of two for other pairs of samples. See also Mackinney 1962 (Sec. A), Ingle 1962 (Sec. F), Davidson 1953 (Sec. I).

MACADAM 1942

David L. MacAdam, "Visual Sensitivities to Color Differences in Daylight," *J. Opt. Soc. Am.*, **32**, 247–274 (1942).

This classic paper describes extensive studies of the visual perception of small color differences, and lays the groundwork for the development of the MacAdam color-difference equation [MacAdam 1943 (Sec. F)]. Extended to color differences involving luminance as well as chromaticity by Brown and MacAdam [Brown 1949 (Sec. F)].

MACADAM 1943

David L. MacAdam, "Specification of Small Chromaticity Differences," *J. Opt. Soc. Am.*, **33**, 18–26 (1943).

The studies of the perceptibility of small chromaticity differences [MacAdam 1942 (Sec. F)] are extended to form the basis of a well-known and widely used method of calculating color differences. See also Davidson 1955b (Sec. F), Simon 1958 (Sec. F), and MacAdam 1965 (Sec. I).

NICKERSON 1944

Dorothy Nickerson and Keith F. Stultz, "Color Tolerance Specification," *J. Opt. Soc. Am.*, **34**, 550–570 (1944).

Visual observations were compared with color differences calculated from instrumental measurements by several formulas. Although some equations [for example that of MacAdam 1943 (Sec. F)] were not included here, the general conclusions found in studies of this sort have changed remarkably little in two decades.

SIMON 1958

F. T. Simon and W. J. Goodwin, "Rapid Graphical Computation of Small Color Differences," *Am. Dyestuff Reptr.*, **47**, No. 4, 105–112 (Feb. 1958).

Describes a set of charts, improved over those described by Davidson and Hanlon [Davidson

1955b (Sec. F)], for the rapid calculation of color difference by the MacAdam formula [MacAdam 1943 (Sec. F)]. The charts are available on request from the Circulation Section—Advertising Department, Union Carbide Corp., Plastics Division, 270 Park Avenue, 44th Floor, New York, New York 10017. [In process of revision to refer to MacAdam 1965 (Sec. I) color differences, 1966.]

TILLEARD 1964

D. L. Tilleard, "Evaluation of Small Colour Differences and Tolerances in Colour Matching," *Rev. Current Lit.*, **37**, 143–153 (1964).

A well-written review paper on the calculation of color differences and uniform chromaticity scales. 119 references.

G. Colorants*

ABBOTT 1944

R. Abbott and E. I. Stearns, *Identification of Organic Pigments by Spectrophotometric Curve Shape*, Calco Technical Bulletin No. 754, American Cyanamid Co., Bound Brook, New Jersey (1944).

A description of a practical and relatively simple technique for the identification of organic pigments. See also Saltzman 1959 (Sec. H).

APPS 1958

E. A. Apps, "Fading of Printing Inks," *Paint Manuf.*, **28**, 237–240, 248, 275–278 (1958).

The general subjects of artificial weathering tests and the measurement of fading are discussed with particular reference to paint systems.

ATHERTON 1955

E. Atherton and R. H. Peters, "Colour Gamuts of Pigments." *Congrès FATIPEC*, **III**, 147–158 (1955).

The MacAdam limits defining the theoretical gamuts of ideal colorants [MacAdam 1935 (Sec. G)] are modified to take account of surface reflection losses as in paint films, and the performance of some actual pigments is compared to these limits.

ATHERTON 1957

E. Atherton and D. Tough, "Aspects of Colorimetry Applied to the Colour Gamut of Pigments," *J. Oil Colour Chem. Assoc.*, **40**, 115–128 (1957).

*See also AATCC (Sec. B); Duncan 1962 (Sec. H); Lubs 1955 (Sec. A); NPVLA (Sec. B); SDC 1956 (Sec. B).

Describes the color gamuts of actual pigments and compares them to the theoretical gamuts of Atherton and Peters [Atherton 1955 (Sec. G)].

CHABOT 1957

George B. Chabot, Sr. and Matthew J. Babey, *Identification of Dyes*, Dyes Technical Bulletin No. 846, American Cyanamid Co., Bound Brook, New Jersey (1957).

A brief summary of some useful techniques for dyestuff identification in the standard manner. See also Abbott 1944 (Sec. G).

GAERTNER 1963

H. Gaertner, "Modern Chemistry of Organic Pigments," *J. Oil Colour Chem. Assoc.,* 46, 13–44 (1963).

A beautifully illustrated article describing with unusual accuracy the structures and properties of recently developed high-grade organic pigments. For earlier pigments, see Vesce 1956 (Sec. G).

GILES 1963

Charles H. Giles and Robert B. McKay, "The Lightfastness of Dyes: A Review," *Textile Res. J.,* 33, 527–577 (1963).

A review of the literature and the work of the senior author and his co-workers on the lightfastness of dyes. Excellent bibliography.

MACADAM 1935

David L. MacAdam, "Maximum Visual Efficiency of Colored Materials," *J. Opt. Soc. Am.,* 25, 361–367 (1935).

The theoretical gamut (maximum chromaticity at constant lightness) which could be achieved with ideal pigments is calculated for CIE Illuminants A and C.

MUDD 1957

J. S. Mudd, "Precise Measurement of Fading on a Time-Intensity Basis," *J. Soc. Dyers Colourists,* 73, 47–52 (1957).

Visual and instrumental methods for measuring fading are compared. The dependence of fading rate on the spectral energy distribution of the light source is discussed.

SALTZMAN 1963a

Max Saltzman, "Colored Organic Pigments: Why So Many? Why So Few?" *Official Digest,* 35, 245–258 (1963).

The gamuts of colors available with pigments are examined with respect to colorant cost, conditions of use, and chemical and weather resistance. See also the discussion on pages 132–136.

SMITH 1954

F. M. Smith and D. M. Stead, "The Meaning and Assessment of Light Fastness in Relation to Pigments," *J. Oil Colour Chem. Assoc.,* 37, 117–130 (1954).

The authors contend (and how right they are) that the light fastness of a pigment by itself has no meaning, and that it is only the light fastness of a pigmented system which can be measured and has any value. The artificial exposure studies leading to this conclusion are described.

VESCE 1956

Vincent C. Vesce, "Vivid Light Fast Organic Pigments," *Official Digest,* 28, No. 377, Part 2, 1–48 (December 1956).

Structures, properties, samples (in paint formulations) and spectrophotometric curves of the most important organic pigments to 1956. For later developments, see Gaertner 1963 (Sec. G).

VESCE 1959

Vincent C. Vesce, "Exposure Studies of Organic Pigments in Paint Systems," *Official Digest,* 31, No. 419, Part 2, 1–143 (December 1959).

A comprehensive, illustrated, study of the behavior on outdoor exposure of paint systems colored with organic pigments. Results are given in terms of numerical color differences as a function of time, with the pigments identified as to structure. In all cases, several paint formulations were used.

VICKERSTAFF 1949

T. Vickerstaff and D. Tough, "The Quantitative Measurement of Lightfastness," *J. Soc. Dyers Colourists,* 65, 606–612 (1949).

One of the earliest and best papers on the subject. The method presented by the authors, utilizing the Adams chromatic value formula to indicate total color change after exposure to a known amount of light, is, in our opinion, a method which will one day be widely used.

H.   Color Matching and Formulation*

ALDERSON 1961

J. V. Alderson, E. Atherton, and A. N. Derbyshire, "Modern Physical Techniques in Colour

*See also Peacock 1953 (Sec. A).

Formulation," *J. Soc. Dyers Colourists*, **77**, 657–669 (1961).

Various color-measuring techniques are described, and the dyer's coordinates of strength, shade, and brightness are related to CIE coordinates. The use of a digital computer to formulate opaque colors is discussed.

ALLEN 1965

Eugene Allen, "Analytical Color Matching," *Color Engineering*, **3**, No. 1, 15–20 (Jan.–Feb., 1965).

A description of instrument- and computer-aided methods of color matching (Chap. 5B), treated from the viewpoint of the analytical chemist familiar with spectrophotometry.

BILLMEYER 1960a

F. W. Billmeyer, Jr., J. K. Beasley, and J. A. Sheldon, "Formulation of Transparent Colors with a Digital Computer," *J. Opt. Soc. Am.*, **50**, 70–72 (1960).

This paper describes, for the first time, the use of a digital computer to predict the formulas required to mix dyes to produce a specified color in a transparent system.

DAVIDSON 1955a

H. R. Davidson and Henry Hemmendinger, "Colorimetric Calibration of Colorant Systems," *J. Opt. Soc. Am.*, **45**, 216–219 (1955).

A description of the empirical way in which paint mixtures were prepared to match whole-number designations in the Munsell Renotation System. The resulting paints were used to prepare the glossy edition of the *Munsell Book of Color* [Munsell 1929 (Sec. D)].

DAVIDSON 1963b

Hugh R. Davidson, Henry Hemmendinger and J. L. R. Landry, Jr., "A System of Instrumental Color Control for the Textile Industry," *J. Soc. Dyers Colourists*, **79**, 577–589 (1963); see also Davidson 1963a.

The basic principles of color matching are reviewed, and an analog computer is described which allows the formulations corresponding to opaque colors to be predicted.

DUNCAN 1949

D. R. Duncan, "The Colour of Pigment Mixtures," *J. Oil Colour Chem. Assoc.*, **32**, 296–321 (1949).

A classic paper describing the various types of color mixing and the laws that they follow. The laws best describing the mixing of pigments are applied to show how to predict the colors of pigment mixtures and the range of colors obtainable with a given set of pigments.

DUNCAN 1962

D. R. Duncan, "The Identification and Estimation of Pigments in Pigmented Compositions by Reflectance Spectrophotometry," *J. Oil Colour Chem. Assoc.*, **45**, 300–324 (1962).

The use of the Kubelka-Munk colorant mixing law to determine the colors of pigment mixtures. See also Duncan 1949 (Sec. H).

DUNCAN 1963

D. R. Duncan, "Modern Techniques of Colour Matching," *Rev. Current Lit.*, **36**, 847–854 (1963).

A well-written review paper. 60 references.

GUTHRIE 1962

J. C. Guthrie, Miss J. Moir, and P. H. Oliver, "Two Problems Associated with the Blending of Coloured Fibres," *J. Soc. Dyers Colourists*, **78**, 27–34 (1962).

Continuation of earlier work by Guthrie and Oliver (Guthrie 1957). The selection of the minimum number of colored staple fibers required to give solid effects in two-component blends and the calculation of permissible tolerances are discussed. Comparison of objective color measurement with subjective assessment is shown to be reasonable provided the subjective assessment is made by a large number of observers.

MILLER 1963

Miss A. Miller, Miss J. Moir, J. C. Guthrie and P. H. Oliver, "A Computed Catalogue of Fibre Blends and its Use in Match Prediction," *J. Soc. Dyers Colourists*, **79**, 604–612 (1963).

Details of the calculation of a catalog of 57,000 colors and of the factors affecting the accuracy attainable in its use.

SALTZMAN 1959

Max Saltzman, "Color Matching via Pigment Identification," *Dyestuffs*, **43**, 57–65 (1959).

The use of the spectrophotometer to identify organic pigments is discussed. The usefulness of such identifications for color matching by *colorant* matching is then described. See also Abbott 1944 (Sec. G).

SAUNDERSON 1942

J. L. Saunderson, "Calculation of the Color of Pigmented Plastics," *J. Opt. Soc. Am.*, **32**, 727–736 (1942).

The equations of Kubelka and Munk (Kubelka 1931), describing the color-mixing laws for opaque pigmented systems, are extended empirically and applied to the calculation of the colors of known mixtures of pigments in plastics.

TILLEARD 1963b

Miss D. L. Tilleard, "Some Applications of the Davidson and Hemmendinger Colorant Mixture Computer to Paints and Plastics," *J. Soc. Dyers Colourists*, **79**, 590–600 (1963).

Experimental evidence that the COMIC works well for light-colored but not for dark-colored paints, and well for opaque, but not for translucent, plastics. (The reasons for this behavior are discussed on page 122).

I. Color Specifications, Standards, and Tolerances*

BROWN 1957

W. R. J. Brown, "Color Discrimination of Twelve Observers," *J. Opt. Soc. Am.*, 47, 137–143 (1957).

An extension of the classic work of Brown and MacAdam [Brown 1949 (Sec. F)] in which the sensitivities of twelve observers (with normal color vision) to small color differences were studied. Significant differences were noted among the observers in the nature of the color difference most readily seen, as well as in the size of the difference barely seen.

DAVIDSON 1953

Hugh R. Davidson and Elaine Friede, "The Size of Acceptable Color Differences," *J. Opt. Soc. Am.*, **43**, 581–589 (1953).

A large number of visual observations of small color differences in dyed wool samples was used to rate samples as accepted or rejected as a commercial match. The per cent acceptable was compared with color differences calculated by several formulas. A modification of the MacAdam formula [MacAdam 1943 (Sec. F)] correlated best with the visual results.

*See also ASTM D-1535 (Sec. D); Davidson 1955b (Sec. F); Nickerson 1944 (Sec. F).

GRANVILLE 1956

W. C. Granville, "Survey of American Color Specifications—1955," *Official Digest*, **28**, 902–921 (1956).

A reasonably complete list, as of 1955, of the major color order systems, standards for transmitted light and reflected light colors, instruments for color measurement, and color codes. References, but no discussion or annotation. Presently under revision.

JOHNSTON 1963

Ruth M. Johnston, "Pitfalls in Color Specifications," *Official Digest*, **35**, 259–274 (1963).

The errors in each step of the initial formulation and production control of a color match are analyzed for the case where instruments are used throughout for color measurement. Writing practical and realizable color specifications is discussed with these errors considered.

JOHNSTON 1964b

Ruth M. Johnston and Robert P. Ericson, "Control of Color Standards," *Color Engineering*, **2**, No. 11–12, 10–13, 23 (Nov.–Dec., 1964).

"The most difficult and also the most critical part of the production control problem on colored products, maintenance of invariant color standards, is discussed in detail."

MACADAM 1965

David L. MacAdam, "Color Measurement and Tolerances," *Official Digest,* 37, 1487–1531 (1965); errata, *J. Paint Technol.,* 38, 70 (1966).

An outstanding discussion of this subject. A brief review of spectrophotometry and colorimetry with special reference to establishing and using color tolerances based on objective methods. Includes a description of the uniform chromaticity space recently recommended by the CIE (page 141), with a color plate. The 1965 MacAdam color-difference calculation described on page 141 is derived and discussed. The summary on page 1530 of the reference is especially recommended.

RICHMOND 1959

Joseph C. Richmond and William N. Harrison, "Evaluation of Small Color Differences: I. Visual Observations." *Bull. Am. Ceramic Soc.*, **38**, 292–300 (1959).

The sizes of small color differences were measured by groups of experienced and of inexperienced observers. The scatter of the results was large in each case but, on the average, inexperienced observers did just as well as those with experience in color matching. (Subsequent papers in this series had not been published by the end of 1965.)

TILLEARD 1957

D. L. Tilleard, "Tolerances in Colour Matching," *J. Oil Colour Chem. Assoc.*, **40**, 952–975 (1957).

A thorough and careful study of the magnitudes of small color differences normally acceptable in production of painted objects. Limited only in that just a few samples were studied.

WRIGHT 1959

W. D. Wright, "Color Standards in Commerce and Industry," *J. Opt. Soc. Am.*, **49**, 384–388 (1959).

The use of physical standards for specifying and controlling color is discussed. The need for permanent standards, both for visual use and for calibrating instruments, is asserted, but the importance of eliminating metamerism between sample and standard for both visual and instrumental use is not adequately stressed.

Bibliography†

*AATCC

W. H. Cady, editor, *Technical Manual of the American Association of Textile Chemists and Colorists*, Howe Publishing Co., New York, annually.

*Abbott 1944

R. Abbott and E. I. Stearns, *Identification of Organic Pigments by Spectrophotometric Curve Shape*, Calco Technical Bulletin No. 754, American Cyanamid Co., Bound Brook, New Jersey, 1944.

*Adams 1942

Elliot Q. Adams, "X–Z Planes in the 1931 I.C.I. (CIE) System of Colorimetry," *J. Opt. Soc. Am.*, **32**, 168–173 (1942).

*Adams 1961

J. M. Adams, "Control and Specifications of Fluorescent Whites and Colours," *J. Soc. Dyers Colourists*, **77**, 670–677 (1961).

*Alderson 1961

J. V. Alderson, E. Atherton, and A. N. Derbyshire, "Modern Physical Techniques in Colour Formulation," *J. Soc. Dyers Colourists*, **77**, 657–668 (1961).

Alderson 1963

J. V. Alderson, E. Atherton, and D. Tough, "The Practical Exploitation of Instrumental Match Pre-

diction," *J. Soc. Dyers Colourists*, **79**, 723–730 (1963).

Allen 1959

Eugene Allen, "Convenient Color Indices for Near White Samples," *J. Opt. Soc. Am.*, **49**, 1227–1228 (1959).

*Allen 1965

Eugene Allen, "Analytical Color Matching," *Color Engineering*, **3**, No. 1, 15–20 (Jan.–Feb., 1965).

*Apps 1958

E. A. Apps, "Fading of Printing Inks," *Paint Manuf.*, **28**, 237–240, 248, 275–278 (1958).

*ASTM D 1535

Method for Specifying Color by the Munsell System, ASTM Designation: D 1535, American Society for Testing and Materials, Philadelphia, Pa.

*ASTM D 1729

Recommended Practice for Visual Examination of Color Differences of Opaque Materials, ASTM Designation: D 1729, American Society for Testing and Materials, Philadelphia, Pa.

ASTM D 1925

Method of Test for Yellowness Index of Plastics, ASTM Designation: D 1925, American Society for Testing and Materials, Philadelphia, Pa.

†References designated by an asterisk (*) are annotated in Chapter 7.

*ASTM D 2244

Method of Test for Instrumental Evaluation of Color Difference, ASTM Designation: D 2244, American Society for Testing and Materials, Philadelphia, Pa.

ASTM E 259

Recommended Practice for Preparation of Reference White Reflectance Standards, ASTM Designation: E 259, American Society for Testing and Materials, Philadelphia, Pa.

*ASTM E 308

Recommended Procedure for Spectrophotometry and Description of Color in CIE 1931 System, ASTM Designation: E 308, American Society for Testing and Materials, Philadelphia, Pa.

ASTM E 313

Method of Test for Indexes of Whiteness and Yellowness of Near-White, Opaque Materials, ASTM Designation: E 313, American Society for Testing and Materials, Philadelphia, Pa.

*Atherton 1955

E. Atherton and R. H. Peters, "Colour Gamut of Pigments," *Congrès FATIPEC* III, 147–158 (1955).

*Atherton 1957

E. Atherton and D. Tough, "Aspects of Colorimetry Applied to the Colour Gamut of Pigments," *J. Oil Colour Chem. Assoc.*, 40, 115–128 (1957).

Atherton 1965

E. Atherton and F. North, "Two Years' Experience of Colour Matching by Computer," Proceedings of the International Colour Meeting, Lucerne (Switzerland) 1965, pp. 823–830.

*Balinkin 1941

Isay A. Balinkin, "Measurement and Designation of Small Color Differences," *Bull. Am. Ceramic Soc.*, 20, 392–402 (1941).

*Bartleson 1960

C. J. Bartleson, "Memory Colors of Familiar Objects," *J. Opt. Soc. Am.*, 50, 73–77 (1960).

Bassemir 1959

R. W. Bassemir, "Color Measuring Instruments for the Printing Ink Industry," *Am. Ink Maker*, 37, 52–61 (1959).

Beasley 1965

J. K. Beasley, J. T. Atkins, and F. W. Billmeyer, Jr., "Scattering and Absorption of Light in Turbid Media," paper presented at the Second Interdisciplinary Conference on Electromagnetic Scattering, Amherst, Mass., June 28–30, 1965.

*Berger 1964

Anni Berger and Andreas Brockes with N. Dalal,

"*Color Measurement in Textile Industry*," Bayer Farben Revue, special edition No. 3, Farbenfabriken Bayer, Leverkusen, Germany, 1964.

Billmeyer 1953

F. W. Billmeyer, Jr. and A. C. Webber, "Three-Dimensional Color Models Constructed on the CIE and Munsell Systems," *J. Opt. Soc. Am.*, 43, 69–70 (1953).

Billmeyer 1956

Fred W. Billmeyer, Jr., "'Compensated Opal' Working Standard Equivalent to Magnesium Oxide," *J. Opt. Soc. Am.*, 46, 72–73 (1956).

*Billmeyer 1960a

F. W. Billmeyer, Jr., J. K. Beasley and J. A. Sheldon, "Formulation of Transparent Colors with a Digital Computer," *J. Opt. Soc. Am.*, 50, 70–72 (1960).

*Billmeyer 1960b

Fred W. Billmeyer, Jr., "Use of a Digital Readout Unit in Converting Spectrophotometric Data to Color Coordinates," *J. Opt. Soc. Am.*, 50, 137–143 (1960).

Billmeyer 1961

F. W. Billmeyer, Jr., J. K. Beasley and J. A. Sheldon, "Color-Order System Predicting Constant Hue," *J. Opt. Soc. Am.*, 51, 656–666, 1440 (1961).

*Billmeyer 1962

Fred W. Billmeyer, Jr., "Caution Required in Absolute Color Measurement with Colorimeters," *Official Digest*, 34, 1333–1342 (1962).

Billmeyer 1963a

Fred W. Billmeyer, Jr., "Tables of Adams Chromatic-Value Color Coordinates," *J. Opt. Soc. Am.*, 53, 1317 (1963).

Billmeyer 1963b

Fred W. Billmeyer, "An Objective Approach to Coloring," *Farbe*, 12, 151–164 (1963).

*Billmeyer 1965a

Fred W. Billmeyer, Jr., "Precision of Color Measurement with the G. E. Spectrophotometer. I. Routine Industrial Performance," *J. Opt. Soc. Am.*, 55, 707–717 (1965).

Billmeyer 1965b

Fred W. Billmeyer, Jr., "Precision and Accuracy of Industrial Color Measurement," Proceedings of the International Colour Meeting, Lucerne (Switzerland) 1965, pp. 445–456.

Billmeyer 1966a

Fred W. Billmeyer, Jr., "The Present and Future of Color Measurement in Industry," *Color Engineering*, 4, No. 4, 15–19 (July–August, 1966). (Same text as Billmeyer 1965b.)

Billmeyer 1966b

Fred W. Billmeyer, Jr., "Yellowness Measurement

of Plastics for Lighting Use," *Materials Research and Standards*, **6**, 295–301, 1966.

Blackwood 1966
N. K. Blackwood and F. W. Billmeyer, Jr., "A Computer Program for MacAdam 'PQS' Color Differences," *Color Engineering*, **4**, No. 2, 24–25 (March–April 1966); No. 3, 12 (May–June 1966).

Breckenridge 1939
F. C. Breckenridge and W. R. Schaub, "Rectangular Uniform-Chromaticity-Scale Coordinates," *J. Opt. Soc. Am.*, **29**, 370–380 (1939).

Brockes 1960
Andreas Brockes and Otto Koch, "Zwei Zusatzgerate zum Spektralphotometer der General Electric," *Farbe*, **9**, 267–272 (1960), in German.

*Brown 1949
W. R. J. Brown and D. L. MacAdam, "Visual Sensitivities to Combined Chromaticity and Luminance Differences," *J. Opt. Soc. Am.*, **39**, 808–834 (1949).

*Brown 1957
W. R. J. Brown, "Color Discrimination of Twelve Observers," *J. Opt. Soc. Am.*, **47**, 137–143 (1957).

*Brown 1958
Margaret Wise Brown, *The Color Kittens*, Golden Press, New York, 1958.

Buc 1952
G. L. Buc, "Further Tables for Use in Computing Small Color Differences," *Am. Dyestuff Reptr.*, **41**, 353–355 (1952).

Buchmann-Olsen 1950
Bent Buchmann-Olsen, *The Objective Measurement of Color and Color Changes*, Akademiet For De Tekniske Videnskaber, G.E.C. Gad, Copenhagen, Denmark, 1950.

Bunkall 1965
P. R. Bunkall, "Applications of Spectrophotometric Measurement in Dyeing and Finishing," *J. Soc. Dyers Colourists*, **81**, 201–205 (1965).

*Burnham 1949
Robert W. Burnham, "Comparison of Color-Order Systems with Respect to Uniform Visual Spacing," *J. Opt. Soc. Am.*, **39**, 387–392 (1949).

*Burnham 1959
Robert W. Burnham, "Prediction of Shifts in Color Appearance with a Change from Daylight to Tungsten Adaptation," *J. Opt. Soc. Am.*, **49**, 254–263 (1959).

*Burnham 1960
R. W. Burnham and R. J. Malach, "Color Appearance Specification with Adaptation to Daylight and Tungsten Illumination," *J. Opt. Soc. Am.*, **50**, 1071–1074 (1960).

*Burnham 1963
Robert W. Burnham, Randall M. Hanes, and C. James Bartleson, *Color: A Guide to Basic Facts and Concepts*, Wiley, New York, 1963.

Carr 1957
W. Carr and C. Musgrave, "Behavior of Organic Pigments in High Temperature Systems," *J. Oil Colour Chem. Assoc.*, **40**, 51–61 (1957).

Carroll 1960
Lewis Carroll, *Alice's Adventures in Wonderland and Through the Looking Glass*, with introduction and notes by Martin Gardner, Clarkson N. Potter, Inc., New York, 1960.

Carroll 1963
C. W. Carroll, *Color: Industrial Color Measurement, Laboratory Color Matching, Production Color Control*, International Business Machines Corp., Midwestern Region, 1963.

*Chabot 1957
George B. Chabot, Sr., and Matthew J. Babey, *Identification of Dyes*, Dyes Tech. Bull. 846, American Cyanamid Co., Bound Brook, New Jersey, 1957.

*Chamberlin 1955
G. J. Chamberlin, *The C.I.E. International Colour System Explained*, 2nd Ed., The Tintometer Ltd., Salisbury, England, 1955.

Chapanis 1965
A. Chapanis, "Color Names for Color Space," *Am. Scientist*, **53**, 327–346 (1965).

Ciba 1965
Ciba Foundation Symposium, *Colour Vision—Physiology and Experimental Psychology*, edited by A. V. S. de Reuck and Julie Knight, Little, Brown & Co., Boston, 1965.

CIE 1931
International Commission on Illumination, *Proceedings of the Eighth Session*, Cambridge, England, 1931.

*Container Corporation of America 1958
Color Harmony Manual, 4th Ed., Color Standards Department, Container Corporation of America, Chicago, Illinois, 1958.

Cooke 1955
Donald E. Cooke, *Color by Overprinting*, Winston, Philadelphia, Pa., 1955.

Coppock 1965
W. A. Coppock, "The Chemstrand Whiteness Scale," *Am. Dyestuff Rptr.*, **54**, No. 10, 33–38 (1965).

Cutter 1962

J. O. Cutter, "The Inorganic Pigments," Chap. 6, pp. 149–173, in *The Science of Surface Coatings*, H. W. Chatfield, ed., Ernest Benn, Ltd., London, England, 1962.

Davidson 1949

H. R. Davidson and L. W. Imm, "A Continuous, Automatic Tristimulus Integrator for Use with the Recording Spectrophotometer," *J. Opt. Soc. Am.*, **39**, 942–944 (1949).

*Davidson 1950

H. R. Davidson and I. H. Godlove, "Applications of the Automatic Tristimulus Integrator to Textile Mill Practice," *Am. Dyestuff Reptr.*, **39**, 78–84 (1950).

*Davidson 1953

Hugh R. Davidson and Elaine Friede, "The Size of Acceptable Color Differences," *J. Opt. Soc. Am.*, **43**, 581–589 (1953).

*Davidson 1955a

H. R. Davidson and Henry Hemmendinger, "Colorimetric Calibration of Colorant Systems," *J. Opt. Soc. Am.*, **45**, 216–219 (1955).

*Davidson 1955b

Hugh R. Davidson and J. J. Hanlon, "Use of Charts for Rapid Calculation of Color Difference," *J. Opt. Soc. Am.*, **45**, 617–620 (1955).

Davidson 1957

Hugh R. Davidson, Margaret N. Godlove and Henry Hemmendinger, "A Munsell Book in High-Gloss Colors," *J. Opt. Soc. Am.*, **47**, 336–337 (1957) (abstract of paper).

*Davidson 1958

H. R. Davidson and H. Hemmendinger, "Comparison of Munsell and MacAdam Color Space," *J. Opt. Soc. Am.*, **48**, 606–608 (1958).

Davidson 1963a

Hugh R. Davidson and H. Hemmendinger, "Use of Instrumentation in Color Matching Problems," *SPE J.*, **19**, 104–108 (1963).

*Davidson 1963b

Hugh R. Davidson, Henry Hemmendinger and J. L. R. Landry, Jr., "A System of Instrumental Colour Control for the Textile Industry," *J. Soc. Dyers Colourists*, **79**, 577–589 (1963).

Davis 1953

Raymond Davis, Kasson S. Gibson and Geraldine W. Haupt, "Spectral Energy Distribution of the International Commission on Illumination Light Sources A, B, and C," *J. Res. Natl. Bur. Std.*, **50**, 31–37 (1953).

Dearth 1963

Leonard R. Dearth, Wayne M. Shillcox and J. A. Van

den Akker, "Instrumentation Studies LXXXVII. Study of Photoelectric Instruments for the Measurement of Color: Reflectance and Transmittance. Part XIV. The Standard Brightness Tester as a Four-Filter Colorimeter," *Tappi*, **46**, 179A–188A (1963).

De Kerf 1958

J. L. F. De Kerf, "Accuracy of Tristimulus Computations," *J. Opt. Soc. Am.*, **48**, 334–338 (1958); **49**, 102 (1959).

Derby 1952

R. E. Derby, Jr., "Applied Spectrophotometry. I. Color Matching with the Aid of the 'R' Cam," *Am. Dyestuff Reptr.*, **41**, 550–557 (1952).

Donaldson 1947

R. Donaldson, "A Colorimeter with Six Matching Stimuli," *Proc. Phys. Soc.*, **59**, 554–560 (1947).

*Duncan 1949

D. R. Duncan, "The Colour of Pigment Mixtures," *J. Oil Colour Chem. Assoc.*, **32**, 296–321 (1949).

*Duncan 1962

D. R. Duncan, "The Identification and Estimation of Pigments in Pigmented Compositions by Reflectance Spectrophotometry," *J. Oil Colour Chem. Assoc.*, **45**, 300–324 (1962).

*Duncan 1963

D. R. Duncan, "Modern Techniques of Colour Matching," *Rev. Current Lit.*, **36**, 847–854 (1963).

Duntley 1942

Seibert Q. Duntley, "The Optical Properties of Diffusing Materials," *J. Opt. Soc. Am.*, **32**, 61–70 (1942).

*Evans 1948

Ralph M. Evans, *An Introduction to Color*, Wiley, New York (1948).

Fink 1960

Donald G. Fink and David M. Luytens, *The Physics of Television* (Science Study Series No. S8), Anchor Books, Doubleday and Co., Inc., Garden City, New York, 1960.

*Foote 1964

P. V. Foote, "Measurement of Colour and Colour Difference," *Rev. Current Lit.*, **37**, 1–10 (1964).

Foss 1944

Carl E. Foss, Dorothy Nickerson and Walter C. Granville, "Analysis of the Ostwald Color System," *J. Opt. Soc. Am.*, **34**, 361–381 (1944).

Foster 1966a

Robert S. Foster, "A New Simplified System of Charts for Rapid Color Difference Calculations," *Color Engineering*, **4**, No. 1, 17–19, 26 (Jan.–Feb., 1966).

Foster 1966b

Robert S. Foster, "Turbid Media Theory in Practice," *Color Engineering*, **4**, No. 2, 26–30 (March–April, 1966).

Franklin 1962

Sandford G. Franklin, "Digital Tristimulus Computer," *J. Opt. Soc. Am.*, **52**, 604 (1962) (abstract of paper).

Gabel 1949

Joseph W. Gabel and E. I. Stearns, "An Auxiliary Working Standard Equivalent to Magnesium Oxide on a General Electric Spectrophotometer," *J. Opt. Soc. Am.*, **39**, 481–483 (1949).

*Gaertner 1963

H. Gaertner, "Modern Chemistry of Organic Pigments," *J. Oil Colour Chem. Assoc.*, **46**, 13–44 (1963).

*Gibson 1938

Kasson S. Gibson and Harry J. Keegan, "Calibration and Operation of the General Electric Recording Spectrophotometer of the National Bureau of Standards," *J. Opt. Soc. Am.*, **28**, 372–385 (1938).

*Gibson 1949

Kasson S. Gibson, *Spectrophotometry (200–1000 Millimicrons)*, NBS Circular 484, U.S. Government Printing Office, 1949.

*Giles 1963

Charles H. Giles and Robert B. McKay, "The Lightfastness of Dyes: A Review," *Textile Res. J.*, **33**, 527–577 (1963).

Glasser 1952

L. G. Glasser and D. J. Troy, "A New High Sensitivity Differential Colorimeter," *J. Opt. Soc. Am.*, **42**, 652–660 (1952).

Glasser 1955

L. G. Glasser, "An Improved Differential Colorimeter and its Application to the Color Control of Paint," *Congrès FATIPEC* **III**, 47–53, (1955).

Glasser 1958

L. G. Glasser, A. H. McKinney, C. D. Reilly and P. D. Schnelle, "Cube-Root Color Coordinate System," *J. Opt. Soc. Am.*, **48**, 736–740 (1958).

Godlove 1933

I. H. Godlove, "Neutral Value Scales. II. A Comparison of Results and Equations Describing Value Scales," *J. Opt. Soc. Am.*, **23**, 419–425 (1933).

*Godlove 1957

I. H. Godlove, *Bibliography on Color*, Inter-Society Color Council, Rochester, New York, 1957.

Goodwin 1955

W. J. Goodwin, "Measurement and Specification of

Color and Small Color Differences," *Mod. Plastics*, **32**, No. 10, 143–146, 235, 239–240, 245, 248 (June 1955).

*Granville 1944

Walter C. Granville and Egbert Jacobson, "Colorimetric Specification of the *Color Harmony Manual* from Spectrophotometric Measurements," *J. Opt. Soc. Am.*, **34**, 382–395 (1944).

*Granville 1956

W. C. Granville, "Survey of American Color Specifications—1955," *Official Digest*, 902–921 (1956).

Grassmann 1853

H. Grassmann, "Zur Theorie der Farbenmischung," *Ann. der Physik und Chemie*, **89**, 69–84 (1853); Prof. (H.) Grassmann, "On the Theory of Compound Colors," *The London, Edinburgh and Dublin Philosophical Mag. and J. Sci.*, **7[4]**, 254–264 (1854).

Gugerli 1963

U. Gugerli and P. Buchner, "The Gradient Method—A Contribution to Metameric Colour Formulation on the Basis of Colour-difference Measurements," *J. Soc. Dyers Colourists*, **79**, 637–650 (1963).

Guthrie 1957

J. C. Guthrie and P. H. Oliver, "Application of Colour Physics to Textiles," *J. Soc. Dyers Colourists*, **73**, 533–542 (1957).

*Guthrie 1962

J. C. Guthrie, Miss J. Moir and P. H. Oliver, "Two Problems Associated with the Blending of Coloured Fibres," *J. Soc. Dyers Colourists*, **78**, 27–34 (1962).

Hackh 1944

Hackh's Chemical Dictionary, 3rd Edition, revised and edited by Julius Grant, McGraw-Hill, New York, 1944.

Halsey 1959a

Rita M. Halsey, "Identification of Signal Lights. I. Blue, Green, White, and Purple," *J. Opt. Soc. Am.*, **49**, 45–55 (1959).

Halsey 1959b

Rita M. Halsey, "Identification of Signal Lights. II. Elimination of the Purple Category," *J. Opt. Soc. Am.*, **49**, 167–169 (1959).

*Hardy 1935

Arthur C. Hardy, "A New Recording Spectrophotometer," *J. Opt. Soc. Am.*, **25**, 305–311 (1935).

*Hardy 1936

Arthur C. Hardy, *Handbook of Colorimetry*, The Technology Press, Cambridge, Mass., 1936.

*Hardy 1938

Arthur C. Hardy, "History of the Design of the Recording Spectrophotometer," *J. Opt. Soc. Am.*, **28**, 360–364 (1938).

Harkins 1959

T. R. Harkins, Jr., J. T. Harris and O. D. Shreve, "Identification of Pigments in Paints by Infrared Spectroscopy," *Anal. Chem.*, **31**, 541–545 (1959).

*Helson 1956

Harry Helson, Deane B. Judd and Martha Wilson, "Color Rendition with Fluorescent Sources of Illumination," *Illuminating Engr.*, **51**, 329–346 (1956).

Herzog 1965

H. Herzog and J. Koszticza, "The Influence of Resin Finishing on the Shade and the Fastness to Light of Naphtanilide Dyed Piece Goods," *Am. Dyestuff Reptr.*, **54**, 34–38 (1965).

Hodgins 1946

Eric Hodgins, *Mr. Blandings Builds His Dream House*, Simon & Schuster, New York, 1946.

Huey 1956

Sam J. Huey, "Use of Gardner Color Difference Meter for Production Control of Shading Operations," *Official Digest*, **28**, 1285–1293 (1956).

*Hunter 1942

Richard S. Hunter, *Photoelectric Tristimulus Colorimetry with Three Filters*, NBS Circular 429, U.S. Government Printing Office, 1942. Reprinted in *J. Opt. Soc. Am.*, **32**, 509–538 (1942).

*Hunter 1958a

Richard S. Hunter, "Description and Measurement of White Surfaces," *J. Opt. Soc. Am.*, **48**, 597–605 (1958).

*Hunter 1958b

Richard S. Hunter, "Photoelectric Color Difference Meter," *J. Opt. Soc. Am.*, **48**, 985–995 (1958).

*Hunter 1963a

Richard S. Hunter, "Measurement of the Appearance of Paint Finishes," *Official Digest*, **35**, 350–366 (1963).

Hunter 1963b

Richard S. Hunter, "Those Other Aspects of Appearance," *Color Engineering*, **1**, No. 2, 8–14 (June 1963).

*IES 1966

IES Lighting Handbook, Illuminating Engineering Society, New York, 1966.

Ingle 1947

George W. Ingle, "Using 3 Dimensions of color in plastics," *Mod. Plastics*, **24**, No. 9, 131–133 (May 1947).

Ingle 1962

George W. Ingle, Frederick D. Stockton and Henry Hemmendinger, "Analytic Comparison of Color-Difference Equations," *J. Opt. Soc. Am.*, **52**, 1075–1077 (1962).

Interchem 1965

The Color Tree, Interchemical Corporation, New York, 1965.

*IPI 1962

IPI Color Finder, Printing Ink Division, Interchemical Corporation, New York, 1962.

*Jacobson 1948

Egbert Jacobson, *Basic Color: An Interpretation of the Ostwald Color System*, Paul Theobald, Chicago, Illinois, 1948.

*Jenkins 1957

F. A. Jenkins and H. E. White, *Fundamentals of Optics*, 3rd Ed., McGraw-Hill, New York, 1957.

Johnson 1963

Sheila Johnson, D. H. Phillips, A. R. Robertson and W. D. Wright, "High-accuracy Colorimetry—A Review of Some Recent Work," *J. Soc. Dyers Colourists*, **79**, 731–739 (1963).

*Johnston 1963

Ruth M. Johnston, "Pitfalls in Color Specifications," *Official Digest*, **35**, 259–274 (1963).

Johnston 1964a

R. M. Johnston and R. E. Park, "Coloring of Unsaturated Polyester Resin Laminates and Gel Coats," *SPE J.*, **20**, 1211–1217 (1964).

*Johnston 1964b

Ruth M. Johnston and Robert P. Ericson, "Control of Color Standards," *Color Engineering*, **2**, No. 11–12, 10–13, 23 (Nov.–Dec., 1964).

Johnston 1965a

Ruth Johnston, "Analysis and Description of Color with Spectrophotometry," *Color Engineering*, **3**, No. 3, 12–14, 16–18, 25 (May–June, 1965).

Johnston 1965b

Ruth Johnston, "Selecting and Training Color Matchers for a Computer Color Control Program," *Color Engineering*, **3**, No. 6, 20–21 (Nov.–Dec., 1965).

*Judd 1933

Deane B. Judd, "The 1931 I.C.I. Standard Observer and Coordinate System for Colorimetry," *J. Opt. Soc. Am.*, **23**, 359–374 (1933).

Judd 1935

Deane B. Judd, "A Maxwell Triangle Yielding Uniform Chromaticity Scales," *J. Opt. Soc. Am.*, **25**, 24–35 (1935).

*Judd 1950

Deane B. Judd, *Colorimetry*, NBS Circular 478, U.S. Government Printing Office, 1950.

Judd 1952

Deane B. Judd, *Color in Business, Science, and Industry*, first edition. Wiley, New York, 1952.

Judd 1961

Deane B. Judd, *A Five-Attribute System of Describing Visual Appearance*, ASTM Special Technical Publication No. 297, American Society for Testing and Materials, Philadelphia, Pa., 1961.

Judd 1962a

Deane B. Judd, G. J. Chamberlin and Geraldine W. Haupt, "The Ideal Lovibond System," *J. Res. Natl. Bur. Std.*, **66C,** 121–136 (1962).

*Judd 1962b

Deane B. Judd, G. J. Chamberlin and Geraldine W. Haupt, "Ideal Lovibond Color System," *J. Opt. Soc. Am.*, **52,** 813–819 (1962).

*Judd 1963

Deane B. Judd and Günter Wyszecki, *Color in Business, Science and Industry*, 2nd Ed., Wiley, New York, 1963.

Judd 1964

Deane B. Judd, David L. MacAdam, and Günter Wyszecki (with the collaboration of H. W. Budde, H. R. Condit, S. T. Henderson and J. L. Simonds), "Spectral Distribution of Typical Daylight as a Function of Correlated Color Temperature," *J. Opt. Soc. Am.*, **54,** 1031–1040, 1382 (1964).

Keegan 1944

Harry J. Keegan and Kasson S. Gibson, "On the Use of Working Standards of Didymium and Vitrolite Glasses for Spectrophotometric Measurements," *J. Opt. Soc. Am.*, **34,** 770 (1944) (abstract of paper).

*Keegan 1962

Harry J. Keegan, John C. Schleter and Deane B. Judd, "Glass Filters for Checking Performance of Spectrophotometer–Integrator Systems of Color Measurement," *J. Res. Natl. Bur. Std.*, **66A,** 203–221 (1962).

*Kelly 1943

Kenneth L. Kelly, Kasson S. Gibson and Dorothy Nickerson, "Tristimulus Specification of the *Munsell Book of Color* from Spectrophotometric Measurements," *J. Opt. Soc. Am.*, **33,** 355–376 (1943).

*Kelly 1955

Kenneth L. Kelly and Deane B. Judd, *The ISCC–NBS Method of Designating Colors and a Dictionary of Color Names*, NBS Circular 553, U.S. Government Printing Office, 1955.

Kelly 1958

Kenneth L. Kelly, "Centroid Notations for the Revised ISCC–NBS Color-Name Blocks," *J. Res. Natl. Bur. Std.*, **61,** 427–431 (1958).

Kelly 1962

Kenneth L. Kelly, "Coordinated Color Identifications for Industry," *NBS Tech. Note 152*, U.S. Government Printing Office, Washington, D.C., 1962.

Kelly 1965

Kenneth L. Kelly, "A Universal Color Language," *Color Engineering*, **3,** No. 2, 16–21 (March–April, 1965).

*Kodak 1962

Kodak Color Data Book E–74, *Color as Seen and Photographed*, Eastman Kodak Co., Rochester, New York, 1962.

Kodak 1965

Eastman Kodak Co., Rochester, New York, "Uncertainty Searching," [advertisement appearing in *Science*, **149,** 809 (1965) and elsewhere].

*Kornerup 1962

A. Kornerup and J. H. Wanscher, *Reinhold Color Atlas*, Reinhold, New York, 1962.

Kubelka 1931

Paul Kubelka and Franz Munk, "Ein Beitrag zur Optik der Farbanstriche," *Z. tech. Physik.*, **12,** 593–601 (1931) (in German).

Kubelka 1948

Paul Kubelka, "New Contributions to the Optics of Intensely Light-Scattering Materials. Part I," *J. Opt. Soc. Am.*, **38,** 448–457, 1067 (1948).

Kubelka 1954

Paul Kubelka, "New Contributions to the Optics of Intensely Light-Scattering Materials. Part II. Non-homogeneous Layers," *J. Opt. Soc. Am.*, **44,** 330–355 (1954).

Lange 1960

Heinz E. Lange, "The 'Color Analyzer' and its Applications in the Ink Industry," *Am. Ink Maker*, **38,** 60–64, 67, 68, 137 (1960).

*Le Grand 1957

Yves Le Grand, *Light, Colour, and Vision* (translated by R. W. G. Hunt, J. W. T. Walsh, and F. R. W. Hunt), Wiley, New York, 1957.

Lenoir 1959–63

J. Lenoir, *Les Pigments Organiques*. (Translated titles follow): "Origins, terminology, classification," *Peintures, Pigments, Vernis*, **35,** 303–310 (1959); Part 1, "Acetoacetanilide Azoics," *ibid.*, pp. 442–452; Part 2, "Pyrazolone Azoics," *ibid.*, pp. 612–619; Part 3, "Beta-Naphthol Azoics," *ibid.*, **36,** 144–157 (1960);

Part 4, "Azoics of Beta-Hydroxy Naphthoic Acid (BON)," *ibid.*, pp. 388–395; Part 5, "Azoics of Arylides of BON," *ibid.*, pp. 700–715; Part 6, "Naphthol Sulfonic Acid Azo Compounds," *ibid.*, **37**, 331–341 (1961); Part 7, "Phthalocyanines," *ibid.*, **38**, 5–20 (1962); Part 8, "Anthraquinone and Indigoid Pigments," *ibid.*, pp. 384–404; Part 9, "Triphenylmethane and related (types of) pigments," *ibid.*, **39**, 68–89 (1963); Part 10 (conclusion), "Miscellaneous Pigments," *ibid.*, pp. 536–550 (in French).

*Little 1963

Angela C. Little, "Evaluation of Single-Number Expressions of Color Difference," *J. Opt. Soc. Am.*, **53**, 293–296 (1963).

*Lubs 1955

H. A. Lubs (ed.), *The Chemistry of Synthetic Dyes and Pigments*, Reinhold, New York, 1955.

*MacAdam 1935

David L. MacAdam, "Maximum Visual Efficiency of Colored Materials," *J. Opt. Soc. Am.*, **25**, 361–367 (1935).

MacAdam 1937

David L. MacAdam, "Projective Transformations of the I.C.I. Color Specifications," *J. Opt. Soc. Am.*, **27**, 294–299 (1937).

*MacAdam 1942

David L. MacAdam, "Visual Sensitivities to Color Differences in Daylight," *J. Opt. Soc. Am.*, **32**, 247–274 (1942).

*MacAdam 1943

David L. MacAdam, "Specification of Small Chromaticity Differences," *J. Opt. Soc. Am.*, **33**, 18–26 (1943).

*MacAdam 1957

David L. MacAdam, "Analytical Approximations for Color Metric Coefficients," *J. Opt. Soc. Am.*, **47**, 268–274 (1957).

*MacAdam 1965

David L. MacAdam, "Color Measurement and Tolerances," *Official Digest*, **37**, 1487–1531 (1965); errata, *J. Paint Technol.*, **38**, 70 (1966).

*Mackinney 1962

Gordon Mackinney and Angela C. Little, *Color of Foods*, AVI Publishing Co., Westport, Connecticut, 1962.

Maerz 1930

A. Maerz and M. Rea Paul, *A Dictionary of Color*, McGraw-Hill, New York, 1930.

Marsh 1964

J. S. Marsh and D. A. Plant, "Instrumental Colour-match Prediction Using Organic Pigments," *J. Oil Colour Chem. Assoc.*, **47**, 554–575 (1964).

Mattiello 1942

Joseph J. Mattiello, editor, *Protective and Decorative Coatings*, vol. II, Wiley, 1942.

McCarley 1965

J. E. McCarley, C. E. Green and K. H. Horowitz, "Digital System for Converting Spectral Data to CIE Coordinates, Dominant Wavelength and Excitation Purity," *J. Opt. Soc. Am.*, **55**, 355–360 (1965).

McLaren 1965

K. McLaren, "Colour-Matching Lamps," *J. Soc. Dyers Colourists*, **81**, 269–270 (1965).

McNicholas 1928

H. J. McNicholas, "Equipment for Routine Spectral Transmission and Reflectance Measurements," *J. Res. Natl. Bur. Std.*, **1**, 793–857 (1928).

*Mellon 1950

M. G. Mellon, editor, *Analytical Absorption Spectroscopy*, Wiley, New York, 1950.

*Michaelson 1938

J. L. Michaelson, "Construction of the General Electric Recording Spectrophotometer," *J. Opt. Soc. Am.*, **28**, 365–371 (1938).

*Middleton 1953

W. E. Knowles Middleton, "Comparison of Colorimetric Results from a Normal-Diffuse Spectrophotometer with those from a 45-Degree-Normal Colorimeter for Semiglossy Specimens," *J. Opt. Soc. Am.*, **43**, 1141–1143 (1953).

*Miller 1963

Miss A. Miller, Miss J. Moir, J. C. Guthrie and P. H. Oliver, "A Computed Catalogue of Fibre Blends and its Use in Match Prediction," *J. Soc. Dyers Colourists*, **79**, 604–612 (1963).

Mitton 1958

Parker B. Mitton and Lawrence S. White, "Pigment Optical Behavior Evaluation on a Physical Basis," *Official Digest*, **30**, 1259–1276 (1958).

Moll 1960

I. S. Moll, "Aspects of Pigment Dispersion Related to Usage," *J. Soc. Dyers Colourists*, **76**, 141–150 (1960).

Moon 1943

Parry Moon and Domina Eberle Spencer, "A Metric for Colorspace," *J. Opt. Soc. Am.*, **33**, 260–269 (1943); "A Metric Based on the Composite Color Stimulus," *ibid.*, pp. 270–277.

*Morse 1956

Mark P. Morse, "Color Measurement with the General Electric Spectrophotometer," *Official Digest,* **28,** 1278–1285 (1956).

*Mudd 1957

J. S. Mudd, "Precise Measurement of Fading on a Time-Intensity Basis," *J. Soc. Dyers Colourists,* **73,** 47–52 (1957).

*Munsell 1929

Munsell Book of Color, Munsell Color Co., Baltimore, Maryland, 1929–1966.

Munsell 1933

A. E. O. Munsell, L. L. Sloan and I. H. Godlove, "Neutral Value Scales I. Munsell Neutral Value Scale," *J. Opt. Soc. Am.,* **23,** 394–411 (1933).

*Munsell 1962

Munsell Color Standards for Plastic Insulated Wire and Cable, 2nd Ed., Munsell Color Co., Baltimore, Maryland, 1962.

*Munsell 1963

A. H. Munsell, *A Color Notation,* Munsell Color Co., Baltimore, Maryland, 1936–1963.

NBS 1939

"Preparation and Colorimetric Properties of a Magnesium-Oxide Reflectance Standard," NBS Letter Circular LC-547, U.S. Government Printing Office, 1939.

NBS 1955

"Standards for Checking the Calibration of Spectrophotometers (200 to 1,000 mμ)," NBS Letter Circular LC-1017, U.S. Government Printing Office, 1955.

NBS 1965

ISCC–NBS Color-Name Charts Illustrated with Centroid Colors, Standard Sample No. 2106, Supplement to NBS Circular 553, National Bureau of Standards, Washington, D.C., 1965.

*Newhall 1943

Sidney M. Newhall, Dorothy Nickerson and Deane B. Judd, "Final Report of the O.S.A. Subcommittee on the Spacing of the Munsell Colors," *J. Opt. Soc. Am.,* **33,** 385–418 (1943).

*Newhall 1957

S. M. Newhall, R. W. Burnham, and Joyce R. Clark, "Comparison of Successive with Simultaneous Color Matching," *J. Opt. Soc. Am.,* **47,** 43–56 (1957).

*Newton 1730

Sir Isaac Newton, *OPTICKS, or a Treatise of the Reflections, Refractions, Inflections & Colours of Light,* (Reprint based on the 4th Ed., London 1730), Dover Publications, New York, 1952.

Nickerson 1935

Dorothy Nickerson, "Disk Colorimetry; Including a Comparison of Methods for Computing Tristimulus Values for Certain Disks," *J. Opt. Soc. Am.,* **25,** 253–257 (1935).

Nickerson 1936

Dorothy Nickerson, "The Specification of Color Tolerances," *Textile Res.,* **6,** 505–514 (1936).

*Nickerson 1940

Dorothy Nickerson, "History of the Munsell Color System and its Scientific Application," *J. Opt. Soc. Am.,* **30,** 575–586 (1940).

*Nickerson 1943

Dorothy Nickerson and Sidney M. Newhall, "A Psychological Color Solid," *J. Opt. Soc. Am.,* **33,** 419–422 (1943).

*Nickerson 1944

Dorothy Nickerson and Keith F. Stultz, "Color Tolerance Specification," *J. Opt. Soc. Am.,* **34,** 550–570 (1944).

Nickerson 1950

Dorothy Nickerson, "Tables for Use in Computing Small Color Differences," *Am. Dyestuff Reptr.,* **39,** 541–549 (1950).

*Nickerson 1957

Dorothy Nickerson, *Color Measurement and Its Application to the Grading of Agricultural Products,* U.S. Dept. of Agriculture Misc. Publ. 580, U.S. Government Printing Office, 1957.

*Nickerson 1960

Dorothy Nickerson, "Light Sources and Color Rendering," *J. Opt. Soc. Am.,* **50,** 57–69 (1960).

Nill 1963

Martin W. Nill, "The Recording Spectrophotometer as a Tool in Paper Mill Color Work," *Tappi,* **46,** No. 1, 133A–136A (Jan. 1963).

Nimeroff 1962

I. Nimeroff, Joan R. Rosenblatt and Mary C. Dannemiller, "Variability of Spectral Tristimulus Values," *J. Opt. Soc. Am.,* **52,** 685–691 (1962).

Nimeroff 1964a

I. Nimeroff, "Field Trial of the 1959 CIE Supplementary Standard Observer Proposal," *J. Opt. Soc. Am.,* **54,** 696–704 (1964).

Nimeroff 1964b

Isadore Nimeroff, "Spectral Tristimulus Values for the CIE (u,v,w) Uniform Spacing System," *J. Opt. Soc. Am.,* **54,** 1365–1367 (1964).

*NPVLA

F. Scofield, editor, *Raw Materials Index,* National Paint, Varnish, and Lacquer Association, Washington, D.C., irregular.

Oehlcke 1954

C. R. M. Oehlcke, "The Use of Organic Colouring Matters in Plastics," *J. Soc. Dyers Colourists*, **70**, 137–145 (1954).

*OSA 1953

Optical Society of America, Committee on Colorimetry, *The Science of Color*, Thomas Y. Crowell Co., New York 1953. Reprinted by the Optical Society of America, 1963.

Ostwald 1931

Wilhelm Ostwald, *Colour Science* (Authorized Translation with an Introduction and Notes by J. Scott Taylor). Part 1, "Colour Theory and Colour Standardization" (1931); Part II, "Applied Colour Science" (1933); Winsor and Newton, Ltd., London, England.

Park 1944

R. H. Park and E. I. Stearns, "Spectrophotometric Formulation," *J. Opt. Soc. Am.*, **34**, 112–113 (1944).

Payne 1961

Henry Fleming Payne, *Organic Coatings Technology*, Vol. II, *Pigments and Pigmented Coatings*, Wiley, New York, 1961.

*Peacock 1953

W. H. Peacock, *The Practical Art of Color Matching*, American Cyanamid Co.; Bound Brook, New Jersey, 1953.

Pivovonski 1961

Mark Pivovonski and Max R. Nagel, *Tables of Blackbody Radiation Functions*, Macmillan, New York, 1961.

Plant 1962

D. A. Plant and D. M. Varley, "The Constitution, Properties, and Applications of Organic Pigments," Chap. 7, pp. 174–200, in *The Science of Surface Coatings*, H. W. Chatfield, editor, Ernest Benn, Ltd., London, England, 1962.

Preston 1965

C. Preston and David Tough, "Automated Shade Matching," *Color Engineering*, **3**, No. 3, 19–25 (May-June, 1965).

Priest 1920

I. G. Priest, K. S. Gibson, and H. J. McNicholas, "An Examination of the Munsell Color System. I. Spectral and Total Reflection and the Munsell Scale of Value," *Technologic Papers of the Bureau of Standards* No. 167, Washington, D.C., 1920.

Priest 1935

Irwin G. Priest, "The Priest-Lange Reflectometer Applied to Nearly White Porcelain Enamels," *J. Res. Natl. Bur. Std.*, **15**, 529–550 (1935).

Pritchard 1952

B. S. Pritchard and E. I. Stearns, "Dye Control with the *R*-Cam and Ruler," *J. Opt. Soc. Am.*, **42**, 752–753 (1952); **73**, 212 (1953).

*Pritchard 1955

B. S. Pritchard and W. A. Holmwood, "New Recording Spectrophotometer," *J. Opt. Soc. Am.*, **45**, 690–695 (1955).

*Pugh 1956

Norman R. Pugh, "An Application of the Beckman Model DU Spectrophotometer to Paint Color Control," *Official Digest*, **28**, 1302–1309 (1956).

Pugin 1965

Andre Pugin, "The Influence of Chemical Structure on the Color and Properties of Dioxazine Pigments," *Official Digest*, **37**, 782–802 (1965).

Rattee 1965

I. D. Rattee, "Discovery or Invention?" *J. Soc. Dyers Colourists*, **81**, 145–150 (1965).

*Richmond 1959

Joseph C. Richmond and William N. Harrison, "Evaluation of Small Color Differences: I. Visual Observations," *Bull. Am. Ceramic Soc.*, **38**, 292–300 (1959).

Richter 1955

Manfred Richter, "The Official German Standard Color Chart," *J. Opt. Soc. Am.*, **45**, 223–226 (1955).

Ridgway 1912

Robert Ridgway, *Color Standards and Color Nomenclature*, published by the author, Washington, D.C., 1912.

*Robertson 1965

A. R. Robertson and W. D. Wright, "An International Comparison of Working Standards for Colorimetry," *J. Opt. Soc. Am.*, **55**, 694–706 (1965).

Rood 1961

Joseph L. Rood, "Color Measurement with the Bausch and Lomb Spectronic 505," *Farbe*, **10**, 105–114 (1962).

Rösch 1929

Siegfried Rösch, "Darstellung der Farbenlehre für die Zwecke des Mineralogen," *Fortsch. der Mineralogie, Kristallographie, und Petrographie*, **13**, 73–234 (1929) (in German).

Rushton 1962

W. A. H. Rushton, *Visual Pigments in Man*, Liverpool Univ. Press, 1962. See also W. A. H. Rushton, "Visual Pigments in Man," *Sci. Am.*, **207**, No. 5, 120–123, 125, 126, 128–130, 132 (November 1962).

*Saltzman 1959

Max Saltzman, "Color Matching via Pigment Identification," *Dyestuffs*, **43**, 57–65 (1959).

*Saltzman 1963a

Max Saltzman, "Colored Organic Pigments: Why So Many? Why So Few?" *Official Digest,* **35,** 245–258 (1963).

Saltzman 1963b

Max Saltzman, "Color as an Engineering Material," *SPE J.,* **19,** 476–479 (1963).

Saltzman 1965

Max Saltzman and A. M. Keay, "Variables in the Measurement of Color Samples," *Color Engineering,* **3,** No. 5, 14–19 (Sept.–Oct., 1965).

*Saunderson 1942

J. L. Saunderson, "Calculation of the Color of Pigmented Plastics," *J. Opt. Soc. Am.,* **32,** 727–736 (1942).

Saunderson 1946

J. L. Saunderson and B. I. Milner, "Modified Chromatic Value Color Space," *J. Opt. Soc. Am.,* **36,** 36–42 (1946).

Schofield 1939

R. K. Schofield, "The Lovibond Tintometer Adapted by Means of the Rothamsted Device to Measure Colours of the C.I.E. System," *J. Sci. Inst.,* **16,** 74–80 (1939).

Schultz 1931

Ludwig Lehmann, *Farbstofftabellen von Gustav Schultz,* 7th Ed., Akademische Verlagsgesellschaft M.B.H., Leipzig, Vol. I, 1931, Supplement 1934; Vol. II, 1932; Supplement 1939 (in German).

*SDC 1956

Society of Dyers and Colourists and American Association of Textile Chemists and Colorists, *Colour Index,* 2nd Ed., 1956; Supplement, 1963.

*Simon 1958

F. T. Simon and W. J. Goodwin, "Rapid Graphical Computation of Small Color Differences," *Am. Dyestuff Reptr.,* **47,** No. 4, 105–112 (Feb. 1958).

Simon 1961

Frederick T. Simon, "Small Color Difference Computation and Control," *Farbe,* **10,** 225–234 (1961).

Simpson 1962–3

J. E. Simpson, "Color in Plastics is Everybody's Business," (Part I of a series). *Mod. Plastics,* **40,** No. 1, 84–87 (Sept. 1962); "Choosing the Right Coloring Method," (Part II), *ibid.,* No. 3, 94–97, 202, 204–206 (Nov. 1962); "How to Choose the Right Colorant for the Right Resin," (Part III), *ibid.,* No. 4, 90–93, 175–176, 179, 182 (Dec. 1962); "Know Your Colorant Characteristics," (Part IV), *ibid.,* No. 7, 88–91, 199, 201–2, 204–5, 209–10 (March 1963); "Coloring Thermoplastic Resins," (Part V), *ibid.,* No. 9, 107–110, 184, 187–188, 190, 192–194, 196, 198 (May 1963); "Coloring Thermosetting Resins," (Part VI), *ibid.,* No. 10, 89–92, 162, 165–166, 168–169 (June 1963). (Reprinted as *Coloring Plastics,* by Color Division, Ferro Corporation, Cleveland, Ohio, 1963.)

*Smith 1954

F. M. Smith and D. M. Stead, "The Meaning and Assessment of Light Fastness in Relation to Pigments," *J. Oil Colour Chem. Assoc.,* **37,** 117–130 (1954).

Smith 1962

F. M. Smith, "An Introduction to Organic Pigments," *J. Soc. Dyers Colourists,* **78,** 222–231 (1962).

Smith 1963

Daniel Smith, "Visual Color Evaluation: Lighting and the Observer," *Am. Dyestuff Reptr.,* **53,** P207–P209, P213 (1963).

*Southall 1937

James P. C. Southall, *Introduction to Physiological Optics,* (Reprint based on the 1937 Ed., Oxford). Dover Publications, New York, 1961.

Stearns 1944

E. I. Stearns, "Spectrophotometry and the Colorist," *Am. Dyestuff Reptr.,* **33,** 1–6, 16–20 (1944).

*Stiles 1962

W. S. Stiles and G. Wyszecki, "Field Trials of Color-Mixture Functions," *J. Opt. Soc. Am.,* **52,** 58–75 (1962).

*Teevan 1961

Richard C. Teevan and Robert C. Birney, *Color Vision (An Enduring Problem in Psychology: Selected Readings),* D. Van Nostrand Co., Princeton, New Jersey, 1961.

*Thurner 1965

Karl Thurner, *Colorimetry in Textile Dyeing—Theory and Practice,* Badische Anilin & Soda Fabrik AG, Ludwigshafen am Rhein, Germany, 1965.

*Tilleard 1957

D. L. Tilleard, "Tolerances in Colour Matching," *J. Oil Colour Chem. Assoc.,* **40,** 952–975 (1957).

*Tilleard 1963a

D. L. Tilleard, "Colour Systems and Colour Atlases," *Rev. Current Lit.,* **36,** 931–940 (1963).

*Tilleard 1963b

Miss D. L. Tilleard, "Some Applications of the Davidson and Hemmendinger Colorant Mixture Computer to Paints and Plastics," *J. Soc. Dyers Colourists,* **79,** 590–600 (1963).

*Tilleard 1964

D. L. Tilleard, "Evaluation of Small Colour Differences and Tolerances in Colour Matching," *Rev. Current Lit.*, **37**, 143–153 (1964).

Traub 1961

Alan C. Traub and Isay Balinkin, "Proximity Factor in the Judd Color Difference Formula," *J. Opt. Soc. Am.*, **51**, 755–760 (1961).

*Tuttle 1956

Henry A. Tuttle and Melvin M. Gerson, "An Application of the 'Colormaster' Differential Colorimeter for Control and Evaluation of Maintenance Paints," *Official Digest*, **28**, 1310–1318 (1956).

Van den Akker 1937

J. A. Van den Akker, "Chromaticity Limitations of the Best Physically Realizable Three-Filter Photoelectric Colorimeter," *J. Opt. Soc. Am.*, **27**, 401–407 (1937).

Venkataraman 1952

K. Venkataraman, *The Chemistry of Synthetic Dyes*, Academic Press, New York, 1952.

*Vesce 1956

Vincent C. Vesce, "Vivid Light Fast Organic Pigments," *Official Digest*, **28**, Part 2, 1–48 (1956).

*Vesce 1959

Vincent C. Vesce, "Exposure Studies of Organic Pigments in Paint Systems," *Official Digest*, **31**, Part 2, 1–143 (1959).

*Vickerstaff 1949

T. Vickerstaff and D. Tough, "The Quantitative Measure of Lightfastness," *J. Soc. Dyers Colourists*, **65**, 606–612 (1949).

Völz 1962

Hans G. Völz, "Ein Beitrag zur phänomenologischen Theorie licht-streuender und -absorbierender Medien," *Congrès FATIPEC* **VI**, 98–103, (1962) (in German).

Völz 1964

Hans G. Völz, "Ein Beitrag zur phänomenologischen Theorie licht-streuender und -absorbierender Medien. Teil II; Möglichkeiten zur experimentellen Bestimmung der Konstanten," *Congrès FATIPEC* **VII**, 194–201 (1964) (in German).

Wald 1964

George Wald, "The Receptors of Human Color Vision," *Science*, **145**, 1007–1016 (4 September 1964).

Walton 1959

William W. Walton and James I. Hoffman, "Principles and Methods of Sampling," Chap. 4 in *Treatise on Analytical Chemistry*, I. M. Kolthoff, Philip J.

Elving and Ernest B. Sandell, eds., Interscience, New York, 1959, Part I, Vol. 1, pp. 67–97.

Webster 1961

Webster's Third New International Dictionary—Unabridged, G. and C. Merriam Co., Springfield, Mass., 1961.

Wegmann 1960

J. Wegmann, "Effect of Structure on the Change in Colour of Vat Dyes on Soaping," *J. Soc. Dyers Colourists*, **76**, 282–300 (1960).

White 1960

G. S. J. White, "How Much Research? A Critical Problem in the Manufacture of Textile Dyes," *J. Soc. Dyers Colourists*, **76**, 16–22 (1960).

Wood 1917

Robert William Wood, *How to Tell the Birds from the Flowers and Other Woodcuts*, (Reprint of the original edition, Dodd, Mead and Co., New York, 1917). Dover Publications, New York, 1959.

*Wright 1959

W. D. Wright, "Color Standards in Commerce and Industry," *J. Opt. Soc. Am.*, **49**, 384–388 (1959).

*Wright 1961

W. D. Wright, "Colour and its Measurement; Instrumental Methods of Colour Measurement; Colour Theory and Measurement Applied to the Textile and Dyeing Industries; Bibliography," *CIBA Review*, 1961/2, 2–34 (1961).

*Wright 1964

W. D. Wright, *The Measurement of Colour*, 3rd edition, D. Van Nostrand Co., New York, 1964.

Wurzburg 1963a

F. L. Wurzburg, Jr., "Survey of Instruments for Color Specification," *Tappi*, **46**, No. 7, 155A–159A (July, 1963).

Wurzburg 1963b

F. L. Wurzburg, Jr., "Instrumental Color Specifications in the Graphic Arts," *Color Engineering*, **1**, No. 4, 20–22 (December 1963).

Wyszecki 1960

G. Wyszecki, *Farbsysteme*, Musterschmidt Verlag, Berlin, Germany, 1960 (in German).

Wyszecki 1963

Günter Wyszecki, "Proposal for a New Color-Difference Formula," *J. Opt. Soc. Am.*, **53**, 1318–1319 (1963).

Wyszecki 1965

G. Wyszecki and H. Wright, "Field Trial of the 1964 CIE Color-Difference Formula," *J. Opt. Soc. Am.*, **55**, 1166–1174 (1965).

AUTHOR INDEX*

Abbott, R., 113, 155–157
Adams, E. Q., 49, 85, 150, 154
Adams, J. M., 152
Alderson, J. V., 111, 122, 123, 143, 156
Allen, E., 122, 143, 153, 157
American Association of Textile Chemists and Colorists, 95, 97, 100, 136, 148, 149, 155
American Dyestuff Reporter, 148
American Society for Testing and Materials, 51, 52, 57, 77, 150, 152, 154, 158
Ames, A., Jr., 2
Apps, E. A., 155
Atherton, E., 111 (Alderson 1961), 122 (Alderson 1961), 123 (Alderson 1961), 133, 134, 143, 155, 156
Atkins, J. T., 111 (Beasley 1965), 143 (Beasley 1965)

Babey, M. J., 156
Balinkin, I. A., 84, 154
Bartleson, C. J., 89, 146, 149
Bassemir, R. W., 72, 80
Beasley, J. K., 49 (Billmeyer 1961), 110 (Billmeyer 1960a), 111, 122 (Billmeyer 1960a), 143, 157
Bednar, W. A., 125
Berger, A., 127, 146
Billmeyer, F. W., Jr., 42, 45, 49, 51, 57, 70, 71, 77, 79, 82, 85, 86 (Blackwood 1966), 108, 110, 111 (Beasley 1965), 122, 141, 143 (Beasley 1965), 152, 154, 157
Birney, R. C., 148
Blackwood, N. K., 86, 141
Breckenridge, F. C., 46
Brockes, A., 75, 127 (Berger 1964), 146
Brown, M. W., 146
Brown, W. R. J., 58, 154, 155, 158
Buc, G. L., 85

Buchmann-Olsen, B., 67
Buchner, P., 122 (Gugerli 1963)
Budde, H. W., 5 (Judd 1964), 137 (Judd 1964)
Bunkall, P. R., 143
Burnham, R. W., 46, 54 (Newhall 1957), 146, 149, 150

Carr, W., 100, 136
Carroll, C. W., 152
Carroll, Lewis, 94
Chabot, G. B., Sr., 156
Chamberlin, G. J., 26 (Judd 1962a,b), 46, 62 (Judd 1962a,b), 150, 151
Chapanis, A., 28
Ciba Corporation, 12
Clark, J. R., 54 (Newhall 1957), 150
Color Engineering, 148
Colour Index, 95–97, 100, 136, 149
Condit, H. R., 5 (Judd 1964), 137 (Judd 1964)
Container Corporation of America, 30, 150
Cooke, D. E., 108
Coppock, W. A., 52
Cutter, J. O., 100, 136

Dalal, N., 127 (Berger 1964), 146
Dannemiller, M. C., 58 (Nimeroff 1962)
Davidson, H. R., 17, 28, 79, 84, 86, 87, 111, 112, 121, 150, 152, 154, 155, 157, 158
Davis, R., 38
Dearth, L. R., 67, 74
De Kerf, J. L. F., 79, 153
Derby, R. E., Jr., 118, 127
Derbyshire, A. N., 111 (Alderson 1961), 122 (Alderson 1961), 123 (Alderson 1961), 156
Donaldson, R., 62
Duncan, D. R., 111, 155, 157
Duntley, S. Q., 111

Eastman Kodak Co., 12, 108, 147
Ericson, R. P., 158
Evans, R. M., 3, 11, 17, 18, 23, 110, 146, 149

Fink, D. G., 108
Foote, P. V., 153
Foss, C. E., 30
Foster, R. S., 86, 11, 141
Franklin, S. G., 79
Friede, E., 84 (Davidson 1953), 86 (Davidson 1953), 87 (Davidson 1953), 158

Gabel, J. W., 77
Gaertner, H., 96, 142, 149, 156
Gerson, M. M., 73 (Tuttle 1956)
Gibson, K. S., 26 (Kelly 1943), 38 (Davis 1953), 51 (Priest 1920), 77 (Keegan 1944), 82, 153
Giles, C. H., 156
Glasser, L. G., 49, 51, 67, 73
Godlove, I. H., 17 (Davidson 1950), 51, 146
Godlove, M. N., 28 (Davidson 1957), 152
Goodwin, W. J., 86 (Simon 1958), 87 (Simon 1958), 128, 155
Grant, J., 20 (Hackh 1954)
Granville, W. C., 30, 151, 158
Grassmann, H., 8, 31, 32, 38, 65, 105
Green, C. E., 42 (McCarley 1965)
Gugerli, U., 122
Guthrie, J. C., 120 (Miller 1963), 157

Hackh's Chemical Dictionary, 20
Halsey, R. M., 60
Hanes, R. M., 146
Hanlon, J. J., 86 (Davidson 1955b), 154, 155, 158 (Davidson 1955b)
Hardy, A. C., 6, 40, 42, 77, 82, 142, 146
Harkins, T. R., 113
Harris, J. T., 113 (Harkins 1959)

*Except in Chapter 7, Annotated Bibliography, coauthors are not named in the text, but they are cited in this index. For example, the entry "Dannemiller, M. C., 58 (Nimeroff 1962)" means that M. C. Dannemiller is one of the coauthors whose work in referred to on page 58 by the words "Nimeroff 1962." The full citation may be found in the Bibliography (pages 161–172) under the citation "Nimeroff 1962."

Harrison, W. N., 158
Haupt, G. W., 26 (Judd 1962a,b), 38 (Davis 1953), 62 (Judd 1962a,b), 150 (Judd 1962a,b), 151
Helson, H., 150
Hemmendinger, H., 28 (Davidson 1957), 84 (Ingle 1962), 86 (Ingle 1962), 111 (Davidson 1963b), 112 (Davidson 1955a), 121 (Davidson 1963b), 150, 154, 157
Henderson, S. T., 5 (Judd 1964), 137 (Judd 1964)
Herzog, H., 100
Hodgins, E., 25
Hoffman, J. I., 55 (Walton 1959)
Holmwood, W. A., 82 (Pritchard 1955)
Horowitz, K. H., 42 (McCarley 1965)
Huey, S. J., 73
Hunter, R. S., 11, 46, 51, 52, 67–69, 72, 73, 84, 128, 150, 153, 154

Illuminating Engineering Society, 7, 146
Imm, L. W., 79 (Davidson 1949)
Ingle, G. W., 84, 86, 128, 154
Interchemical Corporation, 23
International Commission on Illumination, 6, 31, 33, 36, 38, 41, 137, 139–141
Inter-Society Color Council News Letter, 148
IPI Color Finder, 151

Jacobson, E., 30, 146, 147, 151
Jenkins, F. A., 147
Johnson, S., 153
Johnston, R. M., 57, 88, 116, 125, 142, 158
Journal of Paint Technology, 149
Journal of the Oil and Colour Chemists' Association, 149
Journal of the Optical Society of America, 149
Journal of the Society of Dyers and Colourists, 149
Judd, D. B., 3, 5, 11, 13 (Kelly 1955), 15, 25, 26, 28 (Kelly 1955; Newhall 1943), 31, 36, 40, 43, 46, 51 (Newhall 1943), 52, 62, 72, 77 (Keegan 1962), 80, 85, 111, 113, 137, 139, 140, 147, 150–153

Keay, A. M., 57 (Saltzman 1965), 88 (Saltzman 1965)
Keegan, H. J., 77, 82 (Gibson 1938)
Kelly, K. L., 13, 26, 28, 29, 59, 60, 88, 147, 150, 151
Koch, O., 75 (Brockes 1960)
Kornerup, A., 151
Koszticza, J., 100 (Herzog 1965)
Kubelka, P., 111, 158

Landry, J. L. R., Jr., 111 (Davidson 1963b), 121 (Davidson 1963b), 157
Lange, H. E., 82

Le Grand, Y., 147
Lehmann, L., 95 (Schultz 1931)
Lenoir, J., 100, 136
Little, A. C., 40 (Mackinney 1962), 77 (Mackinney 1962), 84, 85 (Mackinney 1962), 86, 147, 154
Lubs, H. A., 96, 147, 155
Luytens, D. M., 108 (Fink 1960)

MacAdam, D. L., 5 (Judd 1964), 42, 46, 85, 86, 127, 132, 137 (Judd 1964), 141, 150, 151, 154–156, 158
Mackinney, G., 40, 77, 84–86, 147, 155
Maerz, A., 26
Malach, R. J., 149
Marsh, J. S., 122
Mattiello, J. J., 96
McCarley, J. E., 42
McKay, R. B., 156
McKinney, A. H., 49 (Glasser 1958), 51 (Glasser 1958)
McLaren, K., 38
McNicholas, H. J., 51 (Priest 1920), 62
Mellon, M. G., 63, 147
Michaelson, J. L., 82
Middleton, W. E. K., 69, 153
Miller, A., 120, 157
Milner, B. I., 49 (Saunderson 1946), 152
Mitton, P. B., 11
Moir, J., 120 (Miller 1963), 157
Moll, I. S., 100, 133, 136
Moon, P., 49
Morse, M. P., 82
Mudd, J. S., 156
Munk, F., 111 (Kubelka 1931), 158 (Kubelka 1931)
Munsell, A. E. O., 51
Munsell, A. H., 147, 152
Munsell Book of Color, 26, 27, 150, 151, 157
Munsell Color Standards for Plastic Insulated Wire and Cable, 59, 151
Musgrave, C., 100 (Carr 1957), 136 (Carr 1957)

Nagel, M. R., 6 (Pivovonski 1961)
National Bureau of Standards, 28, 77, 147
National Paint, Varnish and Lacquer Association, 149, 155
Newhall, S. M., 28, 42 (Nickerson 1943), 51, 54, 150–152
Newton, Sir Isaac, 1, 4, 31, 65, 147
Nickerson, D., 26, 28 (Newhall 1943), 30 (Foss 1944), 42, 51 (Newhall 1943), 60, 79, 84–86, 150–153, 155, 158
Nill, M. W., 82
Nimeroff, I., 58, 140
North, F., 143 (Atherton 1965)

Oehlcke, C. R. M., 136
Oliver, P. H., 120 (Miller 1963), 157
Optical Society of America, 6, 7, 37, 40, 77, 148, 153
Ostwald, W., 30

Park, R. E., 88 (Johnston 1964a), 125 (Johnston 1964a)
Park, R. H., 122
Paul, M. R., 26 (Maerz 1930)
Payne, H. F., 96
Peacock, W. H., 57, 124, 148, 156
Peters, R. H., 133 (Atherton 1955), 134 (Atherton 1955), 155, 156
Phillips, D. H., 153 (Johnson 1963)
Pivovonski, M., 6
Plant, D. A., 100, 122 (Marsh 1964), 136
Preston, C., 122, 143
Priest, I. G., 51, 62
Pritchard, B. S., 82, 111, 118
Pugh, N. R., 82
Pugin, A., 142

Rattee, I. D., 143
Reilly, C. D., 49 (Glasser 1958), 51 (Glasser 1958)
Review of Current Literature on the Paint & Allied Industries, 149
Richmond, J. C., 158
Richter, M., 46
Ridgway, R., 26
Robertson, A. R., 153
Rood, J. L., 82
Rösch, S., 42
Rosenblatt, J. R., 58 (Nimeroff 1962)
Rushton, W. A. H., 12

Saltzman, M., 56, 57, 88, 113, 130, 134, 135, 155–157
Saunderson, J. L., 49, 111, 152, 158
Schaub, W. R., 46 (Breckenridge 1939)
Schleter, J. C., 77 (Keegan 1962)
Schnelle, P. D., 49 (Glasser 1958), 51 (Glasser, 1958)
Schofield, R. K., 26, 150
Sheldon, J. A., 49 (Billmeyer 1961), 110 (Billmeyer 1960a), 122 (Billmeyer 1960a), 157
Shillcox, W. M., 67 (Dearth 1963), 74 (Dearth 1963)
Shreve, O. D., 113 (Harkins 1959)
Simon, F. T., 83, 86, 87, 155
Simonds, J. L., 5 (Judd 1964), 137 (Judd 1964)
Simpson, J. E., 100, 136
Sloan, L. L., 51 (Munsell 1933)
Smith, D., 58
Smith, F. M., 100, 136, 156
Society of Dyers and Colourists, 95, 100, 136, 149, 155
Southall, J. P. C., 12, 148
Spencer, D. E., 49 (Moon 1943)
Stead, D. M., 136 (Smith 1954), 156
Stearns, E. I., 77 (Gabel 1949), 111 (Pritchard 1952), 113, 118 (Pritchard 1952), 122 (Park 1944), 155, 156, 157 (Abbott 1944)

Stiles, W. S., 150

Stockton, F. D., 84 (Ingle 1962), 86 (Ingle 1962), 154

Stultz, K. F., 84 (Nickerson 1944), 155, 158 (Nickerson 1944)

Teevan, R. C., 148

Thurner, K., 72, 83, 87, 148

Tilleard, D. L., 150, 152, 155, 158, 159

Tough, D., 122 (Preston 1965), 143 (Alderson 1963), 155, 156

Traub, A. C., 84

Troy, D. J., 67 (Glasser 1952), 73 (Glasser 1952)

Tuttle, H. A., 73

Van den Akker, J. A., 67, 74 (Dearth 1963)

Varley, D. M., 100 (Plant 1962), 136 (Plant 1962)

Venkataraman, K., 96

Vesce, V. C., 100, 136, 156

Vickerstaff, T., 156

Völz, H. G., 111, 143

Wald, G., 12

Walton, W. W., 55

Wanscher, J. H., 151

Webber, A. C., 42 (Billmeyer 1953), 45 (Billmeyer 1953)

Webster's Third New International Dictionary, 20, 93

Wegmann, J., 100

White, G. S. J., 143

White, H. E., 147

White, L. S., 11 (Mitton 1958)

Wilson, M., 150

Wood, R. W., 101

Wright, H., 141 (Wyszecki 1965)

Wright, W. D., 49, 77, 84, 148, 153, 154, 159

Wurzberg, F. L., Jr., 72, 80, 154

Wyszecki, G., 5 (Judd 1964), 15 (Judd 1963), 25, 31 (Judd 1963), 40 (Judd 1963), 52 (Judd 1963), 72 (Judd 1963), 80 (Judd 1963), 85 (Judd 1963), 111 (Judd 1963), 113 (Judd 1963), 137 (Judd 1964), 139 (Judd 1963), 140 (Judd 1963), 141, 147, 150, 153 (Judd 1963)

SUBJECT INDEX

A

A, *see* CIE illuminants, CIE sources

AATCC (American Association of Textile Chemists and Colorists) *Technical Manual*, 97, 100

Abridged spectrophotometry, 73, 75

"Absolute" color measurements, 69–72, 77

Absorption, absorbed light, 9, 110–111

Acceptability, 54, 57

Acceptability vs. perceptibility, 87–88

Accuracy (of color measurement), 141–142

Achromatic samples, 16

Adams chromatic value system, 49, 85

Adams color-difference equations, 84–85

Adaptation, 18

Additive color matching, 32, 61–63

Additive color mixing, 104–107

Additive primary colors, 32, 105

Additives, 136

Adjusted-Hue system, 49

Adjustment (of color match), 123–128

Alpha, beta system, 46, 48, 84

Analog computers (*see also* Computers), 111, 121–122

Appearance (of color), 18–23, 149–150
other aspects of, 11, 128

Applied Physics Corp., 80–81

Assessment (of colors), 54, 83

Atherton limits, 133–134

Azo dyes, 96

B

B, *see* CIE illuminants, CIE sources

Barium sulfate (BaSO$_4$), 77

Bausch and Lomb Co., 80–82

Beckman Instruments, Inc., 81–82

Beer's law, 10, 110

Binder, 94–95

Blackbody, 5–6, 41

Bleed, 94

Brightness, dyer's, 17

C

C, *see* CIE illuminants, CIE sources

Calculated catalogs, 120

Calibration, of colorimeters, 71–72
of spectrophotometers, 77

Carl Zeiss, Inc., 74–75

Cary Spectrophotometer, 80–81

Charts, color-difference, 85–86, 141

Chroma, 17, 26–27

Chromatic samples, 16

Chromatic value system (Adams), 49

Chromaticity coordinates, 40

Chromaticity diagram (CIE), 40–43
uniform, systems, 44–50

C.I. *(Colour Index)*, 95–97, 100

CIE (Commission International d'Eclairage), 31–45, 46, 48, 69–70, 77–79, 137–142

CIE chromaticity coordinates, 40

CIE chromaticity diagram, 40–43

CIE color-difference equation, 141

CIE color-matching functions, 36, 38

CIE Committee E-1.3.1 on Colorimetry, 137

CIE coordinate system, three-dimensional, 42–43

CIE daylight illuminants, 137–138

CIE dominant wavelength, 41–42

CIE illuminants A, B, C, 38–39, 77, 137–138

CIE illuminants D$_{6500}$, etc., 137–138

CIE luminance, luminous transmittance or reflectance, 38

CIE primaries, 37–39

CIE purity, 41–42

CIE reflectance standard, 138

CIE R, G, B system, 31–36

CIE Sources A, B, C, 38–39, 41

CIE standard observer, 1931, 38–39, 41

CIE standard sources, 38

CIE standard observer, supplementary, 138–141

CIE system, 31–45

CIE tristimulus values, 32, 35, 38, 69–70, 77–79, 142

CIE uniform chromaticity (u, v) system, 46, 48, 140–141

CIE u, v system, 46, 48, 140–141

CIE U^*, V^*, W^* system, 141

CIE Wyszecki U^*, V^*, W^* system, 141

CIE X, Y, Z system, 35–45

CODIC color-difference computer, 86

Color, appearance of, 18–23
appropriateness of, 130
assessment of, 53–54, 83
vs. colorant, 92
definition, 1
description of, 14–17
designer's concept of, 129
education for, 144
engineering aspects of, 129–136
examination of, 53–54, 83
meaning of, 129
perception of, 149–150
stylist's concept of, 129

"Color-Brightness Tester," 74–75

Color comparator, 61–62

Color coordinates, 17, 69

Color difference, 71–72, 84–88, 141, 154–155
acceptability vs. perceptibility, 87–88
bibliography, 154–155
charts for calculating, 85–86, 141
classification of calculation methods, 87
comparison of units, 86
computers for, 86
equations for, 84–87, 141
measurement of, 71–72

"Color-Eye," 73–74

Color Forecasts of the Color Association of the United States, Inc., 26

Color gamuts, 110, 112, 132–136

Color Harmony Manual, 30

Color match, conditional, 23, 113
"exact," 88
invariant, 23, 113
metameric, 113
spectrophotometric, 113

Color matching, 20–23, 32, 112–124, 143–144, 156–158
additive, 32
adjustment, 123–124
bibliography, 156–158
colorant, 112
by colorant identification, 113
colorant selection for, 112–114
computer, 119–123, 143–144
conditional, 113

control in, 124–128
initial, 114–123
instrumental, 115–124, 143–144
instrumentation for, 88
invariant, 113
laws of, 103–112
metameric, 113
metamerism and, 20–23
by mixing lights, 32
new trends in, 143–144
spectrophotometric, 113
tolerances in, 88
visual, 115
Color measurement, 53–89, 141–142,
    152–154
"absolute," 69–72, 77
accuracy of, 141–142
basic principles, 53
bibliography, 152–154
with colorimeters, 69–72
differential, 71–72
precision of, 141–142
sample preparation for, 55–57
with spectrophotometers, 77
visual, 57–60
Color-measuring instruments, 60–83,
    142
colorimeters, 66–74, 142
photoelectric, 63–83
spectrophotometers, 74–82, 142
visual, 60–66
Color memory, 89
Color mixing, 103–112
additive, 103–107
complex-subtractive, 111–112
simple-subtractive, 107–110
Color models, 42, 45
Color names, 43
Color-order systems, 25–52
bibliography, 150–152
Color photography, 108
Color rendition, 18
Color scales, 50–52, 60
of lightness, 51
single-number, 50–52
of whiteness, 52
of yellowness, 51
Color specification, 53–89, 158–159
Color standards, 158–159
Color television, 107–108
Color temperature, 5
correlated, 8
Color tolerances, 88, 158–159
Color wheel, 107, 108
Colorant (French), 92–93
Colorant pour cuve (French), 92–93
Colorant pigmentaire (French), 92–93
Colorants (see also Dyes, Pigments), 1,
    55–56, 91–101, 112–114, 142–
    144, 155–156
bibliography, 155–156
binders and, 94–95
books on, 97, 100

chemical nature, 94
classification of, 95–96
cost, 114, 130–131, 134–135, 142–
    143
definition, 1, 91
fastness, 114, 131, 142–143
identification, 113
information sources, 97, 100
light fastness, 142–143
metallic, 144
new research on, 142–143
opacifying, 94
optical properties of, 144
pearlescent, 144
preparation for measurement, 55–56
price, 114, 130–131, 134–135, 142–
    143
selection of, 97–100, 112–113, 136
shade cards, 97–99
solubility, 93–94
terminology, 91–93
transparency, 95
Colorimeters, 61–63, 66–75, 119, 126–
    128, 142
"absolute," 69–71
calibration, 71–72
Carl Zeiss, 74–75
chemical, 61
"Color-Brightness Tester," 74–75
"Color-Eye," 73–74
"Colormaster," 73–74
in color matching, 119
"Color-Rad," 74
commercial instruments, 72–74
coordinate scales, 69
differential use, 71–72
disk, 61, 105
Donaldson, 62–63
"Elrepho," 74–75
Gardner, 72–73
Hunter, 72–73
Instrument Development Laboratories
    (IDL), 13–24
Manufacturers' Engineering and
    Equipment Corp. (MEECO), 74–
    75
Martin Sweets, 74–75
new designs, 142
in production control, 126–128
readings of, 69
scales of, 69
source-detector response, 66–71
spectral response, 66–71
standardization, 71–72
Zeiss, 74–75
Colorimetry (see also Colorimeters), 66–
    74
Color Index (see Colour Index)
Coloring (definition), 1
"Colormaster," 73–74
"Color-Rad," 74
Colors, primary, 105–108
wavelengths of spectral, 4

Colour (British), 92–93
Colour Index, 95–97, 100
COMIC colorant mixture computer, 121–
    122
Commission International d'Eclairage
    (see CIE), 31
Complex-subtractive mixing, 111–112
Computer color matching, 119–124,
    143–144
Computers, 79, 86, 110–111, 121–123,
    142–144
analog, 111, 121–122
CODIC, 86
for color difference, 86
for color matching, 110–111, 121–
    123, 143–144
COMIC, 121–122
digital, 110–111, 122–123
tristimulus (integrators), 79, 142
tristimulus difference (TDC), 122
Conditional match, 23, 113
Control, in matching, 124
in production, 124–128
Correlated color temperature, 8
Cost, of colorants, 114, 130–131, 134–
    135, 142–143
Cotton, grading for color, 60
Cube-root lightness scale, 51
Cube-root system, 49–50

D

D,D$_{6500}$ (CIE daylight illuminants), 137–
    138
Davidson and Hemmendinger, Inc., 86,
    121–122
Daylight, 5, 137–138
Degrees Kelvin (definition), 5
Description (of color), 14–17
"Desert island" experiment, 15–17
Designer, 129–130
Detectors (of light), 12
Differential color measurement, 71–72
Differential colorimeters, see Colorim-
    eters
Diffraction grating, 74–75
Digital computers (see also Computers),
    110–111, 122–123
DIN (Deutsche Industrie Norm) system,
    46, 49
Disk colorimetry, 61, 105
Disperse dyes, 93
Dominant wavelength, 41–42
Donaldson colorimeter, 62–63
Dyeing, direct, 100
of plastics, 108
Dyer's brightness, 17
Dyes (see also Colorants), 93–96
azo, 96
binders and, 94–95
chemical nature, 94
classes of, 96
definition, 93
disperse, 93

and pigments, 93–95
  solubility, 93–94
  transparency, 95
  vat, 93, 96

E

Education, for color, 144
"Elrepho," 74–75
Engineering aspects of color, 100, 112, 129–136
Equal visual perception, *see* Uniform Visual perception
Examination (of colors), 53–54, 83
Eye, 12, 14
  color-matching functions of, 32–33, 36–38, 138–141
  as null detector, 59, 83

F

Farbstoff (German), 92–93
Fastness, 114, 131, 142–143
Federal Color Card for Paint (Federal Specification TTC-595), 26
Fibers, dyed, 100
Flexographic inks, 100
Fluorescence, 11, 128
Fluorescent materials, measurement of, 67, 138
Formulation, *see* Color matching
Foster color-difference charts, 141

G

Gamuts (of color), 110, 112, 132–136
Gardner Laboratory, Inc., 72–73
General Electric Co., 75, 82, 142
Gloss, 12, 17, 113, 128
  in color matching, 113
  and surface roughness, 12
Grassmann's laws, 32, 38, 65, 105–107

H

Hayes G. Shimp, Inc., 26, 62
Haze, 11, 128
House and Garden Colors, 26
Hue, 16, 26–27
Hues, wavelengths of common, 4
Hunter alpha, beta system, 46, 48
Hunter Associates Laboratory, Inc., 72–73
Hunter color coordinates, 69
Hunter color-difference equation, 84
Hunter colorimeters, 72–73
Hunter *L, a, b* coordinates, 69
Hunter uniform-chromaticity system, 46, 48

I

Identification (of colorants), 113
Illuminant (*see also* Source), 18–23, 38–39, 77, 137–138
  A, B, C, 38–39, 77, 137–138
  CIE, 77, 137–138
  daylight, 137–138

definition, 39
  mode of viewing, 3, 105
Illuminating and viewing conditions, 67–69, 75, 142
Index of refraction, 8, 10, 11
Infrared light, 4
Initial color match, 114–124
Inks, flexographic, 100
Institute of Paper Chemistry, 74
Instrument Development Laboratories (IDL), 73–74
Instrument metamerism, 69–70
Instrumental color matching, 115–124
Instruments, color-measuring, 60–83, 142
  colorimeters, 66–74, 142
  photoelectric, 63–83
  spectrophotometers, 74–82, 142
  visual, 60–66
Integrating sphere, 63–69, 75, 80–82, 142
Integrators, tristimulus, 79, 142
International Commission on Illumination (*see also* CIE), 31
Invariant match, 23, 113
ISCC-NBS system, 28–29
Iteration, 120

J

Judd unit, 84

K

Koenig-Martens photometer, 62–63
Kubelka-Munk equations, 111, 118, 122, 143

L

L, a, b coordinates, 69
Lambert's law, 9
Light absorption, 9
Light fastness, 114, 131, 142–143
Light scattering, 10–11
Light source, *see* CIE source, Source
Light transmission, 8
Lightness, 16
  scales of, 51
Limit standards, 83
Log-density cam, 117
Lovibond glasses, 26, 62
Lovibond Tintometer, 26, 62
Luminance, 38
Luminous reflectance, transmittance, 38

M

MacAdam color-difference equation, 85, 141
MacAdam limits, 42, 44, 132–133
MacAdam uniform-chromaticity system, 46, 48, 140–141
Maertz and Paul Dictionary of Color, 26
Magnesium oxide (MgO), 69, 77, 138
Manufacturers' Engineering and Equipment Corp. (MEECO), 73–74

Martin Sweets Company, The, 74–75
Matching, *see* Color matching
Matière colorante (French), 92–93
Measurement of color, *see* Color measurement
Metallic appearance, 11
  colorants, 144
  reflex, 11, 128
Metameric lights, 32
Metameric match, 20, 113
Metameric objects, 20
Metameric pair, 20
Metamerism, 20–23, 32, 50, 69–70, 126
  instrument, 69–70
  observer, 23
  production control and, 126
  single-number color scales and, 50
Millimicron, 4
Models of color space, 42, 45
Modes of viewing, 3
Monitoring, 125
Monochromatic light, 65
Monochromator, 65
Moon-Spencer system, 49
Munsell Book of Color, 27–28, 134–135, 151
Munsell Chroma, 26
Munsell color-difference equations, 84
Munsell colors, plotted in other systems, 46–49
Munsell Hue, 26
Munsell Notation, 27
Munsell Renotation System, 28
Munsell System, 26–28
Munsell Value, 26, 51

N

Nanometer, 4
NBS color-difference equation, 84
NBS unit of color difference, 84–87
Nessler tube, 61

O

Object mode of viewing, 3
Observer metamerism, 23
  standard (CIE), 38, 138–141
  variability, 58
Omega space, 49
Opacifiers, 112
Opal glass standards, 77
Opaque objects, 9
Organic pigments, 94
Ostwald system, 30–31

P

Paintings, pointillist, 105, 107
Partial derivatives, 123, 126–127
Particle size, and scattering power, 11
Pearlescent colorants, 144
Perceptibility vs. acceptability, 87–88
Perception of color, bibliography, 149–150
Perfect diffuser, 77, 138

Photocells, photodetectors, phototubes, 12, 14
Photography, color, 108
Pigment (German), 92–93
Pigment-dyed fiber, 100
Pigment padding, resin-bonded, 94, 95, 100
Pigments (*see also* Colorants), 11, 93–95
    and binders, 94–95
    bleed, 94
    chemical nature, 94
    definition, 93
    vs. dyes, 93–95
    functional, 93
    light scattering of, 11
    organic, 94
    particle size, 11
    solubility, 93–94
    structural, 93
    transparency, 95
Plastics, dyeing of, 108
Pointillist painting, 105, 107
Precision, of color measurement, 141–142
Pressed BaSO$_4$, MgO, white standards, 77
Price, of colorants, 113, 130–131, 134–135, 142–143
Primary colors, additive, 32, 105
    CIE, 37
    subtractive, 108
    unreal, 36–37
Primary lights, 32
Printing, color, 107, 108
Prism, 4, 9, 65–66, 74–75
Production control, 124–128
    adjusting, 125–127
    controlling, 128
    monitoring, 125
    process variables and, 125
Purity, 41–42

R

"R"-cam, 118
Rectangular Uniform Chromaticity Scale (RUCS) system, 46–47
Reference white standards, 69, 77, 138
Reflectance standards, 69, 77, 138
Reflected light, 11
Reflection, 8, 11
    surface, 8
Refractive index, 8, 10–11
R, G, B coordinates, 69
R, G, B system (CIE), 31–36
Ridgway Color Standards, 26

S

Sampling, 55–57
Saturation, 17
Saunderson-Milner system, 49–50
Scattering, scattered light, 10–11
    and particle size, 11

Selected-ordinate method (of tristimulus integration), 78–79
Shade cards, 97–99
Shading, 123–128
Simon-Goodwin color-difference charts, 85–86
Simple-subtractive color mixing, 107–110
Single-number scales, 50–52, 60
Single-number scales of lightness, 51
Single-number scales of whiteness, 52
Single-number scales of yellowness, 51
Slit, 76
Smoked magnesium oxide (MgO), 77
Solubility, of colorants, 93–94
Source (*see also* CIE source), 4–8, 39, 57–58
    definition, 39
    standard, 7
    for visual matching, 57–58
Specifications, bibliography, 158–159
Spectral energy distribution curves, 5–8
Spectral reflectance curves, 18–23
Spectral response curves, 14–15, 19–22, 68, 72
    of colorimeters, 68, 72
    of detectors, 14–15, 19–22
Spectral transmittance curves, 12
"Spectronic 20," 80
"Spectronic 505," 80–82
Spectrophotometers, 74–82, 113, 115–119, 142
    accessory cams for, 117, 118
    accuracy of, 77
    Applied Physics Corp., 81
    Bausch and Lomb, 80–82
    Beckman, 81–82
    calibration, 77
    Cary, 80–81
    and color matching, 113, 115–119
    and colorant identification, 113
    design of new, 142
    differential use, 77
    General Electric, 82, 142
    log-density cam for, 117
    "R"-cam for, 118
    "Spectronic," 80–82
    standardization, 77
Spectrophotometric curve, *see* Spectral reflectance curves, and Spectral transmittance curves
Spectrophometric match, 113
Spectrum, 4, 32, 41, 75–76
Spectrum colors, 4, 32, 41
Spectrum lights, 32
Spectrum locus, 41
Specular reflection, 68–69
Spin dyeing, spun-dyed fibers, 100, 131
Stabilizers, 114
Standard observer, CIE 1931, 38
    CIE supplementary, 138–141

Standard sources (*see* CIE sources, Sources)
Standards, 57–59, 69, 77, 138, 158–159
    bibliography, 158–159
    in color matching, 57–59
    limit, 59
    reflectance, 69, 77, 138
    target, 59
    white, 69, 77, 138
Stimulus, 15, 19–22
Stylist, 129
Subtractive color mixing, 107–110
    complex, 111–112
    simple, 107–110
Subtractive primary colors, 108
Surround, 17
Surface roughness, 12
Surface texture, 17

T

Tables for color-difference calculation, 85
Technical Manual, AATCC, 97, 100
Television, color, 107–108
Temperature, absolute, 5
    color, 5
    correlated color, 8
    degrees Kelvin, 5
Tolerances, 88, 158–159
Translucent objects, 10
Transmission, transmitted light, 8
Transparency, dyes vs. pigments, 94
Transparent objects, 8
Trichromatic coefficients, 40
Tristimulus difference computer (TDC), 122
Tristimulus integrator, 79, 142
Tristimulus values, 32, 35, 38, 69–70, 77–79, 142
Turbidity, 11

U

Ultraviolet light, 4, 138
Uniform Chromaticity Scale (UCS) system, 46, 47
Uniform-chromaticity systems, 45–50, 84–85, 141
    Adams, 49, 85
    Adjusted-Hue, 49
    alpha, beta, 46, 48, 84
    chromatic-value, 49
    CIE 1960 u, v, 46, 48, 141
    cube-root, 49–50
    DIN, 46, 49
    Hunter, 46, 48
    MacAdam u, v, 46, 48, 141
    Moon-Spencer, 49
    omega-space, 49
    Rectangular Uniform Chromaticity Scale (RUCS), 46, 47
    Saunderson-Milner, 49, 50
    Uniform Chromaticity Scale (UCS), 46, 47

zeta-space, 49, 50
Uniform visual perception, 27–28, 45–
    50
  in CIE system, 41
  color-order systems directed towards,
    45–50
  in Munsell System, 27–28
  possibility of achieving, 49–50
  scales of, 50–52
Union Carbide color-difference charts,
    85–86
Unreal primary colors, 36
u, v System, 46, 48, 141
U^*, V^*, W^* System, 141

V

Value, 16, 26–27
Vat dyes, 93, 95–96
Viewing conditions, 67–69, 75
Visual color matching, 57–59, 115
Visual examination of colors, 53–54

W

Wavelength, units of, 4
  of common hues, 4
Weighted-ordinate method (of tristimu-
    lus integration), 77–79
White standards, 69, 77, 138
Whiteness scales, 52

Wyszecki U^*, V^*, W^* system, 141

X

X, Y, Z system (CIE), 35–45

Y

Yellowness scales, 51

Z

Zeiss, Carl, Inc., 74–75
Zeta-space, 49, 50

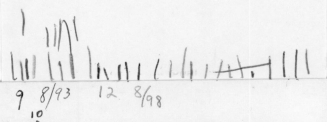